Mathematics in Geology

TITLES OF RELATED INTEREST

Mathematics in Geology

JOHN FERGUSON

Imperial College of Science and Technology,
University of London

London
ALLEN & UNWIN
Boston   Sydney   Wellington

Allen & Unwin, the academic imprint of
Unwin Hyman Ltd
PO Box 18, Park Lane, Hemel Hempstead, Herts HP2 4TE, UK
40 Museum Street, London WC1A 1LU, UK
37/39 Queen Elizabeth Street, London SE1 2QB, UK

Allen & Unwin Inc.,
8 Winchester Place, Winchester, Mass. 01890, USA

Allen & Unwin (Australia) Ltd,
8 Napier Street, North Sydney, NSW 2060, Australia

Allen & Unwin (New Zealand) Ltd
in association with the Port Nicholson Press Ltd,
60 Cambridge Terrace, Wellington, New Zealand

First published in 1988

British Library Cataloguing in Publication Data

Ferguson, John
    Mathematics in geology.
1. Geology——Mathematics
I. Title
510'.24553   QE33.2.M3
ISBN 0–04–550050–9
ISBN 0–04–550051–7   Pbk

Library of Congress Cataloging-in-Publication Data

Ferguson, John.
    Mathematics in geology.
Bibliography: p.
Includes index.
1. Geology – Mathematics.   I. Title.
QE33.2.M3F47   1987   510'.24553   87–14336
ISBN 0–04–550050–9 (alk. paper)
ISBN 0–04–550051–7 (pbk. : alk. paper)

Typeset in 10 on 12 point Times by Latimer Trend & Company Ltd
and printed in Great Britain by Billing & Sons, Worcester

Preface and acknowledgements

During 15 years of teaching mathematics, computing and statistics to undergraduate students studying for a first degree in geology, a number of difficulties have become apparent, not least amongst which is the absence of a suitable textbook setting out the basic mathematics which is required to understand many aspects of modern geology. Another problem, particularly in British universities, is the wide disparity between levels of mathematical achievement among undergraduates starting out on Earth science degree courses. For example, about 25 per cent of a typical class of around 50 students could have no real working knowledge of calculus and at least one-half of these will not have studied the subject at all. It is also normal to find that perhaps only 10 per cent of the class will have encountered matrix algebra before coming to university, while only a similar percentage will have been taught statistics. If we add to this the fact that about one-half of any class can be considered to be non-numerate (although this level is falling as geology becomes more-widely recognized as a numerical subject), there are many problems involved in teaching mathematics.

The difficulty for the teacher lies in trying to encourage those students who are numerate to develop their skills in the context of geology, while trying to bring the knowledge of the remainder to a satisfactory level. In the opinion of the author this minimum level of achievement should consist of a well-developed understanding of the language of mathematics which should enable the student to formulate a geological problem in mathematical terms to facilitate its solution, with help and advice from a professional mathematician; in other words, to equip the potential geologist with a language of communication.

Experience of teaching mathematics courses suggests that the level of application to the topic is greatly enhanced if the student can see a direct geological application of what is being taught. Thus, although there are many excellent mathematics textbooks that are easily and cheaply available, there are very few which are totally oriented towards geology. Looking at the geological literature, there is much good basic mathematics scattered throughout textbooks, not least of which are books such as John Davis' *Statistics and data analysis in geology* or Harbaugh & Bonham-Carter's *Computer simulation in geology,* or journals such as the *Journal of Mathematical Geology.* However, although lists of these and other similar works can be given to students as recommended reading, to locate all of the necessary books in the library, as well as finding the relevant sections, would present the average student with a considerable challenge, added to which must be the consideration that a mathematics course may only be a very small fraction of the total study that the student is expected to make.

This book is offered in order to achieve some of the above objectives, and to attempt to bridge the gap between mathematics and geology. If, by chance, it stimulates fellow geologists to think more frequently in mathematical terms, then it will have achieved its purpose.

I must at this point recognize the help and encouragement of my colleagues in the Department of Geology at Imperial College, and in particular Dr John Cosgrove, who kindly read the text and made many suggestions for its improvement. I must also thank the reviewers, who spent time reading the manuscript and giving the benefit of their experience with helpful suggestions, and the many students who have pointed out the shortcomings of my attempts to teach them mathematics, which hopefully has enabled me to avoid similar errors in the presentation of this work. Finally, thanks are due to my wife, without whose encouragement and bullying the writing would never have been completed.

John Ferguson

Contents

List of tables

Mathematics in Geology

1 Introduction

1.1 Solution of geological problems – are mathematical methods necessary?

A question which is often asked is whether it is necessary for geologists to know and to use mathematics in the practise of their science. There is no simple answer to this question, and it is true that many geologists have had successful careers without ever needing to get involved in anything other than simple mathematics, and all the indications are that this is likely to continue into the future. However, in many branches of the subject the trend has been towards using a numerical approach for the solution of suitable problems. The extent to which this occurs depends on the nature of the area being studied; thus, in structural geology, which is concerned in its simplest aspects with the geometrical relationships between various features, there are many problems which are easily solved. More recently the use of analytical methods has allowed the solution of more-difficult problems. In another area, geochemistry, two things have happened. On the theoretical side there has been a greater integration with physical chemistry, which itself is a highly mathematical subject; and on the practical side there is the need to analyse and interpret the vast quantities of data which modern instrumentation produces.

Within geology the application of numerical methods has been given various names, so we have numerical geology, geomathematics, geostatistics and geosimulation. Most university geology courses which concern themselves with numerical methods for geologists largely deal with statistical applications in the subject, with perhaps a little on simulation and computing thrown in for good measure. Another trend which in some ways is extremely useful is the use of relatively cheap and easily available statistical packages, such as Microtab, published by Edward Arnold (Higginbotham 1985), which allow the rapid processing of large data sets, to give perfectly satisfactory results in most cases. However, experience has shown that in a limited number of situations things can go wrong and, unless the operator is well versed with the particular package being used, the chances of sorting things out for that particular data set can be very slim.

Again, there is the unexpected answer. The author remembers well, as a postgraduate student, looking at results from a trend surface mapping program and commenting 'but I thought that the anticline drawn by the computer was a syncline!'. In this situation a little more knowledge of the 'mathematics' of the algorithm used by the computer program in question would have cleared up the problem. The structure which was being mapped by the program was, indeed, a syncline, and the opposite result produced was a mathematical artefact, due to a problem of round-off error encountered during a matrix-inversion routine. Many more examples could be given of misleading results being produced and accepted, and in some cases published. There is no real excuse for this, but as long as it happens doubts are going to be cast on the validity of using some numerical methods in geology. Not only should we all remember the truth of the old adage 'garbage in equals garbage out', but we should also be aware that the converse of this statement is not always true!

The author firmly believes that some basic training in mathematics can prevent the recurrence of these sorts of problems. This book, then, is offered as one means of rectifying this lack of basic knowledge, and is largely directed towards considering the numerical methods most frequently used in geology today. Since knowledge of basic mathematics is so fundamental to the understanding of the methods, it is humbly suggested that the study of the subject should take precedence over the teaching of most of what passes as numerical geology. If, due to lack of time, a choice has to be made between, say, a course in mathematics or a course in geostatistics, then the former should be favoured. Also, in the field of computer applications in geology there are many who think that the solution is to let students loose with statistical packages. In reality this can be no substitute for hands-on experience gained from writing programs and running data sets.

This book therefore tries to present, in an easily digestible form, some basic mathematics, knowledge of which will be useful to anyone wishing to pursue numerical applications in geology. It is assumed that the basic level of mathematical ability of those using the book includes a knowledge of basic trigonometry, geometry and the manipulation of simple algebraic equations. The work is not rigorous, in the sense that it does not contain theorems and proofs; indeed, there are many cases where phrases such as 'it can be shown that ...' are used. For those who wish to follow up individual algorithms, sufficient references are given. As far as possible, the examples used to illustrate the applications are geological in nature, using the author's own teaching material or material gleaned from other sources and, in particular, from the geological literature. In the latter case, full references are given.

Although there has been no intention to produce another statistics or simulation text, these topics have been included where it has been necessary to demonstrate the link between the mathematical ideas being discussed and the areas of application. These factors can be of particular importance in areas where geological decisions can have economic consequences – the difference between profit and loss may hang on a few parts per hundred million of a potentially interesting deposit.

1.2 Mathematical formulation of a geological problem

As has already been mentioned, some aspects of geology are more explicitly mathematical than others. Thus, for example, if we are interested in rates of change the problem can, if it is reasonably simple, usually be formulated in such a way as to allow the use of differential calculus. This will give an analytical expression whose solution can give an accurate answer. Similarly, in the calculation of volumes, provided some mathematical expression can be found describing the geometry of the object in question, integration can lead to an accurate answer. Even in complex cases where it is difficult to derive an equation describing the object, the use of the principles of integration, using a numerical approach, can often lead to a satisfactory, although not absolute, answer.

In other areas such as sedimentology – where grain size studies, for example, can lead to numerical data – it is generally much more difficult to formulate equations describing large-scale sedimentary processes. However, it is possible to arrive at general expressions which will allow further possibilities to be explored. We can take as an example Elliott's Episodal Theory for coal measure deposition (Elliott 1970). The following simplified résumé has been adapted from the introductory section of Elliott's paper:

(1) Deposition takes place during uninterrupted episodes of sub-delta advance and retreat.
(2) During episodes of retreat, the major distributaries and associated depositional environments give way to more extensive smaller scale distributary systems and environments. This pro-

cess increases the chance of intra-deltaic deposition at any particular locality.

(3) Retreat leads to reductions in sub-delta topographical relief, which gives rise to anaerobic conditions and perhaps later to the spread of conditions favouring the development of seat earth and peat in areas of suitable relief.

(4) Four types of sedimentation are present: an upwards developing clastic succession of faunal mudstones to flaser silt sandstones which are typical of the interdistributary areas; clastic successions of massive siltstones, complex silt sandstones, layered sandstones and rippled sandstones laterally and terminally associated with distributaries; washout and fill successions of sandstones which fill the distributary channels; and lastly, hydrologically controlled seat earths and coals in the swamp areas.

(5) Individual episodes of sedimentation are often terminated by geographical changes associated with delta switching up-stream. In areas outside this influence characteristic deposition is uninterrupted. When episodes are terminated by delta switching, individual cyclotherms can show markedly differing boundaries from area to area.

(6) Major environment sub-groups recognized during each episode are: swamp, prodeltaic–interdistributary and interdistributary. Geographic changes referred to in (5) above, are considered to give rise to a random ordering of the deposits. It follows from this that a coal seam found at one locality may arise from several episodes of deposition within the swamp region or, similarly, a prodeltaic environment could persist during several episodes.

(7) The thickness of successions which accumulate during one episode can be influenced by contemporaneous compaction of underlying deposits which can give rise to thicker than normal deposition; this mechanism is particularly dominant where intradeltaic deposits overlay thick peats.

(8) Variations in thickness of deposits accumulated during individual episodes can also be influenced by regional subsidence.

(9) The geometry of some sedimentary bodies, for example levees, can also influence local variations in thickness.

In other words, throughout the delta, characteristic sedimentary sequences are being deposited at any particular geographical locality. Such deposition continues until it is interrupted by changes brought about by delta-switching due to natural phenomena. For example, big storms or hurricanes can cause sediment to block the major distributary channel, and can bring about extensive changes in the delta geography. Thus characteristic sequences are built up because of random changes in geography.

A mathematical model should take into account at least the more important elements of this theory. Consider the processes which have controlled the deposition of a typical coal measure sequence at a single point in space, through which we have drilled an exploratory bore hole. The relationship between sediment and process can be expressed in the form of a function:

$$Y = f(A, B, \ldots)$$

(functions and function notation will be discussed in detail in Section 2.1.5). Putting this expression into words: Y, the sediment deposited during the interval under study, is equal to a combination of equations which describe the various sedimentological processes concerned in the deposition of the sediment. They are:

A, subdelta advance and retreat (leading to changes in the local environment)

B, typical sequences developed in relation to geography;

C, local sedimentation episodes (controlled by A);

D, changes in the thickness of units (due to compaction of the underlying peat);

D', changes in the thickness of units (due to regional compaction);

E, effect of the geometry of the individual bodies; and

F, major changes brought about by natural catastrophes.

Thus, we can say that

$$Y = f(A, B, C, D, D', E, F)$$

In his original paper, Elliott (1970) presents a simulation model based on the nine elements of his theory, which allow the simulation of a stratigraphic sequence by combining individual sedimentary episodes, based on the following.

(a) A schematic map showing the subdivision of the delta into 100 sedimentation zones. For purposes of the simulation, the co-ordinates of the corners of each zone are used as data to enable the correct sedimentation sequence to be assigned, for each depositional episode.

(b) A series of 45 sedimentation sequences cross-referenced to the zones of the map, each of which depicts a facies or sequence to be deposited during one episode.

(c) Changes in delta geography are simulated by selecting co-ordinate pairs (eastings and northings) at random, and by assigning episodes according to (a) and (b), above.

(d) The thickness of sequences is assigned by generating random numbers with known mean and standard deviation. Two frequency distributions taken from actual stratigraphic sequences are used (Elliott 1970, p. 326, text fig, 4), one relating to the thickness of seat earths and the other to all other depositional episodes. Coal thickness is derived from the second of these, dividing the selected thickness by 12.

Using this approach it was not necessary to define any of the contributing functions A–F, mathematically. However, it would be possible to define these functions precisely, and to build a totally mathematical simulation model. To show how this might be achieved, we can consider the effect of the compaction of peat. In a recent paper Elliott (1985) has shown that the compaction ratio for peat has a linear relationship with moisture content:

$$M_v = 100 - 5R_c$$

where M_v = moisture content by volume and R_c = compaction ratio, calculated as $\Delta Z / \Delta Z'$ as in Figure 1.1.

Another expression relating to the compaction of peat has been presented by Falini (1965, p. 1336), where the pore index p is related to the loading stress σ by

$$p = 21e^{-3\sqrt{10^{-4}\sigma}}$$

where e is the base of natural logarithms and σ is expressed in $kg\,m^{-2}$. The compressibility, K, is given by

$$K = \frac{dz/z}{d\sigma}$$

where the thickness passes from z to $(z - dz)$, i.e. from ΔZ to $\Delta Z'$ in Figure 1.1.

These two equations can be related back to that given by Elliott (1985), through the pore index p, which for original peaty material

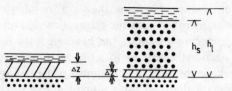

Figure 1.1 Diagrammatic representation of the reduction in thickness of peat, from original thickness ΔZ to $\Delta Z'$, due to overlying sediment column of thickness h_s and water column height h_l (after Falini 1965).

with 95% moisture content is taken as 20. Brown coals with moisture contents of between 50 and 70% have pore indices of 1–2 and bituminous coals with moisture contents of less than 10% have pore indices of less than unity (Falini 1965, p. 1336). For the purposes of our model we need only consider the early effects, i.e. forest loading and sediment loading (Elliott 1985, p. 169, fig. 6). Between these limits the compaction ratios are between 1 and 3.7, pore indices are between 20 and 4, and moisture content (by volume) between 97 and 82%.

Thus, we could, if we so desired, build one of these equations into Elliott's model to replace the present method of assignment of thickness for coal deposition. It would not be difficult to develop a similar equation relating the compaction of other sedimentary types in response to overburden pressure. This process of finding mathematical expressions to replace our unknowns can, of course, be continued, but it should be borne in mind that even without doing so the approach adopted by Elliott has led to a useful and valid model, albeit based on geological rather than mathematical data. If such an exercise were undertaken, the outcome would be to lead us to a deeper understanding of the geological processes which we are studying.

1.3 Computational aids

The traditional aids to computation, the slide-rule and the book of logarithmic tables (and other functions) are rapidly becoming historical relics. In the mid-1970s hand-held calculators with extensive mathematical function keys were relatively expensive. Today, for the same financial outlay a desk-computer can be purchased and hand-held calculators have become so cheap that when a fault occurs in one, it is thrown away and a new one is bought. Also, until relatively recently, in the field of education, computers were restricted to universities, but now they are in infants' classrooms. Geology, like many other scientific subjects, moved uneasily into the computing age during the 1960s, but having got the bit between the teeth it has steadfastly refused to let it go. Gone are the days of tediously working through long columns of figures by hand. Data are now automatically filed using some suitable interface between machine and computer, so that the data are ready for analysis almost as soon as they are produced.

Concurrent with advances in computational aids and their availability is a decrease in numeracy among many students. A very noticeable feature among classes of undergraduate students today is that if a ban is put on the use of a calculator, then their ability to do even the simplest numerical operations drops dramatically. Gone are the days when the result of 11×12 came out automatically. Even the facility of using logarithmic tables has been lost, and blank faces greet the teacher who has the temerity to introduce logarithms into his lecture. Of course, these are extremes, but the point should be made that there is no substitute in the learning process for sitting down and working through a problem by hand. Indeed, if test data are not treated in this way, how is one to assess the validity of the machine-generated output in the first instance?

Thus, although computer programs which are designed to solve many of the problems considered in this book are given, it is suggested that students work through some of the examples by hand. This will enable the intermediate steps in the calculation to be seen, as well as providing data which will enable the working of the computer program concerned to be checked.

1.3.1   Computers and computer languages

The technology of computer production is advancing so rapidly that any comments other than the most general are likely to be out of date before any book on the subject is published. However, some comments are in order. There are currently two distinct groups of machines: the mainframe computer and the microcomputer (usually referred to as the micro). The former is usually static and physically very large. It is very fast computationally, and is capable of supporting many different input and output devices. The micro, on the other hand, is small, often mobile, and usually supports a limited number of input and output devices. Again, roughly, micros can be divided into two groups by their initial cost: one group is priced in the range £2000–£10 000, while the other group ranges from around £100 to £1000. Of these two groups the cheaper ones are often regarded as mere toys, although many have been used for scientific application with great success.

Most students, at least initially, are more likely to be involved with micros rather than mainframes although, depending on the facilities available, the graduation from one to the other can be relatively rapid, particularly since many micros can now be easily adapted for use as remote terminals to mainframe computers. The mode of operation of the two types need not be considered here, although the differences in how the two types go about their business can be confusing to the uninitiated, as can the terminology used. At this stage we need only note that hardware refers to the machine itself and the peripheral devices such as printers, tape-drives, etc., whereas software refers to the 'programs' (note that it is conventional to use the American spelling of the word in this context) which are used to instruct the machine on how to perform the task at hand.

Programs are written in the form of instructions, which the computer can translate into a code which will enable it to perform the task required and, when all of the necessary instructions are at hand, to carry them out and present the results, in a form which can be understood. As human beings communicate with one another via language, so we communicate with the computer via language. There are many languages available for use in this area; some are quite specific to a given machine, whereas others are designed with a particular purpose in mind. Thus, the choice of a language will depend on machine availability and the problem being tackled. Many computer languages – like their human counterparts – have dialects, which have been developed to suit either a particular purpose or a particular machine. Languages also have rules which relate to their use, as well as syntax. The objective of these languages is to enable the user to communicate with the computer in an easily understood fashion (from the user's point of view), to enable it to perform the operation required.

Finally, we must always remember that today's computers are idiots; they can interpret instructions as they are given, but cannot yet interpolate in the sense that human beings can or supply missing instructions. In general, a computer needs an explicit instruction at every point.

1.3.2 Computers in geology

There is an extensive literature on the application of computers to solve geological problems, and many programs have been published. Notable contributions have come from Krumbein & Graybill

(1965), Harbaugh & Merriam (1968), Harbaugh & Bonham-Carter (1970) and Davis (1973). Some of these books contain computer programs which enable the reader, if he or she so desires, to solve a vast number of geological problems, but are mainly concerned with either statistics or simulation. The programs are written in **Fortran** (FORmula TRANslation) programming language, a high-level language which allows easy translation of mathematical expressions into program statements. Indeed, until comparatively recently most published geological programs have been written in this language and its use has been widespread in geology since the mid-1960s. Some very early programs were written in **Algol** (ALGOrithmic Language), but these often appeared translated into Fortran later. Several versions of Fortran exist but currently most computers use Fortran 77, a standard version of the language. Most published geological programs are in the version of the language known as Fortran IV, but it should not prove difficult to update them if necessary.

More recently, because of the easy availability of microcomputers, many geological programs have been written in **BASIC** (Beginners All-purpose Symbolic Instruction Code). This change has occurred because of technical difficulties in implementing the Fortran language on a micro. There are many versions of BASIC and, in the UK at least, much geological work has been done using a version known as BBC-BASIC, which is implemented on the BBC microcomputer. The language is not unlike Fortran, and conversion from one to the other is relatively simple. However, there are some facilities which are unique to both languages. Another language which has received much attention in scientific work generally is **Pascal**, which can be implemented on most micro computers. Both BASIC and Pascal languages are also available for use on mainframe computers.

Throughout this book a number of programs are referred to which enable some of the more-complex mathematical operations to be carried out more easily; listings are given in Appendix 3. The programs are written in BASIC, because of its relatively wider availability on microcomputers, although it should be stressed that it is BBC-BASIC which has been used and some of the programs contain statements or functions which are specific to the BBC operating system. A number of programs are taken from the author's own collection of material, while others are taken from the literature. A few have been written specifically for this book, and these are the only ones which are not adaptations of Fortran originals. Thus, if the majority of programs look like Fortran programs, this is the reason. All have been extensively tested and should prove to be relatively robust in use. Unfortunately, there is no way of guaranteeing robustness under every circumstance, and it is always possible to find a data set which will cause a program to crash.

Although the programs, as written, will stand alone, they are probably most useful if they are used as subroutines as part of larger, more-complex packages designed with a specific task in mind. Indeed, one of the virtues of having to learn a programming language is that it not only teaches geologists to write their own programs, but it also enables them to bring together and use parts of already-published programs in such a way that the parts perform specific tasks, obviating the necessity of writing complete programs from scratch, to suit each individual problem as it arises.

1.4 Speed and accuracy

Speed and accuracy are two problems which, although they may appear peripheral to the majority of matters discussed in this book, turn out to be important in practice. Needless to say, they affect some algorithms more than others. Later, and particularly in the context of numerical analysis, some of the detail will be discussed more fully. At this point a few general comments can be made. Since it is fairly safe to say that these are usually not factors of concern to the average mainframe-computer user, the comments are particularly directed at users of micros. Some of the comments, especially those concerned with accuracy, also apply when using hand-held calculators.

Problems related to speed and accuracy arise in many ways, but most importantly they relate to the word-length and the speed of the machine being used. In some applications the efficiency of the program itself will play an important part, particularly with regard to the speed of execution. Since accuracy is related to word-length, i.e. the number of significant figures which can be carried as a number, it is fairly easy to check. It is possible to write a program to evaluate a number such as 1/3, which cannot be expressed as a rational number, and then successively to multiply the result by the fractions 1/10, 1/100, etc., for say 50 increments. Performing such a calculation on the BBC micro using the BASIC compiler, it is found that the dynamic range of the exponent is down to 10^{-39}, while the mantissa is expressed to seven-figure accuracy. Beyond 10^{-39} the program is terminated with a floating point underflow. Another area which can be troublesome, and which is worth looking at, is the conversion from a real number to its logarithm and back again. Some quite surprising results can be obtained by checking these and other functions. It is recommended that similar checks be made if other compilers are being used. For example, A. R. Miller (1981) has shown that there are considerable differences in the numerical accuracy of different commercially available Pascal compilers.

1.5 Computer literature

Although computer programming is an important aspect of numerical geology, it is not proposed to follow the example of some earlier texts by including some simple instruction on programming. It is suggested that those interested in following up this aspect of the work use some of the excellent books already available on the subject.

A number of books which can be recommended include the following. For an introduction to computers generally, the work by Hollingdale & Toothill (1975), in the Pelican Series is excellent. The user-guides issued with individual computers are generally good, but several do assume much more knowledge than the beginner normally has, and are not really written with the simple application aspect in mind. The BBC User Guide by Coll (1982) is essential for those using a BBC micro. This book is clearly written, and straightforward to use. Of a more-specific nature and giving listings of useful programs are A. R. Miller's (1981) text on the use of Pascal in scientific programming generally, and Unwin & Dawson (1985), on geographical programming applications. Shelley's (1984) text on the essentials of Fortran 77 should prove invaluable for those using mainframe computers.

2 Useful mathematical ideas

To provide the basic level of mathematics needed to work through this book, it is necessary to start by looking at some simple mathematical ideas in the fields of algebra, geometry and trigonometry. For most students this will be revision. However, since throughout the book we are attempting to link mathematics to geology, it is not intended that this chapter should be skipped on the basis of having covered the ground at an earlier stage. Indeed, to establish firmly the idea of thinking of geological problems in mathematical terms, the topics covered in this chapter start with geological data or problems which are then expressed mathematically.

2.1 Algebra

2.1.1 Linear equations

(a) THE EQUATION OF A STRAIGHT LINE

A number of specimens of the Jurassic brachiopod *Epithyris oxonica* (Buckman) were measured, and the length and width of the pedicle valve were recorded. The data are shown in Table 2.1a and graphically in Figure 2.1.

As can be seen from Figure 2.1, a straight line passing through the origin of the graph which honours most of the points, can be fitted to the data. The equation of this line will be of the general form

$$y = ax$$

where y = the length of the pedicle valve, x = the width of the pedicle valve and a = the slope of the line. The slope can be conveniently found by either of two methods. If the graph is drawn so that the scale for the two axes is the same and the slope of the line is no steeper than about 60°, then measuring the angle that it makes with the horizontal axis and finding its tangent will suffice. This angle is normally denoted by the symbol θ. Alternatively (and

Table 2.1 Measurements of (a) *Epithyris oxonica* (Buckman), Jurassic, Bathonian, Blisworth Limestone, collected from Irchester, Northamptonshire, and (b) *Turitella* sp., Eocene, Bracklesham Beds, collected from Bracklesham Bay, Hampshire.

(a) *Epithyris oxonica*		(b) *Turitella* sp.	
Length of pedicle valve (mm)	Width of pedicle valve (mm)	Length of shell (mm)	Diameter of last chamber (mm)
18.0	16.0	10.0	3.0
19.0	17.0	13.0	3.5
20.0	19.0	16.0	5.0
21.5	19.0	22.0	6.0
26.5	23.5	24.0	6.5
29.0	25.0	28.0	6.0
33.5	29.0	35.0	8.0
36.0	31.0	39.0	8.0

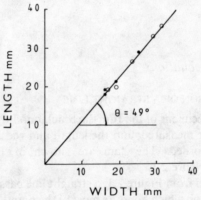

Figure 2.1 Plot of length against width for the measurements given in Table 2.1a, of the Jurassic brachiopod *Epithyris oxonica* (Buckman). Length = length of pedicle valve; width = maximum width of shell at right angles to length.

particularly if the two axes are not equally scaled), the vertical rise per unit length increase along the horizontal axis can be calculated. Whichever method is used, the sign for the slope is determined by its direction, being positive if the slope is upwards from left to right, and negative if the slope is upwards from right to left. In this example the measured angle $\theta = 49°$ and $\tan \theta = 1.15$.

Alternatively, we can measure; thus for a rise of 36 units on the (vertical) y-axis, we have 31 units on the (horizontal) x-axis, so

$$36/31 = 1.16$$

Thus, we can express the growth of the terebratullid shell in terms of the length and width of the pedicle valve:

$$\text{length} = 1.15 \times \text{width}$$

Plotting the data relating to *Turitella* sp. from Table 2.1, which is illustrated in Figure 2.2, we find that the best-fit line no longer passes through the origin of the graph, but has an intercept on the *y*-axis, at -8.5 mm. Any equation describing the line must take this factor into account, so the general equation is

$$y = ax + b$$

where $y =$ the length of the spire, $x =$ the diameter of the last chamber, $a =$ the slope of the line and $b =$ the intercept of the line on the vertical axis. Proceeding as before,

$$\theta = 79°, \quad \tan \theta = 5.145$$

or

$$39/8 = 4.875$$

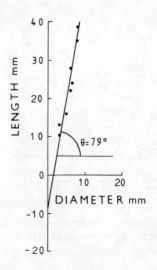

Figure 2.2 Plot of length against diameter for the measurements given in Table 2.1b, of the Eocene gastropod *Turitella* sp. Diameter = diameter of last preserved whorl; length = length of preserved spire.

Note here that a small inaccuracy incurred in measuring the angle has made a significant difference in the result; this follows since, for angles greater than 60°, the value of the tangent increases very rapidly for very small changes in the steepness of the slope.

Since the intercept is -8.5, we can express the growth of our gastropod as

length of spire = (4.875 × last chamber diameter) -8.5
(measurements in mm).

Another example can be studied using results from experiments designed to examine the phase change of aragonite to calcite, and the effect of magnesium-ion inhibition on the reaction. Bischoff (1968, fig. 6) presented data relating to the removal of magnesium ions from solution, before the visual detection of calcite precipitation, in the form of a diagram. The data in Table 2.2 are taken from this diagram, and are also replotted as Figure 2.3.

Table 2.2 Data relating to the depletion of Mg^{2+} in 0.02 м NaCl solution before visible aragonite–calcite transformation was observed.

Time (h)	$[Mg^{2+}]$ (ppm)
0.0	5.5
1.5	5.1
3.0	5.375
7.0	4.75
21.5	3.75
32.0	2.5
36.0	1.75

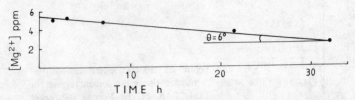

Figure 2.3 Plot of the concentration of Mg^{2+} in aqueous solution against time, recorded during an experimental study of the phase change aragonite–calcite in the presence of magnesium (after Bischoff 1968).

The first thing which is apparent is that the slope of the line is in the opposite sense to the previous examples. If we follow the rules we have already used, we find

$$\theta = -6°, \quad \tan \theta = -0.105$$

remember, since the line slopes from left to right the sign of the angle θ is reversed; alternatively

$$\theta = (1.75 - 5.5)/32$$
$$= -0.117$$

The intercept on the y-axis is 5.5. Therefore, we can express the rate of reduction of Mg^{2+} in solution during the experiment as

$$\text{ppm } Mg^{2+} = (-0.117 \times \text{time}) + 5.5$$

(time measured in hours).

From these three examples, we can now give a general equation for a straight line:

$$y = ax + b$$

where a = the slope of the line
               positive if slope is upwards from left to right
               negative if slope is upwards from right to left
      b = the intercept on the y-axis
               zero if intercept is at the origin of the axes
               positive if intercept is above the origin
               negative if intercept is below the origin

In these three examples we have 'eyeballed' in the best-fit line to our data, attempting to honour as many data points as possible. Clearly, this is not the most objective way to achieve this, and later (Section 4.5.1) we shall be looking at methods of fitting these lines mathematically.

Unfortunately, not all of the parameters in which geologists are interested turn out as a data plot which can be honoured by a straight line. Take, as another example, data from grain-size analysis of sediments. Table 2.3 shows an hypothetical data set representing the cumulative weight percentage of various grades of sand retained on a set of British Standard sieves, which split the sample into

Table 2.3 Hypothetical grain-size data after a sieve test using British Standard sieves at approximately half-φ intervals

Size class		Particle diameter		Cumulative weight percentage
		mm	φ units	
		2.00	−1.00	9
	very coarse	1.40	−0.49	18
		1.00	0.00	27
	coarse	0.71	0.49	36
		0.50	1.00	45
Sand	medium	0.355	1.49	54
		0.25	2.00	63
	fine	0.18	2.47	72
		0.125	3.00	81
	very fine	0.09	3.47	90
		0.063	3.97	100

fractions according to the accepted size classes in the sand grade. Two scales of measurement are shown, these are mm and φ units (explained below).

If we plot cumulative percentage against the mm scale, then the best-fit line is curved, whereas if we plot the same data against the φ-value we get a straight line. These plots are illustrated in Figure 2.4. The straight-line φ-value plot is much easier to deal with than the curve obtained using the mm plot. The reason for this becomes apparent if we look at the relationship between the boundaries of the size classes (very coarse, coarse, etc.) in terms of the sieve size in mm. The classes are based on a geometric scale, i.e. 2, 1, 0.5, 0.25, 0.125, ..., so going from the largest to the smallest size class the ratio between each interval is one-half. In order to arrive at a linear scale for the class boundaries with this sort of scale we can use the formula

$$\varphi = -\log_z d$$

where d = diameter in mm and φ is a dimensionless number. It should be remembered that to calculate the logarithm to base z of any number x

$$\log_z x = \ln x / \ln z$$

The convention used to denote logarithms in this book is that the abbreviation 'ln' denotes a logarithm to the base e (natural logarithm), 'log' denotes logarithm to the base 10, and '$\log_z$' denotes logarithm to any other base, specified by the numerical value of z.

The principal advantages of using the φ scale in grain-size studies are the following.

(a) If the data are plotted on ordinary graph paper a straight line is produced, i.e. the plot is linear.
(b) The calculation of various statistical parameters used in sediment grain-size analysis is much simplified.

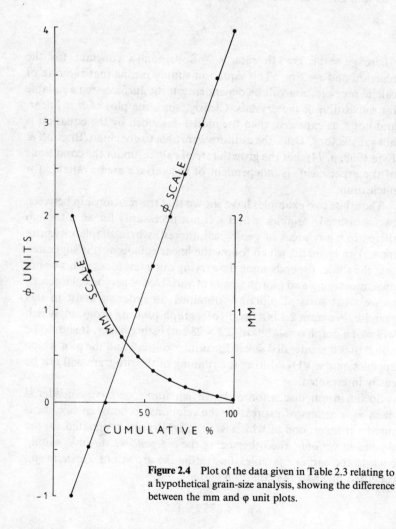

Figure 2.4 Plot of the data given in Table 2.3 relating to a hypothetical grain-size analysis, showing the difference between the mm and φ unit plots.

For further information on this important topic, students are referred to a standard sedimentology textbook such as that of Friedman & Sanders (1978, pp. 642ff.).

Another example involving curved plots can be taken from details of other experimental work on the aragonite–calcite inversion problem, published by Bischoff & Fyfe (1968). In these experiments they found that plots for the rate of precipitation of calcite against time in their experiments were non-linear. However, a plot of the percentage of calcite against the square of the time gave a straight line. This was an extremely significant result, as one model which was thought to describe the rate of precipitation is

$$g_{(t)} = k_g t^3$$

where $g_{(t)}$ = the growth rate, k_g = Boltzmann's constant for the reaction and t = time. This equation simply means that the rate of calcite precipitation will be dependent on the surface area available for nucleation of the crystals. Clearly, since the plot of t^2 is linear, and not t^3 as expected, then the model described by the equation is not satisfactory. Thus, the authors were able to conclude (Bischoff & Fyfe 1968, p. 74) that the growth rate of calcite, under the conditions of the experiment, is independent of the surface area available for nucleation.

These last two examples have shown that the relationship between two measured variables x and y is not necessarily linear, although there are many areas of geological interest, where simple measurements can be made, which follow the linear equation. It is suggested that the student spends some time trying out a few ideas of his or her own, measuring and plotting pairs of variables of geological interest, to see what sorts of plots are obtained. In order to assist in this exercise, Program 2.1 is a listing of a graph-plotting program, which will plot a graph on standard (22 × 28 cm) listing paper. It should be noted that it is intended solely for printer output, and the plot which appears on the VDU during the running of the program will not be easily interpreted.

So far in our discussion of linear equations we have considered them as a means of expressing the relationship between two measured variables, one of which is, or is arbitrarily designated as, the *dependent variable*, the other being the *independent variable*. Going back to the earlier example, illustrating the growth of *Turitella* sp., the fitted line had the equation

$$y = 4.875x - 8.5$$

where $x =$ the diameter of the last chamber (the independent variable) and $y =$ the length of the spire (the dependent variable). In this example the coefficient of the x-value is defined as being a measure of the slope of the line, the constant -8.5, is the intercept on the y-axis, and the coefficient of the y-value is unity. We can rewrite this more conveniently, with the unknowns x and y on one side of the equation (rounding-off in the process) as

$$5x - y = 8.5$$

Now if we arbitrarily alter the coefficient of the y-value in the equation, then we will change the slope of the curve as well as the intercept on the y-axis. However, the intercept on the x-axis will remain the same; some examples are shown in Figure 2.5a. On the other hand, if we hold the coefficients of the x- and y-values constant and change the intercept value, then we will obtain a series of parallel lines cutting both axes at different points, as in Figure 2.5b.

It follows from these two simple exercises that the slope of a curve is governed by the ratio of the coefficient of the x-value to that of the y-value, and the intercept on the x-axis by the ratio of the intercept on the y-axis to the coefficient of the x-value.

If a general expression for the linear equation is

$$ax + by = c$$

where a, b and c are numerical constants, then in general the slope of the line is given by a/b. Also, if the intercept on the y-axis is given by c, then the intercept on the x-axis is given by c/a. Thus, in the examples studied earlier, where y is unity, the coefficient of the x-value is the slope of the curve.

Returning to Figure 2.5a, it is apparent that if we draw the line $x = 5$, the corresponding y-values for each of the equations plotted can be read directly from the points of intersection. Thus, if

$$5x - y = 8.5$$

$$y = 16.5 \quad \text{(when } x = 5\text{)}$$

Similarly, using Figure 2.5b and drawing the line $y = 10$, if

$$5x - y = 0$$

$$x = 2 \quad \text{(when } y = 10\text{)}$$

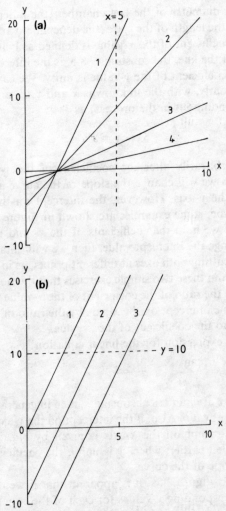

Figure 2.5 Plot of families of functions related to the linear equation $5x - y = 8.5$.
(a) Curves produced by altering the coefficient of the y-value
1. $5x-y=8.5$
2. $5x-3y=8.5$
3. $5x-5y=8.5$
4. $5x-10y=8.5$
(b) curves produced by altering the intercept or constant value.
1. $5x-y=0$
2. $5x-y=8.5$
3. $5x-y=17$

or, if

$$5x - y = 17$$

$$x = 5.4 \quad \text{(when } y = 10)$$

These results are the same as those obtained by solving the corresponding pairs of simultaneous equations. For example,

$$5x - y = 8.5$$

$$x \quad = 5$$

Multiply the lower equation by 5 and subtract:

$$5x - y = \quad 8.5$$

$$- 5x \quad = 25$$

$$\overline{\qquad\qquad\qquad}$$

$$- y = -16.5$$

Similarly, the point of intersection of the curves in Figure 2.5a can be found by solving any pair of equations simultaneously:

$$5x - \quad y = 8.5$$

$$- 5x - 10y = 8.5$$

$$\overline{\qquad\qquad\qquad}$$

$$9y = 0$$

thus: $y = 0$ and $x = 8.5/5 = 1.7$. This demonstrates a link between the points of intersection of curves on a graph and the solution of simultaneous linear equations, which turns out to be useful in a number of areas, not least of which is linear programming, which will be considered in Section 2.1.7.

2.1.2 *Polynomial equations*

Polynomial equations are equations of the general form

$$y = a_1 x^n + a_2 x^{n-1} + \ldots + a_n x + c$$

The most common forms of the polynomial are:

Quadratic

$$y = ax^2 + bx + c$$

which has one point of inflexion which is either a maximum or a minimum (Fig. 2.6).

Cubic

$$y = ax^3 + bx^2 + cx + d$$

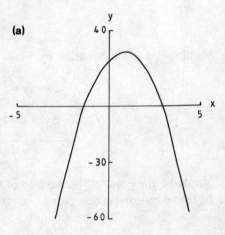

(a)

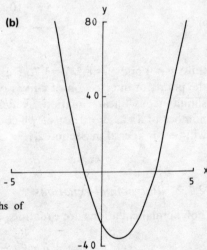

(b)

Figure 2.6 Examples of the graphs of quadratic equations.
(a) $y = -6x^2 + 10x + 24$;
(b) $y = 9x^2 - 18x - 27$.

which can have two points of inflexion; a maximum and a minimum (Fig. 2.7).

Quartic

$$y = ax^4 + bx^3 + cx^2 + dx + e$$

which can have three points of inflexion; either one maximum and two minima, or two maxima and one minimum. The example illustrated (Fig. 2.8) shows only one minimum over the range plotted.

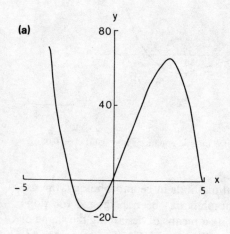

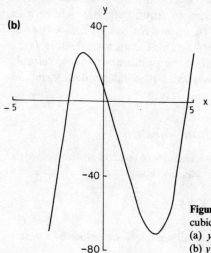

Figure 2.7 Examples of the graphs of cubic equations.
(a) $y = 2x^3 + 5x^2 + 24x$;
(b) $y = 3x^3 - 9x^2 - 27x + 10$.

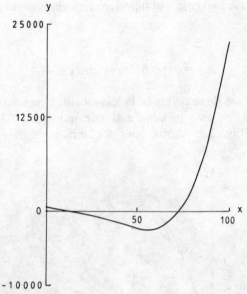

Figure 2.8 Example of the graph of a quartic equation: $y = 0.001x^4 - 0.08x^3 + 0.5x^2 - x + 15$.

In applications of numerical methods in geomorphology, the use of quadratic and cubic polynomials has been suggested for slope analysis, the equations providing a means of describing the shape of a profile (Doornkamp & King 1971, pp. 141ff.). The equations are obtained by calculating a line of best fit using a least-squares method. In geological simulations quadratic equations have also been used combined with other functions, for beach profiles (Fox & Davis 1971). In both of these applications the numerical value y (the dependent variable) is the height of the profile above some suitable datum level, at a point at a distance x (the independent variable) from an origin measured along the datum.

2.1.3 The solution of a quadratic equation

We have already mentioned the quadratic equation in the previous section, where the general form was given as

$$y = ax^2 + bx + c$$

Of particular significance, as we shall see later, are values of x when

$y = 0$, which are known as the roots of the equation. Thus, we need to solve for x when

$$ax^2 + bx + c = 0$$

Extracting the factors is, in many situations, a relatively simple matter. For example, find the roots of the equation

$$y = 2x^2 - 3x + 1$$

The coefficient of the x^2-term as a pair of factors is 2 and 1; thus, the first factors of x are

$$(2x \quad)(x \quad)$$

The factors of the constant term are 1:

$$(2x \quad 1)(x \quad 1)$$

Now all that remains is to find the appropriate signs. If we return to the constant term $+1$, we can obtain this either as $+1 \times +1$; or as -1×-1. However, in order to make the x-term negative, then the factors of the constant in this equation must also be negative, thus

$$(2x - 1)(x - 1) = 0$$

therefore $x = \frac{1}{2}$ or $x = 1$.

The rules for determining the sign of the factors of the constant are:

(a) if both the x-term and the constant term are positive, then the factors of the constant term will also be positive;
(b) if the x-term is negative and the constant term is positive, then the factors of the constant will both be negative;
(c) if the x-term is positive and the constant term is negative, then the factors of the constant term will be positive and negative.

It is wise to check the factors by multiplying out. Indeed, when the signs are different it is essential in order to ensure that they are in the correct order. The simplest way is to use the following:

$$2x - 1 = -x$$
$$x - 1 = -2x \quad +$$
$$\overline{}$$
$$-3x$$

the arrows indicate multiplying and the two products should add up to the middle term of the original expression, the sign will also match if the factorization is correct.

Not all examples are so simple that they can be factored in this way, and a formula which allows solution has to be used. If a and b are the coefficients of the x^2- and x-terms, respectively, and c is the constant, then

$$x = \frac{-b \pm \sqrt{(b^2 - 4ac)}}{2a}$$

For example, solve $3x^2 - 7x - 6 = 0$:

$$x = \frac{7 \pm \sqrt{(49 + 72)}}{6} = \frac{7 \pm (11)}{6}$$

$$x = 3 \text{ or } -2/3$$

Another example; solve $x^2 - 2x + 5 = 0$:

$$x = \frac{2 \pm \sqrt{(4 - 20)}}{2}$$

$$= \frac{2 \pm \sqrt{-16}}{2} = \frac{2 \pm 4\sqrt{-1}}{2}$$

Since it is not possible to find the square root of a negative number, we must write $\sqrt{-1}$ as i, where i is an imaginary number (see Section 2.1.6 for an explanation) then

$$x = (1 + 2i) \text{ or } (1 - 2i)$$

Fortunately, in most situations where the solution of a quadratic occurs in a geological example (see later, particularly Section 6.3) the roots are real. However, we should remember the tests, using the discriminant $b^2 - 4ac$:

if $b^2 - 4ac > 0$ the roots are real and distinct;

if $b^2 - 4ac = 0$ the roots are real and equal;

if $b^2 - 4ac < 0$ the roots are complex.

We can interpret these rules as follows: if we graph the function, and if there are two real roots, then the curve will cut the x-axis twice; if there is one root, then there will be only one point at which the curve cuts the x-axis; finally, if the roots are complex, then the curve will not cut the x-axis at all.

It is also worthwhile to remember that there will be an axis of symmetry for the curve, which can be found from

$$x = -b/2a$$

The problem of solving the roots of a quadratic is very common, therefore a listing of a suitable program for their solution is given as Program 2.2. In its present form the program can be run on its own, removal of REM from statement 10 and changing statement 390 to read 390 ENDPROC would allow it to be used as a procedure within another program, provided a suitable call is made.

Table 2.4 Measurements of specimens of *Gigantoproductus inflatus* (Sarycheva), from the Lower Carboniferous, Crook Burn Limestone, Crook Burn, Northumberland. (a) Adult forms; (b) juvenile forms.

(a) Width (mm)	Curved length (mm)	(b) Width (mm)	Curved length (mm)
140	208	40	57
100	180	55	78
76	127	44	61
100	180	26	36
86	150	50	69
112	195	60	80
110	180	52	65
150	174	64	82
90	162	55	70
77	140		

2.1.4   Other non-linear equations

Table 2.4 gives measurement data for a collection of the productid brachiopod *Gigantoproductus inflatus* (Sarycheva), from the Lower Carboniferous, Visean, Crook Burn Limestone, collected from a locality in Northumberland. The data have been divided into two sets; Table 2.4a refers to adult specimens, while Table 2.4b refers to juveniles. These are plotted as a graph, Figure 2.9, and it is clear that there are two distinct curves relating to the two groups. Also, the distribution of the data points for each collection is honoured by a

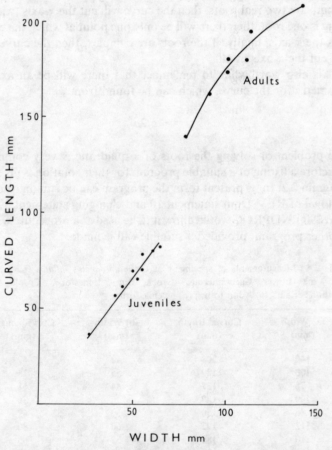

Figure 2.9 Plot of measurements given in Table 2.4, relating to the Carboniferous brachiopod *Gigantoproductus inflatus* (Sarycheva). The curved length is measured around the perimeter of the pedicle valve starting at the tip of the umbo, at right angles to the hinge; the width is measured along the hinge line.

different form of curve. That for the juveniles is a straight line, while that for the adults is a curve. The form of the adult data plot is typical of this genus (Prentice 1956; Ferguson 1978) and illustrates the principle of allometric growth, i.e. the relationship between the size of one part of an organism and the size of another is not linear but follows the general equation

$$y = \beta x^a$$

(see, for example, Reeve & Huxley 1945, p. 121).

If we convert the data for the adult members of the population to logarithms, as in Table 2.5, and replot as in Figure 2.10, the points can be honoured by a straight line. If we estimate the slope and intercept as discussed in Section 2.1.1, then we find that

$$\log CL = 0.75 \log W + 0.72$$

This equation is the linear form of the allometric growth equation, i.e.

$$\log y = \log B + \alpha \log x$$

Thus we can rewrite in the form of the allometric growth equation by taking antilogarithms as appropriate. This gives an estimate of the growth equation for the adult population

$$CL = 5.25 \, W^{0.75}$$

Table 2.5 Data from Table 2.4a expressed as logarithms.

log (Width)	log (Curved length)
2.15	2.32
2.00	2.26
1.88	2.10
2.00	2.26
1.94	2.18
2.05	2.29
2.04	2.26
2.00	2.24
1.95	2.21
1.85	2.15

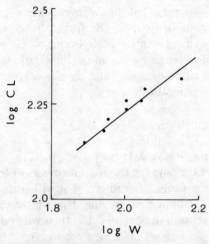

Figure 2.10 Plot of the logarithms of measurements of adult members of the population of *Gigantoproductus inflatus* (Sarycheva) (data from Table 2.5).

Another extremely important equation in a geological context is the exponential equation, which can be written in the general form

$$N_t = N_0 e^{rt} \quad \text{which describes growth}$$

or as

$$N_t = N_0 e^{-rt} \quad \text{which describes decay}$$

Here, N_t = number in population at time t, N_0 = number in population at time $t = 0$, r = a constant, t = time, e = the base of natural logarithms, numerically equal to 2.718282 (to six decimal places). This equation has been used as a descriptor in such diverse topics as population growth, the decay of radioactive isotopes (and hence is used in calculations of geological time), the growth of crystals from a melt and the rate of decay of a slope in stream development. Another significant application is in the determination of rate laws for chemical reactions from experimental data. In the case of the important group of first-order reactions, the equation is

$$C = C_0 e^{-kt}$$

or

$$\ln C = \ln C_0 - kt$$

where C = concentration at a time t during the reaction, C_0 = concentration at the start of the reaction, k = the rate constant and t = time.

One method of finding k for reactions is to determine experimentally the changes of concentration of a reactant with time and to solve the problem graphically (Lasaga 1981, pp. 13ff.). Table 2.6 gives data from experimental cementation of aragonite ooids, showing the rate at which strontium is released from the aragonite during its conversion into calcite. A plot of this data, Figure 2.11a, shows the characteristic exponential curve. Replotting the data using logarithms, as in Figure 2.11b, reduces the curve to two straight lines, which show a break after about 20 days. This result is interpreted as indicating a major change in reaction rate – a slowing down – after the time in question. Based on other evidence, this is thought to be the time of onset of cementation when rim cements start forming around the ooids (Ferguson *et al.* 1984). The rate constants deduced from the graph are 1.017 and 0.5, indicating a drop in rate of just over one-half.

Table 2.6 Data relating to the increase of strontium in sea water during the experimental cementation of aragonite ooids at 200°C and 1 500 lb in.$^{-1}$

Time (days)	ln (time)	$[Sr^{2+}]$ (ppm)	ln $[Sr^{2+}]$
0		7.7	2.04
7	1.95	30	3.4
12	2.49	93	4.53
15	2.71	125	4.83
19	2.95	153	5.03
27	3.30	156	5.05
51	3.93	230	5.44
63	4.14	310	5.74
78	4.36	300	5.70

2.1.5 Functions and function notation

So far we have used simple equations to express relationships between variables, writing them out explicitly. However, as we saw in Section 1.2, it is not always possible to be explicit, and we used the notation

$$y = f(\quad)$$

where the parentheses contained a list of variables. This is handy

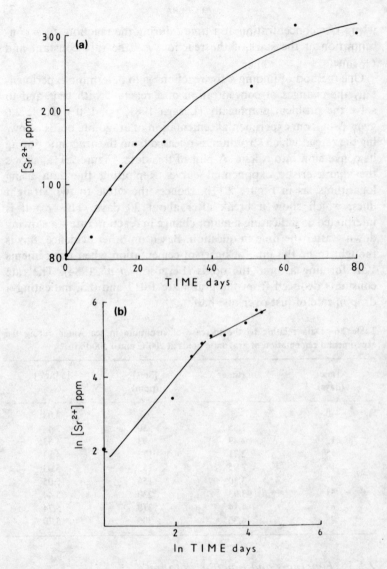

Figure 2.11 Plot of experimental data showing the release of Sr^{2+} from aragonite during its conversion into calcite, plotted against time. (a) Plot of raw data; (b) plot of logarithms of data. (Data as in Table 2.6.)

shorthand notation which is extensively used in mathematics, and it is now convenient to explain its meaning and use.

The original meaning of the word 'function' in mathematics was that some quantity, denoted by the symbol y, is related to another quantity, denoted by x, by a simple formula or rule. A function is written symbolically as

$$y = f(x)$$

The idea of a function was closely related to the idea of a scientific law: e.g. Boyle's Law, which states that at constant temperature the pressure of a fixed mass of gas is inversely proportional to its volume. Returning to an earlier example, the relationship between the length of the pedicle valve and the width for the brachiopod *Epithyris oxonica* could be expressed in this form, i.e.

$$y = f(x)$$

where y = the length of the pedicle valve and $f(x) = 1.15 \times$ width.

As mathematics developed, the idea that the relationship was a simple one was dropped. This followed because it was recognized that some graphs which were originally thought not to represent single functions, but rather to be combinations of different functions, could be described by a single series, the Fourier Series which, as will be discussed in Section 5.5, involves sines and cosines. Further difficulties arose, particularly concerning the calculus of variations where problems involving curves or surfaces are met, so it is now accepted that x and y in the original definition, can stand for any object whatever. In modern mathematics the term 'mapping' is often used in place of 'function'. Their meaning is interchangeable.

A geological example of the definition of a function, which is very similar to that used earlier in Chapter 1, can be taken from Sloss (1962), where conceptual models for near-shore sedimentation are considered. If S represents the gross geometry of a body of sedimentary rocks, Q is the quantity of material supplied at the site of deposition, R is the rate of subsidence at the site, D is the rate of dispersal and M is the nature of the material supplied, then

$$S = f(Q,R,D,M)$$

In other words, the geometry of a sedimentary body is defined by a function which relates the amount of material supplied, the rate of subsidence, the rate of dispersal and the nature of the material. Also, although the nature of the relationship, i.e. the function, is not defined, then the concept has allowed the development of a simple computer simulation model (Harbaugh & Bonham-Carter 1970, pp. 373ff.).

2.1.6 Complex numbers

It was noted during the solution of some quadratic equations (Section 2.1.3) that there were occasions when it was necessary to consider the problem of finding a value for the square root of a negative number. As an example we were asked to find the roots of the quadratic

$$x^2 - 2x + 5 = 0$$

Using the equation it was found that the roots are given by:

$$\frac{2 \pm 4\sqrt{-1}}{2}$$

and by writing $\sqrt{-1}$ as i, where i is an **imaginary number**, then the roots are

$$x = (1 + 2i) \text{ or } (1 - 2i)$$

A **complex number** can be defined as the sum of a real number and the square root of a negative number.

To recap, the square of any real number, be it positive or negative, is always positive, hence the square roots of negative numbers must be a new type of number. These numbers are referred to as imaginary numbers. Also, since a complex number can be defined as the sum of a real number and the square root of a negative number, and every negative number is the product of (-1) and the corresponding positive number, it is sufficient to introduce a new type of number for $\sqrt{-1}$. This is the imaginary unit denoted by the symbol i, hence the sum of a real and imaginary number is referred to as a complex number. The solution to the quadratic equation, the roots given above are, therefore, complex numbers. A complex number whose imaginary part is equal to zero is a real number. As with other numbers, there are rules of representation and manipulation for complex numbers. These are not dealt with here, since most geological problems have real solutions.

2.1.7   Linear programming

Linear programming is a method of finding the best solution to a problem in maximization (or minimization), in the presence of constraints. Thus, we might be asked to maximize the production from an enterprise taking into account certain operational restrictions (constraints) or, in the opposite sense, we could be asked to minimize production costs taking into account financial constraints. This method of solution depends on expressing the problem in the form of a linear function which is to be maximized (or minimized), and combinations of the constraints in the form of linear inequalities. The method is best understood by considering some simple examples.

A mine produces two grades of ore, A and B. Because of operational restrictions, the maximum production of ore grade A is twice that of ore grade B, whose maximum daily output is 15 tonnes. There are two smelting companies who buy ore, one is situated 10 km away and requires to be supplied with at least 10 tonnes of grade B ore. The second is 25 km away and requires at least 16 tonnes of grade A ore. Unfortunately, the mine transport resources are only 750 tonne-km day^{-1}. If the profit on grade A ore is £25 tonne^{-1} and on grade B ore is £20 tonne^{-1}, obtain the tonnage of each grade of ore per day which yields the greatest profit.

Let x = tonnes of grade A ore and y = tonnes of grade B ore. The constraints on production are

$$16 < x < 30$$

$$10 < y < 15$$

which relate requirements to production. The constraints on delivery are

$$25x + 10y < 750$$

which relate distance to the smelters to transport availability. Finally,

$$25x + 20y = z$$

relating profit from each grade of ore to the overall profit from the operation should be maximized. This is known as the **objective function**.

In order to solve the problem the constraints are plotted on a graph, as in Figure 2.12. The curves represent the maximum and minimum of each grade of ore as well as the function relating to distance and transport availability, which are

$$x = 16; \quad x = 30$$

$$y = 10; \quad y = 15$$

and

$$25x + 10y = 750$$

Notice that the inequality signs have now been replaced by equals signs. Working through each, it should be noted that:

(a) x must be greater or equal to 16, therefore the area to the left of $x = 16$ cannot be considered;
(b) x must be less or equal to 30, therefore the area to the right of $x = 30$ cannot be considered;
(c) y must be greater or equal to 10, therefore the area below $y = 10$ cannot be considered;

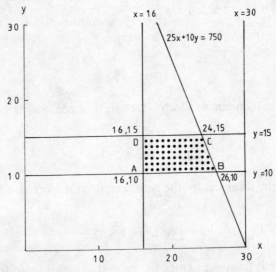

Figure 2.12 Graphical solution of first mine scheduling problem. The objective function is maximized at $x = 24$ and $y = 15$.

(d) y must be less or equal to 15, therefore the area above $y = 15$ cannot be considered; and

(e) since the distance travelled cannot be greater than 750 tonne-km day^{-1}, then the area to the right of the line $25x + 10y = 750$ cannot be considered.

Thus, we have defined the boundary of an area marked ABCD on Figure 2.12, within which solutions are feasible. If we consider just the corners of the quadrilateral and substitute the values for x any at each into the objective function, we get

x, y	$25x + 20y = z$
16, 15	700
16, 10	600
26, 10	850
24, 15	900

Thus, we find that the maximum profit of £900 is made if we supply daily 24 tonnes of grade A ore and 15 tonnes of grade B ore. It can be shown that a maximum (or a minimum) will occur at one of the corners of the inscribed polygon defined by the constraints in a linear-programming problem – the shaded area on the figure.

If we change this example slightly and, instead of having the output of grade A ore controlled by the maximum output of grade B ore, replace these constraints by saying that the maximum total amount of ore produced of either type is 45 tonnes, then our constraints are

$$16 < x \qquad 10 < y$$

which relate to requirements, and

$$x + y < 45$$

which relates to mining capacity, with the delivery constraints and the objective function as before. The graph of their constraints is as in Figure 2.13, and the area of feasible solutions is delineated as before. In this situation the objective function is maximized at the point C on the graph, where $x = 20$ and $y = 25$, which leads to a daily profit of £1000 for the operation.

A graphical solution to a linear programming problem such as

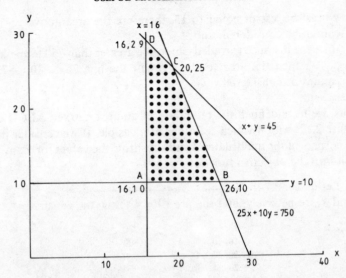

Figure 2.13 Graphical solution of second mine scheduling problem. The objective function is maximized at $x = 20$ and $y = 25$.

those illustrated is quick and reasonably foolproof. However, if there are more than two variables to consider, then, because of the limitations of drawing graphs, the method is inappropriate. We have shown that the possible solution to any two-dimensional linear programming problem lies at one of the points of intersection of the curves representing the constraints. It was shown in Section 2.1.1 that the point of intersection of two curves also represent the solution of the two equations solved simultaneously, this leads us on to an algebraic method of solution for these problems. We start with an example.

A small company produces three types of fireplace, made out of varying combinations of Cotswold limestone and Delabole slate. Fireplace type A needs 10 cwt of Cotswold stone and 2 cwt of Delabole slate, and sells for a profit of £30. Fireplace type B needs 3 cwt of Cotswold stone and 8 cwt of Delabole slate, and sells for a profit of £50. The third type, C, needs 6 cwt of Cotswold stone and 4 cwt of Delabole slate and sells for a profit of £25. If the maximum amount of Cotswold stone available is 200 cwt week^{-1} and the maximum amount of Delabole slate is 150 cwt week^{-1}, how many of each type of fireplace should be produced to maximize the profit, assuming that all of the production can be sold. We can tabulate the data as follows.

	Cotswold stone (cwt)	Delabole slate (cwt)	Profit (£)
fireplace A	10	2	30
fireplace B	3	8	50
fireplace C	6	4	25
maximum rock available per week	200	150	

Let us denote the number of fireplaces of types A, B, C by x_1, x_2 and x_3, respectively, and the profit by z. Then the constraints are

$$10x_1 + 3x_2 + 6x_3 < 200$$

$$2x_1 + 8x_2 + 4x_3 < 150$$

$$x_1 \geqslant 0, \quad x_2 \geqslant 0, \quad x_3 \geqslant 0$$

The objective function is

$$30x_1 + 50x_2 + 25x_3 = z$$

which is to be maximized. First we need to get rid of the inequality signs in our constraint equations. To do this we add a 'slack variable' to each equation:

$$10x_1 + 3x_2 + 6x_3 + x_4 \quad\quad = 200$$

$$2x_1 + 8x_2 + 4x_3 + x_5 \quad\quad = 150$$

We now have two linear equations in five unknowns. We cannot solve these directly, since the problem is **underdetermined**, i.e. there are more unknown variables than there are equations. However, we can choose to set three variables to zero and solve for the remainder.

Set x_3, x_4 and $x_5 = 0$:

$$10x_1 + 3x_2 = 200$$

$$2x_1 + 8x_2 = 150$$

Solving these equations, we find

$$x_1 = 15.54, \quad x_2 = 14.86, \quad x_3 = 0$$

This is a **basic feasible solution**. Rounding-off (we cannot produce fractions of fireplaces), so that $x_1 = 16$ and $x_2 = 15$, we can substitute into the objective function, which gives a value of £1230 for the profit.

We can also set x_2, x_4 and $x_5 = 0$, in which case

$$10x_1 + 6x_3 = 200$$

$$2x_1 + 4x_3 = 150$$

Solving these equations, we find

$$x_1 = -3.56, \quad x_2 = 0, \quad x_3 = 39.28$$

However, this is not a basic feasible solution, since a constraint is that $x_1 \geqslant 0$ and we have found that $x_1 = -3.56$.

We can also set x_1, x_4 and $x_5 = 0$, in which case

$$3x_2 + 6x_3 = 200$$

$$8x_2 + 4x_3 = 150$$

Solving these equations, we find

$$x_1 = 0, \quad x_2 = 2.78, \quad x_3 = 31.94$$

which is a basic feasible solution. Substituting these values (after rounding) into the objective function we find that the profit is £950.

We have now found that by producing 16 fireplaces of type A and 15 fireplaces of type B the company will maximize its profits, which will be £1230 per week. As we noted earlier, the figures used in maximizing the objective function have been rounded, since we assume that we cannot produce fractions of fireplaces. Also, in this example, since the problem was underdetermined, it is impossible to calculate production figures for all three types of fireplace simultaneously. At an early stage we chose to set some variables to zero in an apparently arbitrary fashion. This procedure is legitimate, and it is possible to show that at each corner of the feasible space, only two variables will have non-zero values.

Problems where the objective function is to be minimized are solved in exactly the same way, except that the minimum value for the objective function is sought. For further information on the use of linear programming in a geological context, textbooks such as Harbaugh & Bonham-Carter (1970, ch. 8) and Koch & Link (1971, ch. 14.2) should be consulted. Both give a number of examples, and references for further reading.

2.2 Geometry and trigonometry

2.2.1 Pythagoras' Theorem

Let us suppose that three samples of rock have been collected, in each sample we have found two unique minerals which can be labelled 1 and 2. By point-counting thin sections of the three rocks, the percentage of the two minerals has been determined. On the basis of this information, is it possible to express the closeness of the relationship between the three rocks, numerically? A hypothetical data set is listed in Table 2.7.

Table 2.7 Hypothetical data relating to the amounts of two unique mineral components in three samples of rock.

	Mineral 1 (%)	Mineral 2 (%)
rock A	10	10
rock B	30	15
rock C	25	45

If we plot these data on a graph, as in Figure 2.14, then it is apparent that one method of quantifying the relationship between the three rocks is to calculate the distances $D_{A,B}$, $D_{A,C}$ and $D_{B,C}$, using Pythagoras' Theorem, which states:

The square of the hypotenuse of a right-angled triangle is equal to the sum of the squares on the two adjacent sides.

From Figure 2.14 we can see that the distances (in geometrical terms) between the minerals are given by:

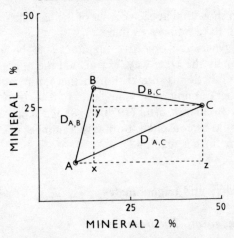

Figure 2.14 Plot of the percentage of two minerals for three rock samples A, B and C, showing their relationship using the Pythagorean distance coefficient (data as in Table 2.7).

$$D_{A,B} = \sqrt{(Ax)^2 + (Bx)^2}$$

$$D_{A,C} = \sqrt{(Az)^2 + (Cz)^2}$$

$$D_{B,C} = \sqrt{(By)^2 + (Cy)^2}$$

Thus, for example, the distance between the two rocks *A* and *B* using this is

$$D_{A,B} = \sqrt{(10 - 15)^2 + (10 - 30)^2}$$

$$= \sqrt{425}$$

$$= 20.62$$

Similarly,

$$D_{A,C} = 38.08$$

$$D_{B,C} = 30.4$$

An advantage of tackling the problem using Pythagoras' Theorem is that if we increase the number of variables, then

$$D_{A,B} = \sqrt{\sum_{i=1}^{n} (A_i - B_i)^2}$$

where $D_{A,B}$ = the distance coefficient, A_i = the ith measured variable for A, B_i = the ith measured variable for B and n = the number of variables. Note that here, as elsewhere in this text, the conventional symbol $\sum$ is used to indicate summation. The indices on it indicates the range of values to be summed.

The measure $D_{A,B}$ has been termed the distance coefficient, and has been used extensively in classification procedures. The smaller the numerical value of the coefficient is, the closer the relationship between the two samples under consideration (see Harbaugh & Merriam 1968, pp. 163ff.). As we shall see in later sections of this book, there are many other mathematical applications of this important theorem.

2.2.2 Trigonometric ratios

In the right-angled triangle ABC Figure 2.15a the ratio of one side to another does not depend on the size of the triangle, but on the size of the angles. These are the 'trigonometric ratios'. They are:

$$\sin \theta = AB/AC$$

$$\cos \theta = BC/AC$$

$$\tan \theta = AB/BC$$

When the triangle does not have a right angle the above ratios do not hold, and neither does Pythagoras' Theorem. Thus, in the triangle ABC shown in Figure 2.15b which does not have a right angle, then to find the unknowns we use the **sine rule**:

$$\frac{\sin A}{a} = \frac{\sin B}{b} = \frac{\sin C}{c}$$

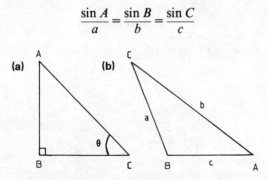

Figure 2.15 The relationship between the length of the sides and the angles of a triangle. (a) A right-angled triangle; (b) an obtuse-angled triangle.

This rule is normally used when one side and two angles are known. If we are given two sides and an angle or three sides, then the **cosine rule** should be used:

$$a^2 = b^2 + c^2 - 2bc \cos A$$

The most useful applications of these ratios and rules in geology are in solving problems related to geological mapping and section construction. To illustrate their use in this important field, we will consider three simple, but frequently occurring, problems.

(a) Find the true thickness of a stratigraphic unit given its apparent thickness at outcrop, its dip and the angle of slope on which the apparent thickness was measured. In Figure 2.16 CA is the apparent (or outcrop) thickness, b is the true dip and a is the slope of the surface. The true thickness AB is given by

$$AB = AC \sin (a + b)$$

(Barnes 1981, p. 74, fig. 6.1). If the surface is horizontal, then $a = 0$, and

$$AB = AS \sin b$$

(Ragan 1968, pp. 10–11, fig. 2.5).

(b) Find the depth D to the top of a stratigraphic unit from a point on the surface at a given distance M from the outcrop, measured at right angles to the strike and also given the true dip b. The depth D is given by

$$D = M \tan b$$

(Ragan 1968, p. 12, fig. 2.10)

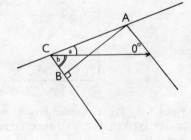

Figure 2.16 To find the true thickness of a stratigraphic unit from its apparent thickness and the angle of dip and the slope of the surface.

(c) To find the dip and strike using three points on a map. The strike is determined by joining two points of equal elevation, where the contour is cut by the top or bottom of the same unit, using points as far apart as possible, to give maximum accuracy. The true dip is found using any third point (again, as far away from the others as is reasonably possible) and the equation

$$\tan b = V/H$$

where b = true dip, V = difference in height between the line of strike and the third point, and H = the horizontal or map distance between the two. The strike can be measured directly from the map (Ragan 1968, p. 19).

Many more examples of the use of the basic geometric and trigonometric concepts can be found in the geological and structural geology literature. A most useful and comprehensive survey of their uses with large numbers of examples is given in Ragan (1968).

Since there are many occasions when geologists are required to measure angles greater than 90° and then convert them to one of the trigonometric functions, it is worthwhile reminding ourselves of the range of values for the functions in the four quadrants of the circle. These are summarized in Table 2.8. It should be remembered that tables of sines, cosines and tangents are normally given only for the first quadrant (0–90°). Thus, if we require, for example, the value for the tangent of 110° we look up the tangent of $(110 - 90)°$, i.e. 20°, and reverse the sign. Similarly, the cosine of 290° is found by getting the value for $(360 - 290)°$, i.e. 70°. In this case the sign is not reversed.

Table 2.8 The ranges of values of the three common trigonometric functions for the four quadrants of the circle. Note that whereas the sine and cosine distributions are continuous, that for the tangent is not.

Angle (degrees)	sin	cos	tan	Circular measure (radians)
0 to 90	0 to +1	+1 to 0	0 to +∞	0 to π/2
90 to 180	+1 to 0	0 to −1	−∞ to 0	π/2 to π
180 to 270	0 to −1	−1 to 0	0 to +∞	π to 3π/2
270 to 360	−1 to 0	0 to +1	−∞ to 0	3π/2 to 2π

2.2.3 Angular measure

In the examples so far discussed in this chapter, and particularly those which are related to problems of geological mapping, the angular measure used is degrees. This is known as **sexagesimal measure**. Fractions of degrees are measured in minutes ($1' = 1/60$ degree) and seconds ($1'' = 1/60$ minute). An alternative to sexagesimal measure is **circular** or **radian measure**. The measurement of an angle in radians is defined as the length of an arc cut off by the angle on a unit circle (i.e. radius 1 unit), with the centre of the circle at the vertex of the angle. The radius and arc are understood to be measured on the same scale. Thus, we have

$$360° = 2\pi \text{ rad} \approx 6.28319 \text{ rad}$$

$$180° = \pi \text{ rad} \approx 3.14159 \text{ rad}$$

$$90° = \pi/2 \text{ rad} \approx 1.57080 \text{ rad}$$

$$\text{or} \quad 1 \text{ rad} = 57° \ 17' \ 44.8''$$

Throughout the remainder of this text the angular unit will be used only in cases where an angle can be directly measured, elsewhere it should be understood that the measure is in radians. Students should also note that in computer programming, functions involving angles (i.e. sin, cos, tan, etc.) use radian measure, and therefore angles given or calculated in sexagesimal measure should be converted accordingly.

2.2.4 Trigonometric identities

There are a number of common trigonometric identities which are used throughout this text and which occur in a number of mathematical applications in the geological literature. Although it is not intended to prove or use them at this stage, a list of the standard identities follows.

(a) Basic identities:

 (i) $\sin^2 A + \cos^2 A = 1$
 (ii) $1 + \tan^2 A = \sec^2 A$
 (iii) $1 + \cos^2 A = \csc^2 A$

(b) Sum and difference formulae:

 (i) $\sin (A + B) = \sin A \cos B + \cos A \sin B$
 (ii) $\sin (A - B) = \sin A \cos B - \cos A \sin B$

(iii) $\cos (A + B) = \cos A \cos B - \sin A \sin B$

(iv) $\cos (A - B) = \cos A \cos B + \sin A \sin B$

(v) $\tan (A + B) = \dfrac{\tan A + \tan B}{1 - \tan A \tan B}$

(vi) $\tan (A - B) = \dfrac{\tan A - \tan B}{1 + \tan A \tan B}$

(c) Double- and triple-angle formulae:

(i) $\sin 2A = 2 \sin A \cos A = \dfrac{2 \tan A}{1 + \tan^2 A}$

(ii) $\sin 3A = 3 \sin A = 4 \sin^3 A$

(iii) $\cos 2A = \cos^2 A - \sin^2 A = 1 - 2 \sin 2A = 2 \cos^2 A - 1$

$\qquad = \dfrac{1 - \tan^2 A}{1 + \tan^2 A}$

(iv) $\cos 3A = 4 \cos^3 A - 3 \cos A$

(v) $\tan 2A = \dfrac{2 \tan A}{1 - \tan^2 A}$

(vi) $\tan 3A = \dfrac{3 \tan A - \tan^3 A}{1 - 3 \tan^2 A}$

(d) Half-angle formulae:

(i) $\sin A = \dfrac{2 \tan \frac{1}{2}A}{1 + \tan^2\frac{1}{2}A}$

(ii) $\cos A = \dfrac{1 - \tan^2\frac{1}{2}A}{1 + \tan^2\frac{1}{2}A}$

(iii) $\tan A = \dfrac{2 \tan \frac{1}{2}A}{1 - \tan^2\frac{1}{2}A}$

(e) Factor formulae:

(i) $\sin A + \sin B = 2 \sin \frac{1}{2}(A + B) \cos \frac{1}{2}(A + B)$

(ii) $\sin A - \sin B = 2 \cos \frac{1}{2}(A + B) \sin \frac{1}{2}(A - B)$

(iii) $\cos A + \cos B = 2 \cos \frac{1}{2}(A + B) \cos \frac{1}{2}(A - B)$

(iv) $\cos A - \cos B = 2 \sin \frac{1}{2}(A + B) \sin \frac{1}{2}(B - A)$

(v) $\tan A + \tan B = \dfrac{\sin (A + B)}{\cos A \cos B}$

(vi) $\tan A - \tan B = \dfrac{\sin (B - A)}{\sin A \cos B}$

Consideration of the angular relationship between shear planes in rock provide a good, simple, geological example of the value of trigonometric identities. For simplicity the two-dimensional case can be considered; that is, the biaxial stress field as illustrated in Figure 2.17b. In this situation there are two principal stresses, σ_1 and σ_3, mutually at right angles to one another. From the biaxial stress analysis, equations can be derived that give the normal stress σ and the shear stress τ along any plane inclined at $\theta°$ to σ_1. Then

$$\sigma = \sigma_1 \sin^2\theta + \sigma_3 \cos^2\theta$$

$$\tau = (\sigma_1 - \sigma_3) \sin\theta \cos\theta$$

Using the trigonometric identities

$$\sin 2\theta = 2 \sin\theta \cos\theta$$

$$\cos 2\theta = \cos^2\theta - \sin^2\theta$$

we can express the biaxial stress equations in terms of the angle 2θ, which is the angle between the shear planes (Fig. 2.17a)

$$\sigma = \tfrac{1}{2}(\sigma_1 + \sigma_3) - \tfrac{1}{2}(\sigma_1 - \sigma_3) \cos 2\theta$$

$$\tau = \tfrac{1}{2}(\sigma_1 - \sigma_3) \sin 2\theta$$

As will be demonstrated in Section 4.2.5, we can use this pair of equations to calculate a theoretical value for the angle 2θ, which can then be compared with the observed angle in rock.

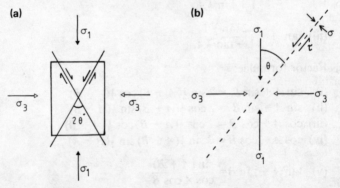

Figure 2.17 (a) The biaxial stress field acting on a small block of rock, producing shear failure. (b) The biaxial stress field showing the relationship between the normal stress (σ) and the shear stress (τ).

2.3 Probability theory

In some of the chapters which follow, the concepts of probability theory are used or alluded to in a number of important applications. Therefore, although this is not intended as a statistical textbook, it is necessary to include a brief introduction to the basic concepts, for completeness. For more-detailed accounts of this topic the student is referred to statistical works. However, the following summary, based on Gray (1967), together with the examples to be found in this section and in later chapters, should provide an introduction to the basic concepts and its potential use in geology. We shall start with the basic definitions.

There are situations in which, when an operation is performed on a system, there are a number of different possible outcomes and where a particular outcome is not under the control of the operator. Probability theory should provide a method of defining how likely a specified outcome is, as a result of the operation. Also, the theory should be able to define how the probabilities that certain basic events occur can be combined to give the probability of the occurrence of complex events. In an ideal situation it should be possible to arrive at a measure of probability from a description of the system and trial; unfortunately, this ideal is only achieved in special situations.

In general, the probability of an event $p(E)$, is measured on the scale 0–1.0 (0–100%), i.e.

$$0 \leqslant p(E) \leqslant 1$$

The measure $p(E)$ can be regarded as the limiting value of the relative frequency of E. This follows since it can be shown that, when repeated independent trials can be made, the relative frequency of E converges to a limit as the number of trials increases. Thus, if we spin a coin the relative frequency of the occurrence of heads tends towards 50 per cent as the number of trials increases. Impossible events have zero relative frequency, and hence zero probability, while events that are certain have unit relative frequency, and hence unit probability. However, it should be remembered that if the frequency of E is 0 (or 1), then it does not mean that E is impossible (or certain). The following axioms, sometimes known as the 'laws of chance', are not proven, but can be justified by the agreement between practical trials and theoretical calculations using them.

2.3.1 The addition axiom

If E_1 and E_2 are two mutually exclusive events (i.e. E_1 and E_2 cannot occur together), then the probability that E_1 or E_2 happens is the sum of their individual probabilities:

$$p(E_1 \text{ or } E_2) = p(E_1) + p(E_2)$$

In general,

$$p(E_1 \text{ or } E_2 \text{ or } \dots \text{ or } E_n) = \sum p(E_1)$$

In systems which are symmetrical, such as a coin or a six-sided die all possible outcomes of a trial can be considered to be equally likely. In this situation, if F is the event which occurs, then the probability of it occurring is given by

$$p(F) = \frac{\text{number of equally likely favourable outcomes}}{\text{total number of equally likely possible outcomes}}$$

2.3.2 Multiplication axiom

If two events E_1 and E_2 are independent, such that the outcome of one does not affect the outcome of the other, then the probability that both E_1 and E_2 happen is the product of their individual probabilities:

$$p(E_1 \text{ and } E_2) = p(E_1) \times p(E_2)$$

In general,

$$p(E_1 \text{ and } E_2 \text{ and } \dots \text{ and } E_n) = \prod_{i=1}^{n} p(E_i)$$

Note the use here, as elsewhere in this book, of the symbol $\prod$, which is the conventional shorthand for multiplication. The indices indicate the range of values to be multiplied together.

2.3.3 Complementary events

When an event E_1 does not happen as the result of a trial, then the complementary event E_2 happens. Since E_1 and E_2 are mutually exclusive,

$$p(E_1 \text{ or } E_2) = p(E_1) + p(E_2)$$

Further, since E_1 or E_2 is certain with unit probability, it follows that

$$p(E_1) = 1 - p(E_2)$$

The result of throwing a pair of dice a large number of times (60), plotted as a histogram, is shown in Figure 2.18. The theoretical distribution is indicated by the dotted lines on the figure. These show how the axioms operate when there is a combination of independent events (i.e. two dice) and mutually exclusive events (i.e. the numbers given by the face of a single die). Thus, the probability that a six will result from one throw of a single die is given by

$$p(6) = 1/6$$

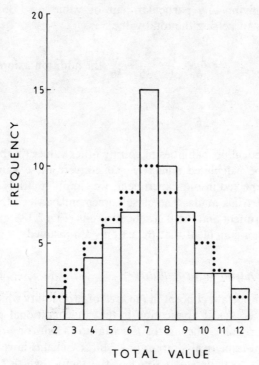

Figure 2.18 Histograms showing the frequency distributions of values obtained from a pair of dice. ——————— , Distribution obtained after throwing a pair of dice 60 times; • • • • • • •, the theoretical distribution for throwing a pair of dice 60 times.

whereas the probability of getting two sixes, throwing two dice is

$$p(6 \text{ and } 6) = \tfrac{1}{6} \quad \tfrac{1}{6} \text{ (the multiplication axiom)}$$

$$= 1/36$$

The result of getting two sixes gives a total of 12. On the other hand, if we wish to calculate the probability of getting the total value five, then there are four ways from which this may arise:

(a) die 1 can show 4 and die 2 can show 1,
(b) die 1 can show 1 and die 2 can show 4,
(c) die 1 can show 2 and die 2 can show 3, and
(d) die 1 can show 3 and die 2 can show 2.

Since these are complementary events, and since the probability of two dice giving any particular pair of values is 1/36, then the probability of getting the total value 5 is

$$p_{(\text{total} = 5)} = \frac{1}{36} + \frac{1}{36} + \frac{1}{36} + \frac{1}{36} \text{ (the addition axiom)}$$

$$= \frac{4}{36}$$

The theoretical probabilities of getting other values (in the range 2–12), can be calculated similarly. To convert these values to the number expected in our experiment, we simply multiply by 60, the number of trials made. The close agreement between this limited-trials experiment and the theoretical results (Fig. 2.18), gives weight to the earlier statement that the axioms are justified.

2.3.4 Conditional probability

Another important concept in the area of probability which has had extensive geological application is that of conditional probability and, in particular, the use of the Markov chain or process. For example, in numerical stratigraphy Markov chains have been used in attempts to understand some of the factors which control the order of deposition of sedimentary sequences. Fundamental to the ideas behind the Markov chain is that the outcome of an event is related to previous events. They can be relatively simple, in that only the immediately preceding event has any influence; or may be complex, where a number of previous events in different combinations have influence. Examples of the use of Markov chains will be given in Section 6.4.1, along with references which will allow the interested reader to follow up the matter.

3 Sequences and series

3.1 Definitions

3.1.1 The idea of infinity

If n takes successively the positive integer values (1, 2, 3, etc.), then there is no limit to the values which n can assume. It does not matter how large a number we may think of, n will eventually exceed it. If n increases in this fashion we can say that n tends to **infinity**, i.e. $n \to \infty$.

Also, if $f(n) = n^x$, where x is a positive integer and n increases without limit, $f(n)$ also increases without limit and will exceed and remain greater than any positive number which n takes, however large. Here, as n tends to infinity, so does $f(n)$, i.e. $f(n) \to \infty$ as $n \to \infty$.

If, for example, $f(n) = n + 1/n$, then $f(n)$ will still approach infinity as $n \to \infty$, provided that n takes on positive integer values as before. On the other hand, if the function is $\varphi(n) = 1/n - n$, then the series will increase without limit through the negative values as n approaches infinity. Thus, we can write $\varphi(n) \to -\infty$ as $n \to \infty$.

3.1.2 Definitions relating to series

A **sequence** is a set of ordered terms with a rule for obtaining each term. It can be written as

$$u_1, u_2, u_3, \ldots, u_n$$

A **series** is formed when the terms of the sequence are added

the sequence $u_1, u_2, u_3, \ldots, u_n +$

gives rise to the series $u_1 + u_2 + u_3 + \ldots + u_n +$

S_n is the sum of the first n terms of a series

S_∞ is the sum to infinity of a series

$\sum_{r=a}^{b} u_r$ is the sum of all the terms u_r, where r is an integer in the range a to b, inclusive

$\prod_{r=a}^{b} u_r$ is the product of all terms u_r, where r is an integer in the range a to b inclusive

A series may be finite or infinite:

the series $u_1 + u_2 + u_3 + \ldots + u_n$ is finite

the series $u_1 + u_2 + u_3 + \ldots + u_n +$ is infinite and its sum is denoted either by $\sum_{r=1}^{\infty} u_r$ or, when it would not be ambiguous, by $\sum u_r$.

3.1.3 The idea of a limit

Taking, as an example, the function $f(n) = 1 + 1/n$, if n takes successively the values 1, 10, 100, 1000, 10 000, etc., then the values for the function are

$$2, 1.1, 1.01, 1.001, 1.0001, \ldots$$

Thus, as the value of n increases, the value of the function gets closer to 1.0, although it never quite reaches it. We can describe this by saying that $f(n)$ tends to 1, as n tends to infinity, i.e. $f(n) \to 1$ as $n \to \infty$. Alternatively, the **limit** of $f(n)$ is 1 as n tends to infinity, symbolically

$$\lim_{n \to \infty} f(n) = 1$$

As we shall see in the following two chapters, one of the more important applications of the limit is in calculus. Here some small but finite increment, usually denoted by Δx, is made infinitely small, i.e. in the limit $\Delta x \to 0$. This then allows the analytical solution of various problems related to rates of change (differential calculus, Ch. 4) and areas and volumes (integral calculus, Ch. 5).

3.1.4 Convergence of a series

If we have a series whose sum to n terms is given by

$$S_n = u_1 + u_2 + u_3 + \ldots + u_n$$

where n tends to infinity (i.e. increases without limit) and, if the sum of the terms of the series tends to a finite limit S as n approaches infinity, then the series is said to be **convergent** and S is its **sum to infinity**.

On the other hand, if the sum tends to infinity as n tends to infinity, then the series is said to be **divergent** to $+\infty$. Also, if the sum tends to $-\infty$ as n tends to infinity, then the series is said to be divergent to $-\infty$.

If we consider the series

$$1 - 1 + 3 - 3 + 5 - 5 + \ldots$$

then the sum $S_{2n} = 0$ and the sum $S_{2n+1} = 2n + 1$. Thus, when $n \to \infty$, then $S_{2n} \to 0$ and $S_{2n+1} \to \infty$. This series **oscillates infinitely**.

If $u_1 + u_2 + u_3 + \ldots$ is a convergent series, then $u_n \to 0$ as $n \to \infty$, and the value of any term is given by

$$u_n = S_n - S_{n-1}$$

Also,

$$\lim_{n \to \infty} u_n = \lim_{n \to \infty} S_n - \lim_{n \to \infty} S_{n-1}$$

$$= 0$$

This is a necessary condition for convergence, but does not guarantee it absolutely. It does not work for example, with the harmonic series.

3.1.5   The time series

In geology, so-called time series play an extremely significant role in many areas. Such series are frequently true time series, i.e. data recorded at set time intervals, or a series relative to some parameter which may be related to time. An example of the first category is the measurement of the release of Sr^{2+} as aragonite is converted to calcite, already used in Section 2.1.4. In the second category we might include data recorded at set intervals, throughout a stratigraphic sequence. In this situation, since the measurement made is relative to thickness and it is likely that there is some relationship between thickness and time, the measurements are also implicitly related to time.

The timespan of measurement will always be finite, whereas the number of possible measurements can be either finite or infinite.

This follows since, however small the timespan may be, it is possible to sample at increasingly smaller intervals. Thus, if Δx is the sample interval and n is the number of data points sampled, then

$$\lim \Delta x \to 0 \text{ as } n \to \infty$$

i.e. we have a continuous record.

Many time series of interest in geology oscillate at approximately regular intervals and with differing amplitudes. The first example mentioned does not fall into this category since, as we have already seen, the release of strontium follows an exponential function. On the other hand, stratigraphic sequences frequently show cyclicity, and many parameters which can be measured for such a sequence reflect this and give rise to oscillating data sequences of great complexity. For the analysis of such time series it is more convenient if the data are sampled at regular intervals, the size of the interval and hence the number of points usually being controlled by either the phenomena being measured or by economic or time considerations. Fortunately, there are very few situations where equal spacing is not possible. We shall consider one method of time series analysis of oscillating data in Section 5.4.

3.2 Some common series

3.2.1 Arithmetic series

An arithmetic series is of the general form

$$a + (a + d) + (a + 2d) + (a + 3d) + \ldots$$

where $a = $ the first term and $d = $ the common difference – to find d subtract any term from the next one. The series a, b, c forms an arithmetic series if the result

$$b = \tfrac{1}{2}(a + c)$$

holds, and b is called the arithmetic mean.

In general, the arithmetic mean is given by

$$\frac{1}{n} \sum_{i=1}^{n} x_i$$

3.2.2   Geometric series

A geometric series is of the general form

$$a + aR + aR^2 + aR^3 + \ldots$$

where $a =$ the first term and $R =$ the common ratio term – to find R divide any term by the previous one. The series can be either convergent or divergent. The nth term u_n is given by

$$u_n = aR^{n-1}$$

and the sum of the first n terms by

$$S_n = \sum_{r=1}^{n} aR^{n-1}$$

The series x, y, z forms a geometric series if

$$y = \sqrt{(xz)}$$

and y is called the geometric mean of x and z.

In general, the geometric mean is given by

$$\sqrt[n]{\prod_{i=1}^{n} (x_i)}$$

3.2.3   The harmonic series

A harmonic series is of the general form

$$a + \frac{a}{a + ((n) - 1)} + \frac{a}{a + ((n) - 1)} + \ldots$$

where $a =$ the first term and $(n) =$ the position of a term in the series. The series can be either convergent or divergent.

The harmonic mean is given by

$$n \Big/ \sum_{i=1}^{n} (1/x_i)$$

3.2.4   The binomial series

The expansion of $(a + x)^n$ for all x and positive integer values of n is given by

$$(a + x)^n = a^n + na^{n-1}x + \frac{n(n - 1)}{2!} a^{n-2}x^2 +$$

$$\frac{n(n - 1)(n - 2)}{3!} a^{n-3}x^3 + \ldots + x^n$$

The general $(r + 1)$ term is given by

$$\frac{n(n-1)(n-2) \ldots (n - r + 1)}{r!} a^{n-r}x^r$$

In some texts the series is denoted by:

$$\sum \binom{n}{r} x^r$$

where $\binom{n}{r} = \dfrac{(n - 1) \ldots (n - r + 1)}{r!}$

and $\binom{n}{0} = 1$

As n is a positive integer, the series has a finite number of terms. We can demonstrate this by expanding simple equations:

$$(a + x)^1 = 1a + 1x$$

$$(a + x)^2 = 1a^2 + 2ax + 1x^2$$

$$(a + x)^3 = 1a^3 + 3a^2x + 3ax^2 + 1x^3$$

$$(a + x)^4 = 1a^4 + 4a^3x + 6a^2x^2 + 4ax^3 + 1x^4$$

The pattern of coefficients of the expansion is most usefully summarized in the form of Pascal's triangle:

n	Pascal's triangle
1	1 1
2	1 2 1
3	1 3 3 1
4	1 4 6 4 1
5	1 5 10 10 5 1
6	etc.

Individual terms in the triangle are obtained by adding the two terms on either side on the previous line:

e.g. $n = 1$ 1   1

     $n = 2$ 1   2   1

     $n = 3$ 1   3   3   1

with the outermost pair of coefficients being set to unity.

3.2.5 Exponential series

An exponential function is one where the variable is in the exponent, e.g. a^x. In the special case e^x (called the exponential function), e is the number such that the gradient $y = e^x$ at $(0,1)$ is unity. Using the binomial series we can expand $f(x) = e^x$, where x is a rational number:

$$e^x = 1 + \frac{x}{1!} + \frac{x^2}{2!} + \frac{x^3}{3!} + \frac{x^4}{4!} + \frac{x^5}{5!} + \ldots$$

this is the exponential series. If x is negative and rational, then

$$e^{-x} = 1 + \frac{x}{1!} + \frac{x^2}{2!} + \frac{x^3}{3!} + \frac{x^4}{4!} + \frac{x^5}{5!} + \ldots$$

We can calculate the value of e to any required degree of accuracy by substituting $x = 1$ in the series e^x as above. This gives

$$e = e^1 = 1 + \frac{1}{1!} + \frac{1^2}{2!} + \frac{1^3}{3!} + \frac{1^4}{4!} + \ldots + \frac{1^9}{9!}$$

whence $e = 2.71828$, to six significant figures. It also follows that $e^0 = 1$.

The logarithmic series is based on the function e^x, which can take any value between 0 and $+\infty$, and corresponding to any real positive number y there is a number x such that

$$y = e^x \quad \text{or} \quad x = \ln y$$

i.e. x is the natural logarithm of y. The series is

$$\ln(1 + x) = x - \frac{x^2}{2} + \frac{x^3}{3} - \frac{x^4}{4} + \ldots$$

which will converge, provided x is in the range -1 to 1.

3.3 Geological applications

3.3.1 The estimation of the mean for a given data set

In statistics there are a number of measures of central tendency which can be used in the statistical description of measurement data. The most commonly used is the mean. However, as we have seen during our consideration of simple series, there are three means which can be calculated, associated with the arithmetic, geometric and harmonic series. In geological data-processing the arithmetic mean (or average) is usually used. However, in some situations it may be more appropriate to use one of the other means. As an example, we can take the data given in Table 2.3 to demonstrate the differences in the arithmetic and geometric mean, by using the data to calculate values for the mean grain size of the sediment sample. If we use the arithmetic mean and the data for the mm-scale, then we find that the mean is 0.607 mm (equivalent to about 0.75 units on the φ-scale), and using the φ-scale data the mean is $1.49\,\varphi$ (equivalent to 0.355 mm). When the geometric mean is used with the mm-scale, then the mean is found to be 0.355 mm, which is equivalent to $1.49\,\varphi$. That is, the geometric mean of the mm-scale gives the same value in φ units, as the arithmetic mean of the φ-scale. This is summarized in Table 3.1.

Table 3.1 The relationship between the arithmetic and geometric means for the grain-size data of Table 2.3.

	Arithmetic mean		Geometric mean	
	mm	equivalent φ	mm	equivalent φ
mm–scale	0.607	0.75	0.355	1.49
	Arithmetic mean			
	φ	equivalent mm		
φ-scale	1.49	0.355		

From the above it is clear that we need some rule which will enable us to decide which mean is appropriate in any particular situation. Distinguishing between the arithmetic and geometric means is relatively straightforward, since things which grow exponentially (such as the mm-scale in our grain-size problem) require the use of the geometric mean. In this context we should also notice that the geometric mean of the lognormal distribution is equal to the median of the distribution. Also, if the natural logarithmic mean $\mu_l(y)$ (throughout this text the Greek symbol μ is used to signify the mean of a data set; unqualified this implies the arithmetic mean, a subscript will signify the mean other than the arithmetic mean, but in this case the subscript l indicates the logarithmic mean) of a set of lognormally distributed data is given by

$$\mu_l(y) = 1/n \sum_{i=1}^{n} \ln y_i$$

and the geometric mean $\mu_g(y)$ is given by

$$\mu_g(y) = \exp(\mu_l(y))$$

where $y = \ln(x - \beta)$ and β is the addition constant, and is equal to zero for small samples. In this case, if x is the measured variable, then

$$y = x$$

As an example, we can take data relating to the measurement of Sr^{2+} on a number of brines from experiments on the early diagenesis of carbonates already referred to earlier (Section 2.1.4). The data quoted in ppm, comprises some 36 points, and is illustrated in Figure 3.1. Although this is not a perfect lognormal distribution, the calculated statistics are as follows:

	arithmetic mean	= 57.31 ppm
raw data	geometric mean	= 39.21 ppm
	median	= 38.50 ppm
ln data	arithmetic mean	= 3.67

and

$$\exp 3.67 = 39.25 \text{ ppm}$$

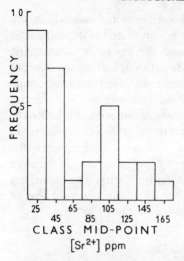

Figure 3.1 Frequency distribution of the data used in the example calculation relating the geometric and arithmetic means. The data are taken from experiments carried out simulating the early diagenesis of carbonate ooids, and represent the concentrations of Sr^{2+} in the brines.

For these data there is a close agreement between the value of the geometric mean of the raw data and the exponential of the arithmetic mean of the transformed set. The difference between the median and the geometric mean probably reflects the nature of the data distribution. For further discussion of these relationships see Rendu (1981, pp. 7ff.).

The use of the harmonic mean is not so clear-cut in geological studies. It may be that in some applications of stratigraphic data analysis the harmonic mean would be more suitable than the generally used arithmetic mean. One important application of the harmonic mean is in the estimation of the tectonic strain ratio. Lisle (1977) was able to show that the strain ratio estimated from the mean shape of deformed elliptical markers varied according to the mean used (Lisle 1977, p. 144, table 1), and the best estimate (when the results were compared with another method of analysis) is given by the harmonic mean. To facilitate calculation of the various means, a computer program, Program 3.1, is listed.

3.3.2 The mean in geothermics

An important factor which controls the temperature gradient of the Earth's crust at a particular point is the thermal conductivity of the constituent minerals of the rocks within the crust, near to the point of measurement. The thermal conductivity, denoted by K, is a measure of the energy flow (heat transfer) per unit area and the temperature gradient, in a one-dimensional heat conductor

(Buntebarth 1984, p. 9). Values of K for rocks and minerals at the Earth's surface range from 1 to $6\,W\,m^{-1}\,K^{-1}$ and is dependent on both the type of rock or mineral and the crystal structure. The thermal conductivity of a rock can be estimated using the thermal conductivities of the individual mineral constituents and their relative occurrence in the rock under consideration.

Thus, a maximum value for thermal conductivity can be calculated from the weighted arithmetic mean

$$K_{max} = \sum_{i=1}^{n} p_i \, K_i$$

and a minimum value from the weighted harmonic mean

$$1/K_{min} = \sum_{i=1}^{n} p_i \, K_i$$

where K_i = the thermal conductivity of the ith mineral species, p_i = the probability of the occurrence of the ith mineral species and n = the number of minerals present. The calculation of the thermal conductivity of a rock using these equations can best be illustrated by reference to an actual example.

A quartz dolerite has the composition given in Table 3.2. Assuming that the pyroxene is augite and the plagioclase labradorite, the thermal conductivities (K) of the minerals are as listed. We are asked to calculate the maximum and minimum thermal conductivities for the rock. The values of K given are taken from Horai & Simmons (1969).

Table 3.2 Mineral composition of a quartz dolerite. The thermal conductivities (K), of the minerals are also given.

Mineral	Percentage	K mcal/cm sec °C
pyroxene	34	9.13
plagioclase	46	3.65
hornblende	4.5	6.07
ilmenite	8	5.25
quartz	5.5	18.37
calcite	2	8.58

$$K_{max} = (0.34 \times 9.13) + (0.46 \times 3.65) + (0.045 \times 6.07) +$$
$$(0.08 \times 5.25) + (0.055 \times 18.37) + (0.02 \times 8.58)$$
$$= 6.6583$$

$$1/K_{min} = (0.34/9.13) + (0.46/3.65) + (0.045/6.07) + (0.08/5.25) +$$
$$(0.055/18.37) + (0.02/8.58)$$
$$= 0.1912$$

and $K_{min} = 5.2289$.

Because K is also dependent on the crystal structure, some rocks can be anisotropic with respect to thermal conductivity. In this situation there are three independent components for K in the directions of the three perpendicular co-ordinate directions x, y and z. Conventionally, K_z is vertical, and K_x and K_y are horizontal and are assumed to be equal.

A value for K_{max} is given by the arithmetic mean:

$$K_{max} = \tfrac{1}{3}(K_x + K_y + K_z)$$

a value for K_{min} is given by the harmonic mean:

$$K_{min} = 3(1/K_x + 1/K_y + 1/K_z)^{-1}$$

while the geometric mean

$$K_g = 3\sqrt{(K_x \, K_y \, K_z)}$$

which lies in the region of

$$K_{min} \leqslant K_g \leqslant K_{max}$$

3.3.3 Discrete distributions

(a) THE BINOMIAL DISTRIBUTION

Let us suppose that we are sorting a pile of material formed of pieces of mineral and gangue, and that the constituents have been well mixed; in other words, the distribution of the two types within the pile is random. Also, because of a coating of mud on each piece, we cannot see what we have chosen until it has been cleaned.

If p is associated with picking a piece of mineral and q is associated with picking a piece of gangue, then because only two events can occur and no others, from the basic concepts of probability theory,

$$p + q = 1$$

Now, using the multiplication axiom of probability theory, if two trials are made, then the probability that we will choose two pieces of mineral is

$$P_{(p \text{ in 2 trials})} = p^2$$

and that we will choose two pieces of gangue is

$$P_{(q \text{ in 2 trials})} = q^2$$

The remaining alternative is that with our two trials we will pick a piece of mineral and a piece of gangue. Now, from the addition axiom, the probability that either p or q will happen twice is

$$p^2 + q^2$$

Thus, the probability that we choose one of each in two trials is

$$1 - (p^2 + q^2)$$

This expression is not very convenient, particularly in complex cases. Thus, an alternative way of approaching the problem is needed. We can argue as follows:

either: mineral can be chosen in trial 1 and gangue in trial 2

or: gangue can be chosen in trial 1 and mineral in trial 2

applying the multiplication axiom, the probability of the first alternative happening is pq, and of the second alternative happening is qp. Combining these, and ignoring the order of events, the probability of choosing a piece of mineral and a piece of gangue in two trials is $2pq$.

Having covered all of the possible outcomes from a two-trial situation, the alternatives can be summarized as follows:

(a) mineral chosen twice: p^2,
(b) either mineral or gangue chosen: $2pq$,
(c) gangue chosen twice: q^2

which are the terms of the binomial expansion

$$(p + q)^2 = p^2 + 2pq + q^2$$

If, instead of picking two pieces of rock (two trials), we pick a number of subsamples of n pieces (n trials), then by extending the above argument it is possible to show that the probability of getting $0, 1, 2, 3, \ldots, n$ pieces of mineral in our subsamples will be given by the successive terms of the expansion of

$$(q + p)^n$$

reading from left to right (*note the order of p and q in this last expression*).

Returning to our example, we may wish to test the hypothesis that the mineral and gangue are mixed in equal proportions. To test this we take 50 subsamples of four pieces each, counting the number of pieces of mineral in each subsample. The data can be tabulated as in Table 3.3.

Table 3.3 Possible numbers of pieces of mineral to be found in a subsample of size 4, and the corresponding number of subsamples found to have those number of pieces of mineral, when 50 subsamples were selected.

No. of possible pieces of mineral in subsample	No. of subsamples
0	2
1	11
2	22
3	12
4	3

The probability P of finding 0, 1, 2, 3 or 4 pieces of mineral in a subsample are given by successive terms of the expansion of

$$(q + p)^4$$

which are

$$P[0] = q^4 \quad P[1] = 4pq^3 \quad P[2] = 6p^2q^2 \quad P[3] = 4p^3q \quad P[4] = p^4$$

numbers in brackets indicate the corresponding number of pieces of mineral. Since our hypothesis was of equal mixing,

$$p = q = 0.5$$

Substituting the values for p and q into each term of the expansion and multiplying the resulting probability values by 50 (the number of subsamples selected), we get theoretical probabilities, and the equivalent expected number of subsamples as given in Table 3.4.

Table 3.4 Theoretical numbers of pieces of mineral in a subsample of size 4, for 50 subsamples, assuming equal mixing of mineral and gangue.

Probability of getting the number of pieces indicated of mineral	Expected no. of subsamples
$P[0] = 0.0625$	3
$P[1] = 0.25$	12
$P[2] = 0.375$	19
$P[3] = 0.25$	12
$P[4] = 0.0625$	3

If we compare the results given in column 2 of Table 3.4 with the original data in column 2 of Table 3.3, then it can be seen that there is a close similarity, which would support our original contention that we had a 50:50 mix of mineral and gangue in our original sample. It should be noted that in a practical application of this method, a statistical test would be used to quantify the similarity between the observed and expected data.

One common use of the binomial distribution is in the situation where there is no *a priori* knowledge as to the values for the probability of an occurrence or non-occurrence. In this situation the required probabilities are estimated from the data. Let us suppose that we have superimposed a grid over an area of interest, and count the number of occurrences of a particular item or event in each grid square. We can tabulate the data to show the number of possible occurrences of the item in any grid square and the number of times each possible occurrence is encountered.

In Figure 3.2 the possible occurrences of the item are: 0, 1, 2 and 3, and there are

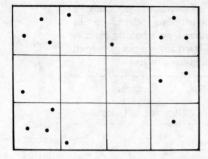

Figure 3.2 Contiguous grid sampling scheme for the binomial distribution. 4 × 3 layout corresponding to the hypothetical example discussed in the text.

3 grid squares with 0 occurrences
5 grid squares with 1 occurrence
1 grid square with 2 occurrences
3 grid squares with 3 occurrences

total grid squares counted = 12
total number of items observed = 16

We can now estimate the probability of an occurrence and the probability of a non-occurrence from the data. The equations are:

$$\text{mean number of events per grid square} = \frac{\text{no. of events observed}}{\text{no. of grid squares counted}}$$

$$p_{(occurrence)} = \frac{\text{mean no. of events per grid square}}{\text{maximum no. of events in any grid square}}$$

$$q_{(non\text{-}occurrence)} = 1 - p_{(occurrence)}$$

It is now possible to use the expansion of $(q + p)^n$ (where n = maximum number of events which occur in any grid square) to give the theoretical probability of the occurrence of 0, 1, 2, 3, ..., n events, calculated by substituting the values for p and q into the successive terms of the expansion. To convert the theoretical probabilities to numbers of occurrences, multiply them by the total number of grid squares counted.

As an example, we can look at data relating to the distribution of the brachiopod *Epithyris oxonica* on a bedding plane in the Blisworth Limestone (Jurassic, Bathonian), at a locality in Northamptonshire. Using a 1-m square grid, the area of exposure was subdivided into 21 squares, and the number of individuals occurring in each square was counted; the data obtained are given in Table 3.5.

Table 3.5 Observed and calculated (assuming a binomial distribution model) data relating to the distribution of *Epithyris oxonica* on a bedding plane in the Blisworth Limestone, Northamptonshire. Observed data based on a 7 × 3 contiguous 1-m grid.

No. of occurrences	Frequency	
	Observed	Calculated
0	3	1
1	4	5
2	6	7
3	4	6
4	2	2
5	2	0

no. of grid squares counted = 21
no. of individuals observed = 46

Mean no. per grid square = 46/21 = 2.19

$$p = 2.19/5 = 0.44$$

$$q = 1 - 0.44 = 0.56$$

Using the expansion $(q + p)^5$ and substituting $q = 0.56$ and $p = 0.44$ into the individual terms of the expansion, the probability of occurrence of 0, 1, 2, 3, 4 and 5, individuals in a grid square were calculated. Multiplication of these probabilities by the total number of individuals observed gives the expected number of grid squares for each class. The values are tabulated, and inspection of Table 3.5 shows that there is a reasonably close agreement between the observed and calculated distributions, which may be of some palaeoecological significance.

The binomial series has been used extensively in statistics as a probability model, and has proved extremely useful in describing certain types of discrete distribution. For applications in geology the reader is referred to Cheeney (1983, pp. 39–40) and Davis (1973, pp. 247ff.).

(b) POISSON DISTRIBUTION

In the previous section, the use of the binomial distribution as a probability model depended on two important points. First, since *n* tends to be a small number there is no difficulty in using the expansion, since there will be only $(n + 1)$ terms. Secondly, by making the two constants q and p add to unity, the sum of the terms of the expansion will also be unity. Let us now consider the exponential series, which might also be used as a probability distribution if it could be arranged for the successive terms to add to 1 and then to assign a meaning to each term.

Since an exponential function has the property

$$a^{x_1} \times a^{x_2} = a^{x_1 + x_2}$$

and if $a = e$, $x_1 = z$ and $x_2 = -z$

then $e^{-z} \times e^z = e^0 = 1$ see Section 3.2.5. This relationship can also be written as

$$1 = e^{-z}\left(1 + z + \frac{z^2}{2!} + \frac{z^3}{3!} + \frac{z^4}{4!} + \ldots\right)$$

or

$$1 = e^{-z} + ze^{-z} + \frac{z^2 e^{-z}}{2!} + \frac{z^3 e^{-z}}{3!} + \frac{z^4 e^{-z}}{4!} + \ldots$$

This arrangement fulfils our first requirement that the successive terms will add up to unity. Unfortunately, the series is infinitely long but, as will become clear from the example, the values of the successive terms quickly become very small. Therefore, we can say that when the number of terms being used is greater than five, the sum approximates to unity. All that remains to be done is to assign a meaning to each term. This is achieved by finding the expectation of the occurrence of an event in a particular situation and assigning this value to z in the last of the above equations. Now, as in the example of the binomial, the first term will record the probability of the occurrence of the zeroth event and the following $(n + 1)$ terms of the expansion will give the probabilities of occurrence of the 1st to nth event, as follows:

$$e^{-z}[0] \quad ze^{-z}[1] \quad \frac{z^2 e^{-z}}{2!}\,[2] \quad \frac{z^3 e^{-z}}{3!}\,[3] \quad \ldots \quad \frac{z^n e^{-z}}{n!}\,[n]$$

If we use the data in Table 3.6 as an example, the total number of *Scrobicularia* counted in all of the samples is 42, and the total

Table 3.6 Data relating to a subfossil *Scrobicularia* community from Gibraltar Point, nr Skegness, Lincolnshire, sampled using random 50-cm^2 quadrats, counting number of *Scrobicularia* in each. P_{exp} calculated according to the Poisson distribution. The expected number of quadrats is calculated by multiplying P_{exp} by the total number of quadrats counted in the original sample.

No. of *Scrobicularia*	No. of quads	P_{exp}	Expected no. of quads
0	67	0.646	62
1	22	0.282	27
2	4	0.062	6
3	1	8.99×10^{-3}	1
4	1	9.82×10^{-4}	0
5	1	8.58×10^{-5}	0

number of quadrats thrown was 96, so the value of z (the expectation or average number of *Scrobicularia* per sample) can be calculated:

$$z = 42/96 = 0.437$$

and

$$e^{-z} = 2.7183^{-0.437} = 0.646$$

i.e.

$$e^{-z} = \ln^{-1}(-0.437) = 0.646$$

Substituting the values of z and e^{-z}, into each term of the expansion, the expected probabilities can be calculated, and from these the expected number of quadrats.

As can be seen from the results in Table 3.6, there is a close match between the observed and expected frequencies of occurrence (as with the binomial distribution, a statistical test of significance should be made, to test the degree of similarity). Used in this way, the Poisson distribution is a useful method which is often used to describe events in a continuum, on the basis of a number of discrete samples. It is normally recommended that this distribution be used when the event is relatively rare, while the binomial distribution should be used when the event is common. Again, the reader is referred to the geological literature for further examples (see Davis 1973, pp. 305–7).

Before leaving the discussion of the use of probability distribution models, based on simple mathematical series, it should be mentioned that several others have been used by ecologists to describe relationships within a community, particularly relating the number of individuals of a species to the number of species present in the community. One particularly important model is the so-called 'Fisher's α distribution', which is a special case of the Poisson distribution where the zero term is not included. This distribution may have important applications in palaeoecology, and is discussed in Section 7.4.1, where an example of its use is also given.

4 Rates of change – differentiation

4.1 Functions: some further definitions

In Section 2.1.5 functions and function notation were defined. Because of the importance the function and its associated notation in calculus, it is necessary at this point to give some further definitions.

4.1.1 Rational functions

A **rational function** is a function of the form

$$\frac{P(x)}{Q(x)}$$

where $P(x)$ and $Q(x)$ are polynomials in x. If the degree of $P(x) <$ the degree of $Q(x)$, then

$$\frac{P(x)}{Q(x)} \text{ is a proper fraction}$$

If, on the other hand, $P(x) \geqslant$ the degree of $Q(x)$, then

$$\frac{P(x)}{Q(x)} \text{ is an improper fraction}$$

4.1.2 Continuous functions

If the graph of a function turns out to be a continuous curve, then it is reasonable to assume that the function is **continuous**. For example, we can draw the graph of

$$f(x) = x + 2$$

as in Figure 4.1a and produce a continuous straight line, whereas if we draw the graph of

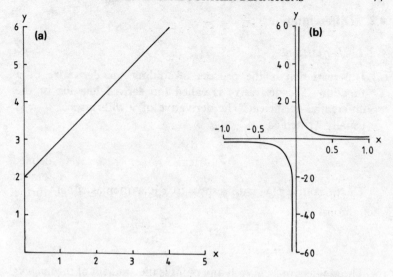

Figure 4.1 Graphs of $f(x)$. (a) The function is continuous, $f(x) = x + 2$; (b) the function is discontinuous, $f(x) = 1/x$.

$$f(x) = 1/x$$

we find that it is continuous except at $x = 0$ (Fig. 4.1b). In the latter case we can say:

as $x \to +0$, $1/x \to +\infty$ and as $x \to -0$, $1/x \to -\infty$,

thus when $x = 0$, $f(x)$ is not defined and the function is **discontinuous.**

More formally:

(a) A function is said to be continuous for $x = a$ if $f(x)$ tends to a limit as $x \to a$, from either side and each of these limits is equal to $f(a)$.
(b) A function $f(x)$ is continuous throughout an interval of values of x if it is continuous for all values of x in that interval. It is continuous everywhere if it is continuous for all values of x.
(c) It can be shown that a polynomial $P(x)$ is continuous for all finite values of x and the rational function $N(x)/D(x)$ is continuous except at values of x where $D(x) = 0$.

4.2 Differentiation

4.2.1 Definitions

(a) **Differentiation** is the process of finding the **derivative** of a function. The derivative is called the **derived function** or the **differential coefficient**. The derivative of y with respect to x is usually written as

$$\frac{dy}{dx}$$

The derivative $f(x)$ with respect to x is written as either

$$f'(x) \quad \text{or} \quad \frac{d[f(x)]}{dx}$$

(b) The **gradient** of a curve at any point is the gradient of the *tangent* to the curve at that point, and is given by the derivative dy/dx at that point.

In other words, the derivative of a function defines a *rate of change* and, having found the derivative, it is relatively easy to find the rate of change at any given point on the curve. A function which is continuous is differentiable, whereas one which is discontinuous is not.

4.2.2 Differentiation from first principles

If we start with some function $y = f(x)$, then the gradient of the chord PQ, joining P to a point Q, near to it on the curve as in Figure 4.2 is

$$\text{grad } PQ = \frac{\delta y}{\delta x}$$

In the **limit** as Q gets closer to P so that δx becomes infinitely small and eventually disappears, then the gradient of the chord becomes the **gradient of the tangent** to the curve at P, i.e.

$$\text{gradient of the tangent at } P = \text{limit } \frac{\delta y}{\delta x} \text{ as } \delta x \to 0$$

or the rate of change of y with respect to x at point P is

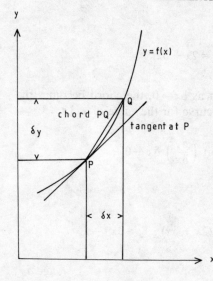

Figure 4.2 Graph of any function $y = f(x)$. The slope of the chord PQ is given by $\delta y/\delta x$. As $\delta x \to 0$ then the chord becomes the tangent to the curve at the point P.

$$\text{limit} \left(\frac{\delta y}{\delta x}\right)_{\delta x = 0} = \frac{dy}{dx}$$

To find dy/dx *when* $y = x^2$

(1) In order to find the slope of the chord near any point on the curve defined by some value of x, we need to add a small increment δx to the right-hand side of the equation and a corresponding increment δy to the left-hand side of the equation, thus we get

$$y + \delta y = (x + \delta x)^2$$

(2) Since $y = x^2$, we can eliminate y from the right-hand side of the equation as follows:

$$\delta y = (x + \delta x)^2 - x^2$$

i.e. we have subtracted x^2 from each side. This gives the increment δy in terms of x.

(3) Expanding the terms in the parentheses, we get

$$\delta y = x^2 + 2x\delta x + (\delta x)^2 - x^2$$

(4) Simplifying,

$$\frac{\delta y}{\delta x} = 2x + \delta x$$

(5) We have already noted that as $\delta x \to 0$, the chord becomes the tangent at the point on the curve for the value of x, i.e.

$$\frac{dy}{dx} = \text{limit} \left(\frac{\delta y}{\delta x} \right) \delta x \to 0$$

which is

$$\frac{dy}{dx} = \text{limit} \, (2x + \delta x)_{\delta x = 0} = 2x$$

Thus,

$$\frac{dy}{dx} = 2x \text{ when } y = x^2$$

We can now consider the general case where the exponent can be any value n. Thus, we find the derivative when $f(x) = x^n$.

To find dy/dx *when* $y = x^n$
Proceeding as before, we get

$$y + \delta y = (x + \delta x)^n$$

Expanding the terms in the parentheses using the Binomial Theorem, where

$$(x + \delta x)^n = x^n + nx^{n-1}\delta x + \frac{n(n-1)}{1 \times 2} x^{n-2}\delta x^2 + \ldots$$

so that

$$(y + \delta y) = x^n + nx^{n-1}\delta x + \frac{n(n-1)}{1 \times 2} x^{n-2}\delta x^2 + \ldots$$

Eliminating y from the right-hand side of the equation:

$$\delta y = x^n + nx^{n-1}\delta x + \frac{n(n-1)}{1 \times 2} x^{n-2}\delta x^2 + \ldots - x^n$$

$$= nx^{n-1}\delta x + \frac{n(n-1)}{1 \times 2} x^{n-2}\delta x^2 + \ldots$$

But

$$\frac{dy}{dx} = \text{limit} \left(\frac{\delta y}{\delta x}\right)_{\delta x \to 0}$$

Therefore

$$\frac{dy}{dx} = nx^{n-1}, \text{ when } y = x^n$$

We can now illustrate this procedure using a simple example. Figure 4.3 shows a plot of data obtained by measuring the length and thickness of specimens of *Homoeorhynchia acuta* (J. Sowerby). The best interpretation of the raw data is the curve as drawn, which

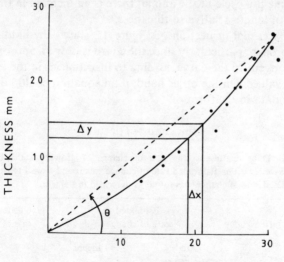

Figure 4.3 Graph of measurements of the Jurassic brachiopod *Homoeorhynchia acuta* (J. Sowerby), showing two simple methods of estimating the rate of growth.

shows that throughout the life-cycle of the animal there are changes in the rate of growth relating the two measurements concerned. If we join the two ends of the curve as indicated by the broken line we can estimate the overall or average rate of growth by finding the tangent of the angle θ, which is

$$\theta = 40°$$

$$\tan \theta = 0.839$$

i.e. the average rate of growth of the thickness of the shell relative to its length is 0.839.

If we wish to know the rate of change for the stage of growth represented by any particular thickness, then we can estimate the value by constructing a chord to the curve near the point by taking a small increment on either side of it and finding the corresponding increment on the other axis. We can then calculate the slope of the chord using these values or, more directly, measure its slope and find the tangent of the angle, using tables. This is also illustrated in Figure 4.3, for the length measurement 20 mm. The results for lengths 10, 20 and 30 mm are given in Table 4.1, which show that during the life-cycle of the animal there is an increase in the rate of change of length relative to thickness.

Even a casual inspection of Figure 4.3 shows the limitations of this approach, particularly since the chord is only an approximation to the tangent to the curve, leading to inaccuracies in the estimated growth values. On the other hand, if an equation could be fitted to the raw data in the form of

$$\text{thickness} = f(\text{length})$$

Table 4.1 Data relating to the rate of change of growth in the brachiopod *Homoeorhynchia acuta*. Estimated rate of change was found from Figure 4.3, while the calculated rate of change was found as described in the text.

Length (mm)	Estimated rate of change		Calculated rate of change
	Angle (degrees)	Tangent	
5	29	0.554	0.503
10	34	0.675	0.726
15	44	0.966	0.900

and if the derivative is then found, then the exact value of the rate of change for any given length could be calculated.

Using a statistical method, the constants α and β of the allometric growth equation (Section 2.1.4) were estimated from the raw data. The equation is

$$\text{thickness} = 0.14\,\text{length}^{1.53}$$

Applying the rule for differentiation to this equation, we get

$$\frac{\mathrm{d}(T)}{\mathrm{d}(L)} = (1.53 \times 0.14)L^{(1.53-1)}$$

$$= 0.2142\,L^{0.53}$$

By putting the values 10, 20 and 30 mm for length into the equation, we can calculate the exact rate of change. The results are given in Table 4.1, and we can make a comparison between those found analytically and the estimates arrived at using the chord method. The differences in the values obtained by the two methods result from difficulties involved in constructing a chord so that it is close to the tangent, and then using the slope of that chord to estimate the rate of change.

Simple functions can be differentiated from first principles, but unfortunately the majority of functions normally met are too complex for such treatment. To facilitate the differentiation of complex functions, two methods are available: (a) the use of rules and (b) the use of standard forms. The application of these two methods is described, with simple examples, in Appendix 1. Readers are reminded that reference should be made to mathematical texts for a more detailed treatment. For example, the books by Hogben (1967) or Graham *et al.* (1984) provide good simple introductions to the topic. More-advanced texts which are useful include those by Gow (1960), Sherlock *et al.* (1982) or Stephenson (1973). Also, since familiarity with the techniques can only be achieved by practice, examples which are to be found in these books should be worked through.

4.2.3 Successive differentiation

If y is a function of x, then in general $\mathrm{d}y/\mathrm{d}x$ is also a function of x. The derivative of $\mathrm{d}y/\mathrm{d}x$, i.e.

$$\frac{d(dy/dx)}{dx}, \quad \text{denoted by } \frac{d^2y}{dx^2}$$

is achieved by successive differentiation. This is the **second differential coefficient**, which can also be denoted by: $f''(x)$, the first-order coefficient being written as $f'(x)$ in this notation, and higher-order derivatives follow the same pattern. During the procedure of successive differentiation the rules and standard forms (Appendix 1) are used as required. The process is illustrated best by a simple example.

Find the third derivative of $4x^3 + 2x^2 + x$;

$$\frac{dy}{dx} = 12x^2 + 4x + 1$$

$$\frac{d^2y}{dx^2} = 24x + 4$$

$$\frac{d^3y}{dx^3} = 24$$

Thus, the third derivative of $4x^3 + 2x^2 + x$ is equal to 24.

There are a number of important uses of successive differentiation, one of which will be dealt with in some detail in Section 4.3.

4.2.4   Partial differentiation

A function frequently contains two or more independent variables, each of which can be differentiated in succession, holding the others constant. In other words, if $y = f(a,b,c)$, then we can differentiate

a   with respect to y, holding b and c constant;
b   with respect to y, holding a and c constant; or
c   with respect to y, holding a and b constant.

The symbol ∂ is generally used to indicate partial differentiation.

Example $y = x^2 + 2z^4 - 3x + z^2 - 4$

Differentiate with respect to x, with z constant:

$$\frac{\partial y}{\partial x} = 2x - 3$$

Differentiate with respect to z, with x constant:

$$\frac{\partial y}{\partial z} = 8z^3 + 2z$$

Example $w = ax^2 + 2bxy + cy^2$

Differentiate with respect to x, with y constant:

$$\frac{\partial w}{\partial x} = 2ax + 2by$$

Differentiate with respect to y, with x constant:

$$\frac{\partial w}{\partial y} = 2bx + 2cy$$

No other rules are required, and partial differentiation is carried out using the rules and standard forms as described in Appendix 1.

4.2.5 *The orientation of shear failure planes in rock*

Before leaving this part of the introduction to differentiation, it is instructive to consider a geological example. For this we return to the problem of shear-plane orientation which was considered in Section 2.2.4. In that section we considered the derivation of two biaxial-stress equations, which were in terms of the angle (2θ) between the shear planes. The equations were

$$\sigma = \tfrac{1}{2}(\sigma_1 + \sigma_3) - \tfrac{1}{2}(\sigma_1 - \sigma_3) \cos 2\theta$$

$$\tau = \tfrac{1}{2}(\sigma_1 - \sigma_3) \sin 2\theta$$

where σ = the normal stress, σ_1 = the stress in the y-direction, σ_3 = the stress in the x-direction and τ = the shear stress.

The Navier–Coulomb criteria for shear failure states that shear failure occurs when the shear stress (τ) along a plane, is equal to the cohesive strength of the material (C_0) plus the resistance to frictional sliding on that plane (= normal stress multiplied by the coefficient of frictional sliding, μ). This was shown diagrammatically in Figure 2.17b. Thus, we have

$$\tau = C_0 + \mu\sigma_n$$

by definition, $\mu = \tan \alpha$, where α is the angle of sliding friction and σ_n is the normal stress. This equation can be rewritten in terms of the angle of sliding friction and the normal stress:

$$\tau = C_0 + \tan \alpha \left[\left(\frac{\sigma_1 + \sigma_3}{2} \right) - \left(\frac{\sigma_1 - \sigma_3}{2} \right) \right] \cos 2\theta$$

The shear stress τ has also been defined in terms of the angle between the shear planes, therefore we can write

$$\left(\frac{\sigma_1 - \sigma_3}{2} \right) \sin 2\theta = C_0 + \tan \alpha \left[\left(\frac{\sigma_1 + \sigma_3}{2} \right) \right] - \left[\left(\frac{\sigma_1 - \sigma_3}{2} \right) \right] \cos 2\theta$$

Now, differentiating with respect to θ,

$$2 \left(\frac{\sigma_1 - \sigma_3}{2} \right) \cos 2\theta = (\tan \alpha) \times 2 \left(\frac{\sigma_1 - \sigma_3}{2} \right) \sin 2\theta$$

which simplifies to

$$\cos 2\theta = \tan \alpha \sin 2\theta$$

or

$$1 = \tan \alpha \frac{\sin 2\theta}{\cos 2\theta}$$

or

$$\tan 2\theta = 1/\tan \alpha = \cot \alpha$$

Therefore,

$$\tan 2\theta = \cot \alpha = \tan(90 - \alpha)$$

thus,

$$2\theta = 90 - \alpha$$

Now, for many rocks the angle of sliding friction, α, is approximately 30°, so

$$\theta = 45 - 15 = 30°$$

and

$$2\theta = 60°$$

When the angle 2θ is measured in rock (see Fig. 2.16a), it is usually found to be close to 60°. Thus, we have demonstrated analytically a result which is in agreement with that observed in rock, showing the power of mathematical analysis applied to this type of problem.

4.3 Maxima and minima

Figure 4.4 is a sketch of the curve of a cubic function. The curve has two turning points at p and q, p being a maximum and q a minimum. We wish to find, analytically, the values of x at these turning points, and which is a *maximum* and which a *minimum*.

To find the position of the turning points p and q, we differentiate and put

$$\frac{dy}{dx} = 0$$

the solution of which gives the turning points required. In order to find which is a maximum and which is a minimum, we need to differentiate with respect to x a second time, i.e. find the second differential coefficient of the original equation. In order to find which is which, we substitute the values of x for the maxima and the minima in this equation and use the rule:

at a maximum position $f''(x)$ has a positive value

at a minimum position $f''(x)$ has a negative value

Example Find the turning points and identify the maxima and minima for the equation

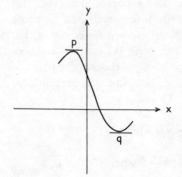

Figure 4.4 Sketch of the curve generated by a cubic function, showing the turning points.

$$3x^3 - 9x^2 - 27x + 10$$

$$\frac{dy}{dx} = 9x^2 - 18x - 27$$

Setting this to zero,

$$0 = (9x + 9)(x - 3)$$

$$x = -1 \text{ or } 3$$

$$\frac{d^2y}{dx^2} = 18x - 18$$

Substituting,

when $x = -1$ $d^2y/dx^2 = -36$, so the function is at a maximum

when $x = 3$ $d^2y/dx^2 = 36$, so the function is at a minimum

Substituting in the original equation, the corresponding values of y are

$$y = 25 \text{ and } -71$$

This is shown diagrammatically in Figure 4.5, which represents graphs of the function and its first and second derivatives. Since finding maximum and minimum values for a cubic function is a relatively common problem, a suitable computer program is listed as Program 4.1.

It should be remembered that a cubic equation need not have turning points, and in this situation there will be a point of *inflexion*. If a sketch of the curve is made this will be apparent, however if no sketch is made and the procedure outlined is followed, then the roots of the quadratic obtained by differentiation will be complex, i.e. there are no real roots, also $f'''(x)$ will be zero. We can test whether the curve is *concave up* or *concave down* as it approaches the point of inflexion, by substituting values on either side of the point of inflexion into the second differential. The rule is

$$y = f(x) \text{ is concave up at } x = 0 \text{ when } f''(x) > 0$$

$$y = f(x) \text{ is concave down at } x = 0 \text{ when } f''(x) < 0$$

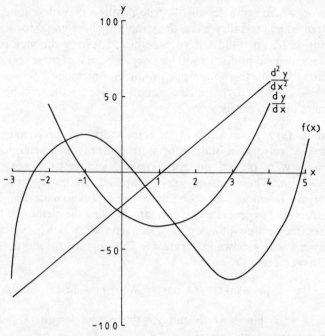

Figure 4.5 Sketch of the cubic function $y = 3x^3 - 9x^2 - 27x + 10$. The first and second differentials are also shown. Note that the turning points of $y = f(x)$ have values of x equal to the values of the points where the curve $y = f'(x)$ cuts the x-axis. Also, when $y = f''(x)$ is negative the turning point of $y = f(x)$ is a maximum, and when $y = f''(x)$ is positive the turning point is a minimum.

The point of inflexion is given by

$$\left(\frac{1}{2a}\right)(-b)$$

where $a = $ the coefficient of the x^2-term in $f'(x)$ and $b = $ the coefficient of the x-term in $f'(x)$.

Thus, having calculated the value for the point of inflexion [a value of x such that $f''(x) = 0$], values of x either side are substituted into $f''(x)$. An example of the use of this will not be given, as the first geological problem covers just this situation.

4.3.1 Geological applications

In a geological context maxima and minima have been used by geomorphologists in the analysis of slope form, particularly in the situation where estimates of the true position of valley floors are required when the valley has a thick infill of alluvium (Doornkamp & King 1971, pp. 148ff.). Two examples, applying the method to simple geological problems will be given. The first of these relates to the growth of the Carboniferous productid brachiopod *Semiplanus latissimus* (J. Sowerby), and the second to finding the thickness of sediment infill in a valley.

Examples (a) Measurements of the hinge width and curved length of the pedicle valve, of a number of individuals of the brachiopod *S. latissimus* were plotted on graph paper, and best-fit lines were eyeballed in. These curves were sigmoidal, indicating that the underlying function was probably a cubic polynomial. The data were then used to generate cubic equations using the method of least squares (see Section 4.5). A plot of one data set, which is typical of those obtained, is shown in Figure 4.6. The equation for this data set was found to be

$$y = 0.00027x^3 - 0.0388x^2 + 2.1x - 14.4$$

where $x =$ the hinge width and $y =$ the curved length of pedicle valve, measurements in mm.

$$\frac{dy}{dx} = 0.00081x^2 - 0.0776x + 2.1$$

$$\frac{d^2y}{dx^2} = 0.00162x - 0.0776$$

The solution of the quadratic is

$$x = 47.9 \pm 17.26i$$

Ignoring the complex part, we can substitute $x = 47.9$ into the second differential, which gives

$$\frac{d^2y}{dx^2} = 0$$

Since $f''(x) = 0$, we have a point of inflexion. Using the rule:

(i) setting $x = 45.0$ (just less than the point of inflexion),

$$f''(x) = (0.00162 \times 45.0) - 0.0776$$

$$= -4.7 \times 10^{-3}$$

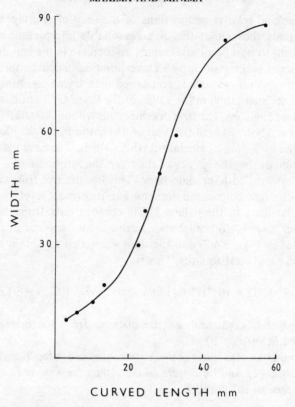

Figure 4.6 Graphical plot of the growth data measured from a single individual of the productid brachiopod *Semiplanus latissimus* (J. Sowerby). The best-fit curve has been eyeballed in.

(ii) setting $x = 50.0$ (just greater than the point of inflexion),

$$f''(x) = (0.00162 \times 50) - 0.0776$$
$$= 3.4 \times 10^{-3}$$

Thus, when $x = 45$, $f''(x)$ is negative and the curve is concave down, and when $x = 50$, $f''(x)$ is positive and the curve is concave up.

From this analysis we can conclude that for the specimens of *S. latissimus* examined, shell increments are laid down in such a way that the change in hinge width relative to the change in valve length (of the pedicle valve), can best be described by a cubic equation. At the point of growth where the hinge width is approximately 48 mm, there is a change in growth pattern (corresponding to a point of inflexion on the curve). Before this the hinge width grew faster than the length, after which the opposite was the case. Consideration of the shape and relative proportions of the shell of many productid brachiopods shows that this is a reasonable interpretation, since there seems to be a point after which an increase in the length of the valves is not accompanied by a corresponding increase in width.

(b) The second example is concerned with trying to estimate the depth of sediment infill in the valley of the River Greta in Kingsdale Beck (near Ingleton, North Yorkshire), above the waterfall Thornton Force. About 50 m to the west of Thornton Force the old valley is blocked by a plug of glacial till which appears to have caused, at some point during the history of the river, the formation of a lake in what is now called Kingsdale Beck. This has drained following the cutting of a new course and deepening to its present level, leaving a broad, flat floor to the valley. Using contour data from the Ordnance Survey (6 in. to 1 mile) map, a cross section was constructed as illustrated in Figure 4.7, and the data were used to obtain a cubic equation using least squares. This is

$$y = (-2.6507 \times 10^{-5})x^3 + (1.204 \times 10^{-2})x^2 - 1.572x + 91.0079$$

where $y =$ the height and $x =$ the distance from the origin, both measured in yards $\times 10^{-1}$.

It should be noted that the measurements were in feet (height) and yards (distance), and both were converted to the scale indicated for convenience of calculation.

$$\frac{\mathrm{d}y}{\mathrm{d}x} = (-7.9521 \times 10^{-5})x^2 + (2.408 \times 10^{-2})x - 1.572$$

$$\frac{\mathrm{d}^2y}{\mathrm{d}x^2} = (1.59042 \times 10^{-4})x + (2.408 \times 10^{-2})$$

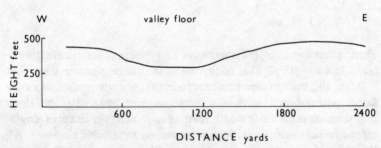

Figure 4.7 Cross section constructed from contour data across Kingsdale Beck, Nr Ingleton, Yorkshire. Note the flat valley floor, which is probably formed from flat-lying sediments, deposited at the bottom of a glacial lake.

The solution of the quadratic is

$$x = 95.2 \quad \text{or} \quad 207.6$$

Substituting these values into the second differential, we get, when $x = 95.2$

$$\frac{d^2y}{dx^2} = 8.93 \times 10^{-3}$$

and, when $x = 207.6$

$$\frac{d^2y}{dx^2} = -8.93 \times 10^{-3}$$

Thus, we have:

when $x = 207.58$ the function is maximized at $y = 46.4$

and

when $x = 95.23$ the function is minimized at $y = 27.6$

For the present purpose, only the minimum value is of interest. Converting our values back to their original units, x the distance in yards from the origin of the plot (west edge of the section):

$$\text{distance} = 952.3 \text{ yd}$$

and y the height in feet from Ordnance Datum (O.D.):

$$\text{height} = 828.1 \text{ ft}$$

Since the measured level at the base of the valley from the map is 850 ft, then the thickness of infill is 21.9 ft.

Using the data given by Wilson (1980), the base of the old river channel at the northern end of the plug of glacial till is at approximately 775 ft O.D. The level of the valley infill at Kingsdale Beck is at 850 ft O.D., therefore assuming no change of level in the old valley floor upstream, the maximum thickness of sediment is 75 ft. If we allow for changes in the valley upstream based on changes downstream, we estimate a change in level of 50 ft to give a base level for the old valley at 825 ft O.D. Thus, a minimum figure for the infill is 25 ft. These maximum and minimum figures should be compared with the calculated value of 21.9 ft.

4.4 Optimization and the method of Lagrange multipliers

In Section 2.1.5 we considered the problem of optimization (either maximization or minimization) of a linear function, subject to certain linear inequality constraints. However, in many situations the functions and constraints may not be linear, but in particular the constraints can be equalities. The method to be described is designed to cater for just this situation.

As an example, let us suppose that we manage two mines A and B and that the total output we require is 100 000 tonnes week^{-1}. We wish to minimize production costs for the two mines. What is the optimum output for each mine when the function relating the cost of the operation is

$$C = 5A^2 + 8B^2 - 3AB$$

subject to (production)

$$A + B = 100\ 000 \text{ tonnes}$$

which can be written as

$$A = 100 - B$$

(A and B in tonnes $\times 10^3$). One method of solution is by substitution. The rewritten constraint for A can be substituted into the cost function:

$$TC = 5(100 - B)^2 + 8B^2 - 3(100 - B)B$$

$$= 50\ 000 - 1300B + 16B^2$$

Taking the first derivative of the constraint equation and setting to zero,

$$\frac{\mathrm{d}(TC)}{\mathrm{d}B} = -1300 + 32B = 0$$

$$B = 40.6 \times 10^3 \text{ tonnes}$$

and the second derivative of the equation:

$$\frac{d^2(TC)}{dB^2} = +32$$

Since the value of the second derivative is positive, the calculated value of 40.6×10^3 tonnes calculated for B is a minimum value. Substitution of this value into the constraint equation gives a value of 59.4×10^3 tonnes as the optimum output for mine A. Substituting these values into the cost function we find that the weekly operating cost is £23 593.76.

This method works well, provided the constraints are not too numerous nor too complex. An alternative method which will work equally well in complex cases is the method whereby artificial unknowns, known as *Lagrange multipliers* are added. As many dummy unknowns can be added as there are constraints.

Returning to the previous problem, we can rewrite our constraint equation as

$$A + B - 100 = 0$$

Multiplying this by the unknown constant λ,

$$\lambda(A + B - 100) = 0$$

and then adding it to the cost function,

$$C_\lambda = 5A^2 + 8B^2 - 3AB + \lambda(A + B - 100)$$

Now, if the constraint is satisfied, then the last term in the Lagrangian cost function will be zero. Therefore, whatever values of A and B minimize the cost C, the same values will minimize C_λ. However, C_λ contains three unknowns: A, B and λ. We can solve the system by partial differentiation and setting the results equal to zero:

$$\frac{\partial C_\lambda}{\partial A} = 10A - 3B + \lambda = 0$$

$$\frac{\partial C_\lambda}{\partial B} = 16B - 3A + \lambda = 0$$

$$\frac{\partial C_\lambda}{\partial \lambda} = A + B - 100 = 0$$

We now have three simultaneous linear equations, which on solution give

$$A = 59.4 \times 10^3 \text{ tonnes}$$

$$B = 40.6 \times 10^3 \text{ tonnes}$$

and

$$\lambda = -472.2$$

The values for production from the two mines are as we calculated using the substitution method, but we also have an additional value λ. The value of λ is significant, and represents the reduction in the total operating cost if only 99×10^3 tonnes were produced instead of 100×10^3 tonnes per week. Thus, the £472.20 is known in economics as the marginal cost of the last unit of production. It should be noted that, having set $\partial C_\lambda / \partial h = 0$, we automatically ensure that the constraint equation is embodied in the system. Additional constraints are handled simply by multiplying each by a different Lagrange multiplier, and including each in the system. For further information on this method students are referred to economics texts such as Glass (1980).

4.5 Differentiation and least-squares methods

4.5.1 Regression of x against y

We have already seen (Section 2.1.1) that if x and y are related by a linear law, then the equation can be expressed in the form

$$y = ax + b$$

In that section we showed that the unknowns a and b in this equation could be estimated from a graph formed by plotting the values for x and y, using a suitable scale and fitting a line by eye, which best honoured the data. We will now consider an analytical solution of the problem using the method of **least squares**. In this method the sums of squares of the differences between the observed and the calculated values will be minimized. Using the data in Table 2.1a, relating to measurements of the brachiopod *Epithyris oxonica*, we can work from first principles following the method outlined by Moroney (1951, p. 280), as follows.

Table 4.2 The predicted y-value and its deviation from the measured values, assuming a linear relationship between x and y and that the x-values contain no error; i.e. y is the dependent variable.

Measured width, x (mm)	Predicted width, y (mm)	Measured length, y (mm)	Deviation (mm)
16	$16a + b$	18	$16a + b - 18$
17	$17a + b$	19	$17a + b - 19$
19	$19a + b$	20	$19a + b - 20$
19	$19a + b$	21.5	$19a + b - 21.5$
23.5	$23.5a + b$	26.5	$23.5a + b - 26.5$
25	$25a + b$	29	$25a + b - 29$
29	$29a + b$	33.5	$29a + b - 33.5$
31	$31a + b$	36	$31a + b - 36$

First, we set out the data showing how the pair of measurements are related, using the equation for the straight line, as in Table 4.2. The deviations can be squared as follows:

$$(16a + b - 18)^2 = 256a^2 - 576a + 32ab + b^2 - 36b + 324$$

$$(17a + b - 19)^2 = 289a^2 - 646a + 34ab + b^2 - 38b + 361$$

$$(19a + b - 20)^2 = 361a^2 - 760a + 38ab + b^2 - 40b + 400$$

$$(19a + b - 21.5)^2 = 361a^2 - 817a + 38ab + b^2 - 43b + 462.25$$

$$(23.5a + b - 26.5)^2 = 552.25a^2 - 1245.5a + 47ab + b^2 - 53b + 702.25$$

$$(25a + b - 29)^2 = 625a^2 - 1450a + 50ab + b^2 - 58b + 841$$

$$(29a + b - 33.5)^2 = 841a^2 - 1943a + 58ab + b^2 - 67b + 1122.25$$

$$(31a + b - 36)^2 = 961a^2 - 2232a + 62ab + b^2 - 72b + 1296$$

which, on summation, gives

$$\Sigma = 4246a^2 - 9669.5a + 359ab + 8b^2 - 407b + 5508.75$$

This equation can be written in the form of a quadratic, in terms of either a or b, to give in terms of a

$$\Sigma = 4246.25a^2 + (359b - 9669.5)a + (5508.75 - 407b + 8b^2) \qquad (4.1)$$

or, in terms of b,

$$\Sigma = 8b^2 + (359a - 407)b + (5508.75 - 9669.5a + 4246.25a^2) \qquad (4.2)$$

We have already seen in Section 4.3 that if we wish to make a value, such as Σ in Eqns 4.1 and 4.2, a minimum then, in general, if

$$S = px^2 + qx + c \qquad (4.3)$$

where $S = \Sigma$ in Eqn 4.2, we need to set the first differential to zero, i.e.

$$\frac{\mathrm{d}S}{\mathrm{d}a} = 0$$

Thus, differentiating Eqn 4.3 and setting to zero, we get

$$\frac{\mathrm{d}S}{\mathrm{d}a} = 2px + q = 0$$

which we can rewrite in terms of x, as

$$x = -q/2p \qquad (4.4)$$

In Eqn 4.1, and by analogy with Eqn 4.3, we find that the values for p and q are

$$p = 4246.25 \qquad q = 359b - 9669.5$$

Substituting these values into Eqn 4.4,

$$a = -\frac{(359b - 9669.5)}{8492.5}$$

which can be rewritten as

$$8492.5a + 359b - 9669.5 = 0$$

which is the partial differential $\partial\sum/\partial a$ of the sums of squares of the deviations, holding b constant. Similarly, using Eqn 4.2 and the procedure just outlined, we find that

$$16b + 359a - 407 = 0$$

which is the partial differential $\partial\sum/\partial b$ of the sums of squares of the deviations, holding a constant. Thus, we have a pair of equations with unknowns a and b:

$$8492.5a + 359b = 9669.5$$

$$359.0a + 16b = 407.0$$

which, on solution, give

$$a = 1.229 \qquad b = -2.129$$

Thus, the equation is

$$length = 1.229 \ (width) - 2.129$$

However, we should remember that we made the assumption at the beginning of the calculation that there was no error in the measurement of the width (denoted by x) hence, by implication, length is the dependent variable. This was a purely arbitrary decision, and we could equally have assumed that the length measurement (denoted by y) contained no error, in which case the width would be the dependent variable. In this case the sums of squares would be:

$$\Sigma = 5508.75a^2 - 9669.5a + 407ab + 8b^2 - 359b + 4246.25$$

which, on solution, gives

$$a = 0.809 \qquad b = 1.859$$

Thus, the equation is

$$width = 0.809 \ (length) + 1.859$$

The first pair of values obtained in the calculations is commonly termed **the regression of x on y**, while the second is **the regression of y on x**. It should be noted that in most situations the dependent and independent variables are known and are not interchangeable, as in this example. Figure 4.8 shows the two regression lines, as well as the estimated fit from the graphical solution of Section 2.1.1. This allows a visual comparison of the results, and it can be seen that the graphical solution runs between the two regression lines, and all three cross at about the same point, the mean of the two measurements.

Let us now look in more-general terms at the rather long-winded calculation we have just completed. Each deviation squared, gave the following terms related to the unknowns a and b in the linear equation

$$y = ax + b$$

which are

$$a^2 \quad -a \quad ab \quad b^2 \quad -b \quad \text{constant}$$

which can be expressed in terms of the two measurements x and y, as

$$x^2 \quad -2xy \quad 2x \quad 1 \quad -2y \quad y^2$$

The sums of squares in terms of x and y, summed from 1 to N, where N is the number of pairs of measurements, were

$$\Sigma x^2 \quad -\Sigma 2xy \quad \Sigma 2x \quad N \quad -\Sigma 2y \quad \Sigma y^2$$

which can be written as a quadratic in terms of the unknown a, as

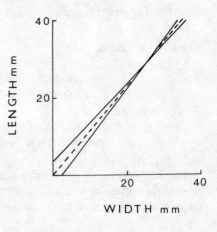

Figure 4.8 Graphical representation of the data from Table 2.1a relating to the Jurassic brachiopod *Epithyris oxonica* (Buckman), showing the best-fit line (broken) and the two calculated regression lines.

$$(\Sigma x^2)a^2 + [(\Sigma 2x)b - \Sigma 2xy]a + (N - \Sigma 2y + \Sigma y^2)$$

and as a quadratic in terms of the unknown b, as

$$(N)b^2 + [(\Sigma 2x)a - (\Sigma 2y)]b + (\Sigma x^2 + 2x + \Sigma y^2)$$

which lead to the two partial differentials

$$\partial\Sigma/\partial a = 0 = 2(\Sigma x^2)a + (\Sigma 2x)b - \Sigma 2xy$$

and

$$\partial\Sigma/\partial b = 0 = 2(N)b + (\Sigma 2x)a - \Sigma 2y$$

These can be written as a pair of simultaneous linear equations

$$2(\Sigma x^2)a + (\Sigma 2x)b = \Sigma 2xy$$

$$(\Sigma 2x)a + 2(N)b = \Sigma 2y$$

that simplify to

$$(\Sigma x^2)a + (\Sigma x)b = \Sigma xy$$

$$(\Sigma x)a + (N)b = \Sigma y$$

which can be solved for the unknowns a and b.

This method can be extended to enable higher-degree polynomials to be fitted to suitable data. Thus, to fit a quadratic equation we can expand our linear equations to give

$$c(N) + b\Sigma x + a\Sigma x^2 = \Sigma y$$

$$c\Sigma x + b\Sigma x^2 + a\Sigma x^3 = \Sigma xy$$

$$c\Sigma x + b\Sigma x^2 + a\Sigma x^4 = \Sigma x^2 y$$

Note that the equations are written slightly differently from those for the linear case; this is simply a matter of convenience, and the pattern can be extended to enable higher-order equations to be fitted as required.

4.5.2 Multiple regression: trend surface analysis

The technique of trend surface analysis, which has had extensive application in geology (see, for example, Harbaugh & Merriam 1968, ch. 5; Davis 1973, pp. 322ff.), is a form of multiple-regression analysis. The method produces surfaces in the form of contour maps, which are described by integer series polynomials which range, in most geological applications, from linear to sixth degree. The method is claimed to provide an objective means of preparing contour maps, and to facilitate the rapid comparison of a number of variables for a given area. Having said this, it should be noted that there are many drawbacks to the method. Some are due to the nature and distribution of the types of data acquired by geologists, but some arise from mathematical problems. Unfortunately, whatever the cause, it is possible to produce surfaces which are purely mathematical artefacts and bear no resemblance to the actual structure being mapped (see Section 7.3 for some discussion of the problems, and particularly Section 7.3.4). Nevertheless, it is a 'quick and dirty' method, which can be particularly useful if one of the following is an objective of the study.

(a) To find the best-fit surface assuming that the differences between the observed and calculated values are due to a random component such as measurement error.
(b) The isolation of components within the data leading to the separation of the regional and local trends.

In general, the surfaces fitted will obey the least-squares criteria for a best fit, where

$$\Sigma(z_{obs} - z_{calc})^2 = minimum$$

where z is the dependent variable – the geological property measured.

Let us consider a simple case, a flat surface which exhibits simple dip and strike. If x and y are the geographical co-ordinates and z is the distance to the surface from some datum such as sea level, then the surface can be described by the linear equation

$$z = A + Bx + Cy$$

given the constants A, B and C, we can for any given point (x,y) calculate

$$z_{calc} = A + Bx + Cy$$

and the deviation between z_{obs} and z_{calc} is given by

$$\text{deviation} = z_{obs} - A - Bx - Cy$$

If the sum of the squared deviations is given by $F(A,B,C)$, then

$$F(A,B,C) = \Sigma(z_{obs} - A - Bx - Cy)^2$$

If $F(A,B,C)$ is to be minimized, then the partial differentials should equal zero:

$$\frac{\partial F}{\partial A} = \frac{\partial F}{\partial B} = \frac{\partial F}{\partial C} = 0.0$$

using the values of z_{obs}, the partial derivatives are

$$\frac{\partial F}{\partial A} = \Sigma 2(z - A - Bx - Cy)(-1) = 0$$

$$\frac{\partial F}{\partial B} = \Sigma 2(z - A - Bx - Cy)(-x) = 0$$

$$\frac{\partial F}{\partial C} = \Sigma 2(z - A - Bx - Cy)(-y) = 0$$

which, on multiplying out and summing the individual terms, gives

$$An + b\Sigma x + c\Sigma y = \Sigma z$$

$$A\Sigma x + B\Sigma x^2 + c\Sigma xy = \Sigma zx$$

$$A\Sigma y + B\Sigma xy + c\Sigma y^2 = \Sigma xy$$

where n = the number of data points and the summation signs imply summing from 1 to n. The solution of these equations is achieved by rewriting them in matrix form as

$$\begin{bmatrix} n & \Sigma x & \Sigma y \\ \Sigma x & \Sigma x^2 & \Sigma xy \\ \Sigma x & \Sigma xy & \Sigma y^2 \end{bmatrix} \begin{bmatrix} A \\ B \\ C \end{bmatrix} = \begin{bmatrix} \Sigma z \\ \Sigma zx \\ \Sigma zy \end{bmatrix}$$

which can be simplified to

$$[A] \quad [\mathbf{b}] = [\mathbf{c}]$$

and the unknown vector [**b**], found by

$$[A]^{-1} \quad [\mathbf{c}] = [\mathbf{b}]$$

The constants for higher-order surfaces are obtained in a similar fashion.

The use of matrix algebra in the solution of simultaneous linear equations will be considered in Section 7.3.3, and an example of the use of trend surface analysis and the calculation of the linear regression coefficients will be given in Section 7.4.2.

5 Areas and volumes: integration

5.1 Integration

Integration is the inverse of differentiation, the process of finding a function when its derivative is given. Theoretically, we should be able to retrace the steps of differentiation to obtain the integral. In practice, this is not easy, as in many cases we cannot put the derivative into the proper form. We saw in Section 4.2.1 that differentiation is concerned with rates of change, integration or integral calculus, on the other hand, is concerned with areas or volumes. Thus, we can say that if a function f is positive and continuous over x, when

$$a \leqslant x \leqslant b$$

then the area under the curve is

$$A = \int_a^b f(x)\mathrm{d}x = [F(x)]_a^b = F(b) - F(a)$$

where $\int$ is the sign indicating integration, $f(x)$ is the **integrand** of $\int f(x)\mathrm{d}x$, and b and a are the limits of integration. Alternatively,

$$A = \lim_{\substack{\Delta x \to 0 \\ n \to \infty}} \sum_{k=1}^{n} f(x_k)\Delta x_k$$

In words, the limit of the sums of the areas of inscribed rectangles, when their width Δx approaches zero and their number becomes infinite, will be equal to the area under the curve $f(x)$ between $x = a$ and $x = b$. This is the **fundamental theorem of integral calculus**.

5.1.1 Numerical integration

The area AA'BB', under a curve $y = f(x)$, as for example in Figure 5.1, can be found by dividing the interval AB into N equal parts,

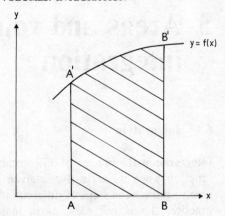

Figure 5.1 The area under the curve $y = f(x)$, between the limits A and B.

each of width Δx, and summing the area of the N strips (the smaller Δx is, then the more accurate the answer will be).

$$\text{area} = (P_1 P'_1)\Delta x + (P_2 P'_2)\Delta x + (P_3 P'_3)\Delta x + (P_4 P'_4)\Delta x$$

$$\approx \int_a^b f(x)\mathrm{d}x$$

i.e. the sum of the areas of the rectangles approximates the area ABCD, as illustrated in Figure 5.2.

For practical purposes we can replace the rectangles with trapezoids, as in Figure 5.3. By this method we calculate

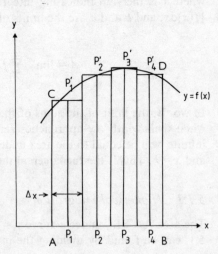

Figure 5.2 The area under the curve $y = f(x)$, between the limits A and B, approximated by rectangles of width Δx and height p_1 p'_1, p_2 p'_2, etc.

$$\text{area } 1 = \tfrac{1}{2}(y_0 + y_1)\Delta x$$

$$\text{area } 2 = \tfrac{1}{2}(y_1 + y_2)\Delta x$$

$$\vdots$$

$$\text{area } 5 = \tfrac{1}{2}(y_4 + y_5)\Delta x$$

$$\text{total area } = \Delta x\{[\tfrac{1}{2}(y_0 + y_5)] + y_1 + y_2 + y_3 + y_4\}$$

Obviously, the smaller Δx is, then the greater the number of strips and the more accurate the final answer. In general,

$$\text{area } = \Delta x\{[\tfrac{1}{2}(y_0 + y_n)] + \sum_{i=1}^{n-1} y_1\}$$

One of the best-known methods of numerical integration is **Simpson's Rule**, where we do not have to integrate or draw a curve of the function. Consider three points

$$(x,y) \quad (x_1,y_1) \quad (x_2,y_2)$$

on the curve $y = ax^2 + bx + c$. Now, our three points give us

$$y_0 = ax^2 + bx + c$$

$$y_1 = ax_1^2 + bx_1 + c$$

$$y_2 = ax_2^2 + bx_2 + c$$

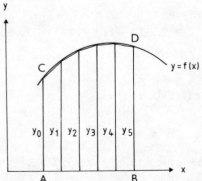

Figure 5.3 The area under the curve $y = f(x)$, approximated by trapezoids of width Δx and ordinates y_0, y_1, etc.

If $x_1 - x = h$, then

$$y_0 = ax^2 + bx + c$$

$$y_1 = a(x + h)^2 + b(x + h) + c$$

$$y_2 = a(x + 2h)^2 + b(x + 2h) + c$$

and the area of the two strips is

$$A = h/3(y_0 + 4y_1 + y_2)$$

Thus, if an area under a curve is divided into an *even* number of *equal* parts with *distance h* between any two successive divisions, the total area will be approximately equal to the sum of the *partial areas*.

The area of the strips is

$$1 \text{ and } 2 = h/3(y_0 + 4y_1 + y_2)$$

$$3 \text{ and } 4 = h/3(y_2 + 4y_3 + y_4)$$

$$(n - 1) \text{ and } n = h/3(y_{n-2} + 4y_{n-1} + y_n)$$

Summing these,

$$S = h/3(y_0 + 4y_1 + 2y_2 + 4y_3 + 2y_4 + \ldots + 4y_{n-1} + y_n)$$

So far, we have labelled the first y-value as y_0; however, this is not very convenient and we shall now return to the normal practice of labelling our values $1, \ldots, n$, where n is an even number. The last equation can now be written as

$$\sum = h/3[(y_1 + y_n) + 4(y_2 + y_4 + \ldots + y_{n-2}) + 2(y_3 + y_5 + \ldots + y_{n-1})]$$

Thus,

$$\sum \approx \int_a^b f(x)\mathrm{d}x$$

provided that

h is small, given by $(b - a)/n$;
n is positive and even; and
b and a are the limits of integration.

Examples Evaluate $\int\limits_1^{2.5} \mathrm{d}x/x$ using six strips

$$h = \frac{2.5 - 1}{6} = \frac{1}{4}$$

It is convenient to tabulate, as follows

x	$1/x$	Weight	Product [weight $\times f(x)$]
1.0	1.0	1	1.0
1.25	0.8	4	3.2
1.5	0.667	2	1.334
1.75	0.571	4	2.284
2.0	0.5	2	1.0
2.25	0.444	4	1.766
2.5	0.4	1	0.4
			$\sum = 10.994$

$$A = \int\limits_1^{2.5} \mathrm{d}x/x = (1/12)(10.994)$$

$$= 0.916 \text{ sq. units}$$

Evaluate $\int\limits_0^1 \ln(4x + 5)\mathrm{d}x$ using four strips

$$h = \frac{1 - 0}{4} = \frac{1}{4}$$

x	$(4x + 5)$	$\ln(4x + 5)$	Weight	Product
0.0	5	1.61	1	1.61
0.25	6	1.79	4	7.16
0.50	7	1.95	2	3.9
0.75	8	2.08	4	8.32
1.0	9	2.20	1	2.20
				$\int = 23.19$

$$A = \int\limits_0^1 \ln(4x + 5)\mathrm{d}x = (1/12)(23.19)$$

$$= 1.9325 \text{ sq. units}$$

Note that the weights or multipliers in the tables come from the general equation for the sum, ie, the first and last strips have a weight of 1 while odd numbered strips have a weight of 2 and even numbered a weight of 4.

Program 5.1 is a computer program for evaluating Simpson's Rule.

5.2 Analytical methods

In the introductory paragraph to this chapter it was mentioned that integration could be considered as the reverse of differentiation. This was followed by a discussion of the integral in terms of finding the area under a curve, and in particular how to approximate this area numerically. It is now necessary to discuss integration analytically. In this context the topic divides naturally into two areas, the *indefinite integral* and the *definite integral*.

5.2.1 The indefinite integral

Let us start with a simple equation

$$y = ax^n$$

Now,

$$\frac{dy}{dx} = nax^{n-1}$$

If we integrate by reversing the process,

$$\int dy = \int (nax^{n-1})dx$$

$$y = \frac{na}{(n-1)+1}x^{(n-1)+1}$$

$$y = ax^n$$

However, suppose that

$$y = 3x^3 + 4$$

then

$$\frac{dy}{dx} = 9x^2$$

Integrating,

$$\int dy = \int (9x^2) dx$$

$$y = \frac{9}{(2+1)} x^{(2+1)}$$

$$= 3x^3$$

Using this approach the constant is lost, and we must take this into account. It should be remembered that the constant must *always* be provided for, so it is normal to write

$$y = 3x^3 + \text{constant}$$

or, more usually,

$$y = 3x + C$$

This is called the **indefinite integral**. If further information is given, it is possible to evaluate the constant. For example, suppose we are given that $x = 2$ when $y = 40$. Then

$$40 = 3(2)^3 + C$$

$$C = 16$$

$$y = 3x^3 + 16$$

Thus, it is possible to show that two functions which have the same derivative differ only by a constant. In general, there are three methods of integrating:

(a) reversing the rules of differentiation;
(b) formulae; and
(c) reference to a table of standard integral forms.

The basic rules of integration and table standard forms can be found in Appendix 2, along with simple examples illustrating their use. Again, as with differentiation, practice is essential and the reader is referred to mathematical texts for more examples and details.

5.2.2   *The definite integral*

The alternative to the indefinite integral is the **definite integral**, where
the limits of integration are given. We have already discussed this
topic in the context of a numerical solution (Section 5.1.1), where the
problem of finding the area under the curve $y = f(x)$ was outlined.
We can, of course, proceed analytically. Given $y = f(x)$ we can
integrate to obtain

$$\int f(x)\mathrm{d}x = F(x) + C$$

Further, if the interval of integration is between a and b, then we can
find:

$$F(x)]_a^b = F(b) = F(a)$$

which is the area between a and b provided $a \leqslant x \leqslant b$, i.e. it is a
proper integral. Since, if $F(x)$ is continuous in the interval $a \leqslant x \leqslant b$,
then $\int_a^b f(x)\mathrm{d}x$ is also continuous.

$F(x)]_a^b$ means that the upper value of b is substituted for x to obtain
$F(b)$ and the lower value of a is substituted for x to obtain $F(a)$.

Example Given $y = x^2$, find the area under the curve from $0 \leqslant x \leqslant 4$

$$\int_0^4 x^2 \, \mathrm{d}x = \tfrac{1}{3}x^3]_0^4$$

$$= \tfrac{1}{3}(4^3 - 0^3)$$

$$= 21.3 \text{ sq. units}$$

Note that $\int_0^4 x^2 \, \mathrm{d}x$ can also be written as

$$\int x^2 \, \mathrm{d}x]_0^4$$

It will have been noticed that the constant of integration was not
used in this example. This follows since it automatically drops out in
the calculation. Thus, given

$$\int_a^b f(x)\mathrm{d}x = F(x) + C]_a^b$$

However,

$$F(x) + C]_a^b = [F(b) + C] - [F(a) + C]$$

$$= F(b) - F(a)$$

$$= f(x)]_a^b$$

As a second example which will be worked through in slightly more detail, we are asked to find the area under the curve $y = 4x + x^2$ when $4 \leqslant x \leqslant 8$

$$\int_4^8 (4x + x^2)dx$$

(1) Integrate $\dfrac{4x^2}{2} + \dfrac{x^3}{3}$ neglecting the constant

(2) Place brackets $2x^2 + x^3/3]_4^8$

(3) Substitute:

$$\text{area} = [2(64) + 512/3] - [2(16) + 64/3]$$

$$= 245.33 \text{ sq. units}$$

It is now convenient to consider the problem in geometric terms. First, the values of y for $y = f(x)$ and $y = \int f(x)dx$ can be calculated, for values of x in the range 1 to 8 as in Table 5.1.

These data are plotted on a graph (Fig. 5.4), from which it can be seen that the area under the curve $y = 4x + x^2$ between the limits $x = 4$ and $x = 8$ (shaded on the figure) is given by the difference in the height of the ordinate for the curve $2x^2 + \frac{1}{3}x^3$ at $x = 8$ (labelled A on the figure) and the ordinate at $x = 4$ (labelled B). We can generalize, and say that the area under any curve $y = f(x)$ between the limits A and B $(A > B)$ is given by the height of the ordinate at A, to the curve $y = \int f(x)dx$ less the height of the ordinate at B. It should

Table 5.1 Values of the function $y = 4x + x^2$ and its integral.

x	1	2	3	4	5	6	7	8
$f(x)$	5	12	21	32	45	60	77	96
$\int f(x)dx$	1.33	10.66	27.0	53.33	91.66	144.0	212.33	298.66

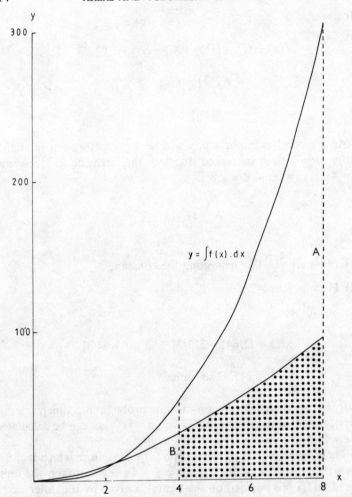

Figure 5.4 Geometric representation of the definite integral. The area outlined in dots, under the curve $y = f(x)$, is given by the difference in height of the ordinates to the curve $y = \int f(x) \mathrm{d}x$, labelled A and B.

be noted that if the curve cuts the x-axis between the limits, then the areas above and below the axis should be calculated separately.

5.2.3 The mean value theorem

The mean value, ξ, of y with respect to x, when $y = f(x)$ over the closed interval $a \leqslant x \leqslant b$ is given by

$$\xi = \frac{1}{b-a} \int_a^b y \, dx$$

The derivation of this is as follows. Let $y_1, y_2, \ldots, y_n$ be values for the function $y = f(x)$ corresponding to the values $x = a$, $x = a + \delta x, \ldots,$ $x = a + (n-1)\delta x$, where $n\delta x = b - a$. We can calculate the mean value for the function by

$$\frac{(y_1 + y_2 + \ldots + y_n)}{n} = \frac{y_1\delta x + y_2\delta x + \ldots + y_n\delta x}{n\delta x}$$

However, since $n\delta x = b - a$, we can rewrite our expression as

$$\frac{1}{b-a} \sum_{n=a}^b y_n\delta x$$

If this expression tends to a limit as $n \to \infty$ (or as $\delta x \to 0$), then the limit is

$$\frac{1}{b-a} \int_a^b y \, dx$$

For example, given $y = x^2$, find the mean value of y in the interval $0 \leqslant x \leqslant 4$.

$$\text{area} = \int_0^4 x^2 \, dx = \tfrac{1}{3}x^3]_0^4$$

$$= 21.3$$

$$\xi = \left(\frac{1}{4-0}\right)(21.3) = 5.325$$

5.3 Volume calculations

In this chapter integration has been treated in the context of finding the area under a curve, given limits in terms of values of one of the unknowns (usually x). This use of integration can be extended to the calculation of volumes, provided the third dimension can be defined. The simplest form of volume calculation involves finding volumes produced by rotating the curve around one or other of the axes.

More formally, the volume generated by rotating the curve $y = f(x)$ once around the x-axis, between the limits a and b is given by

$$\int_a^b \pi y^2 \, dx$$

Similarly, the volume generated by the curve $x = g(y)$ around the y-axis, between the limits c and d is given by

$$\int_c^d \pi x^2 \, dy$$

This can be illustrated by an example where the volume of a solid formed when the curve $y = 3x^2$ is rotated once around the x-axis, between the limits $x = 4$ and $x = 5$, is required. For simplicity, the answer will be left in multiples of π.

$$V = \int_4^5 \pi y^2 \, dx$$

$$= \int_4^5 \pi (3x^2)^2 \, dx$$

$$= \int_4^5 \pi 9x^4 \, dx$$

$$= \frac{\pi 9x^5}{5} \Bigg]_4^5$$

$$= \frac{\pi}{5}[9(5^5)] - [9(4^5)]$$

$$= \frac{\pi}{5}(28\,125 - 9216)$$

$$= \frac{18\,909}{5}\pi \text{ cubic units}$$

In geology problems of volume estimation are more frequently expressed in terms of a three-dimensional Cartesian co-ordinate system. Typically such a situation might occur as a result of an exploration programme, where an estimate of material in place is needed. In this case it may be possible to define the surface mathematically by the use of some technique such as trend surface analysis (as discussed in Section 4.5.2), where the surface is described by a polynomial of the form $z = f(x,y)$, where x and y represent geographical co-ordinates and z represents thickness. Here the volume above some region R in the (x,y)-plane is given by double integration:

$$\iint_R z \, dx \, dy = \iint_R f(x,y) \, dx \, dy$$

In many instances it is simpler to find a numerical approximation than to integrate the function. A numerical solution can be found by dividing the area of interest into a number of conveniently sized cells and calculating the value of z at the centre of each cell, by substituting the co-ordinates into the function. The volume is then found as the sum for all of the cells, of the product of cell area and the thickness z. This technique can also be used where the data have been hand-contoured or where no mathematical equation is available for the surface. In this situation the value of z is estimated at the centre of each cell by a suitable method of interpolation, and the volume is calculated by summation as before.

As an example, we can consider data relating to a thin bed of material of economic interest. The thickness of this unit has been measured at outcrop over an area of around 200 km^2, and from this information a second-degree polynomial has been generated by the method of trend surface analysis. The equation of the surface, in terms of the thickness z (measured in cm) and the geographical co-ordinates x and y (kilometre-grid), is

$$z = 0.32 + 0.104x + 0.0002y - 0.0024x^2 + 0.0013y^2$$

The problem now is to calculate the volume of material in place for the area between the eastings 5 to 20 (x-values) and the northings 1 to 11 (y-values) inclusive. It is assumed that the base of the bed is flat.

An exact analytical solution can be obtained by integration. First, to simplify the integration the coefficients in the equation are replaced by symbols

$$\alpha = 0.32 \qquad \beta = 0.104 \qquad \gamma = 0.0002$$

$$\delta = -0.0024 \qquad \lambda = 0.0013$$

which gives

$$z = a + \beta x + \gamma y + \delta x^2 + \lambda y^2$$

Now the volume is given by

$$V = \int_{y=1}^{11} \int_{x=5}^{20} (a + \beta x + \gamma y + \delta x^2 + \lambda y^2)\,dx\,dy$$

$$= \int_{y=1}^{11} [ax + \beta x^2/2 + \gamma xy + \delta x^3/3 + \lambda y^2 x]_5^{20}\,dy$$

$$= \int_{y=1}^{11} [15a + (\beta/2)(375) + \gamma y(15) + (\delta/3)(7875) + \lambda y^2(15)]\,dy$$

$$= [15ay + (\beta/2)(375)y + (\gamma y^2/2)(15) + (\delta/3)(7875)y + (\lambda y^3/3)(15)]_1^{11}$$

$$= 150a + 3750\beta/2 + 1850\gamma/2 + 78\,750\delta/3 + 19\,950\lambda/3$$

$$= 150a + 1875\beta + 900\gamma + 26\,250\delta + 6650\lambda$$

Putting the coefficient values into this equation, we get

$$V = 48 + 195 + 0.18 - 63 + 8.645$$

$$= 188.465$$

and, after converting scales, we find that the volume of material in place is equal to $1\,884\,650$ m^3.

The following results were obtained for cells of different sizes, using a numerical approximation method. For this the thickness z was found at the centre of each cell, and the cell volume calculated. Summing the volumes for all of the cells gave the total material in place:

cell side 1000 m, volume $2\,208\,800$ m^3

cell side   500 m, volume $2\,045\,632$ m^3

cell side   100 m, volume $1\,883\,762$ m^3

In this example there is good agreement between the result

obtained for the analytical method and those obtained by numerical approximation. This follows as a consequence of the simple surface used to describe the data. Clearly, the more complex the surface is, then the greater the differences between the estimates obtained using different cell sizes. Also, in order to get a value comparable with that obtained by integration, the cell size would need to be reduced further.

5.4 Summation, integration and probability distributions

In Section 4.2.1 it was noted that only continuous functions can be differentiated. Since integration can be considered as the inverse of differentiation (Section 5.1), it follows that only continuous functions can be integrated. We also noted that the area under the curve between the specified limits can be found by one of two methods:

(a) integration using the definite integral, leading to an exact analytical solution or
(b) summation using a numerical method such as Simpson's Rule, which leads to an approximation to the true value.

Thus, for a *continuous* function, the area under the curve can be found by either integration or summation. Functions which are *not continuous*, on the other hand, are not integrable and the summation method is used.

In statistics there are a number of fundamental distributions which are used to describe the probability of the occurrence of events of different types. These distributions can be *continuous* or *discrete*. The two which were introduced in Section 3.3.3, the binomial and Poisson Distributions, belong to the latter group, whereas the extremely important Normal Distribution, for example, is a continuous function. Implicit in statistical theory is the relationship between area and probability; thus, since the probabilities sum to unity, the area under the curve or histogram described by the distribution will also be unity. From the above discussion it is clear that there will be differences in the way in which properties, such as the mean or standard deviation for the two types of distribution, are derived. To illustrate the differences let us consider the derivation of the arithmetic mean. We define the mean as follows.

If x is a *random variable*, the mean of x, denoted by μ_x is given by

(a)
$$\mu_x = \sum_{\text{all } x} x_j f_x(x_j)$$

for a discrete distribution with points x_1, x_2, x_3, ..., x_j and $f_x(x_j)$ is the probability that $x = j$th value also, $\sum_{\text{all } x} f_x(x_j) = 1$.

(b)
$$\mu_x = \int_{-\infty}^{\infty} x f_x(x) \mathrm{d}x$$

for continuous x, with a probability density function $f_x(x)$ and

$$\int_{x_1}^{x_2} f_x(x) \mathrm{d}x = 1$$

Let us now consider the derivation of the mean for the uniform distribution. This distribution, sometimes termed the random distribution, can be either discrete or continuous. For the discrete uniform distribution, the mean is given by

$$\mu_x = \sum_{j=1}^{n} j \frac{1}{N} = \frac{N+1}{2}$$

where x takes all integer values in the range 1 to N, inclusive. For the continuous uniform distribution, the mean is given by

$$\mu_x = \int_{a}^{b} x \frac{1}{b-a} \mathrm{d}x$$

$$= \frac{b^2 - a^2}{2(b-a)} = \frac{a+b}{2}$$

a and b are the interval throughout which the variable x is distributed.

Although the results for the two distributions appear different, and are arrived at by different paths, the observant student will have noted that they have the same meaning. Although many other examples showing the differences in treatment between the two types of distribution in statistics could be given, we shall only emphasize that whereas continuous data can be approximated by a discrete distribution, the converse is not the case. Thus, for example, the binomial distribution is often used as an approximation to the normal distribution, but never the other way round. For further reading on this most important topic, see Cheeney (1983, ch. 5, pp. 58ff.) or any good statistical textbook.

5.5 Fourier series and the analysis of sequential data

In Section 3.1.5 we considered briefly the idea of the time series in geology. It was noted that there were a number of possible types of serially recorded data, some of which exhibit more- or less-complicated oscillations, which could be either explicitly or implicitly related to time, and could be sampled at regular or irregular intervals. Because this information is complex, the underlying trends, which may be related to some geological process of interest, are not always immediately apparent. A large number of techniques have therefore been developed to analyse or filter the data to facilitate the recognition of these trends. In particular, data filtering has become increasingly important in topics such as geophysics. It is not intended to look in detail at these methods in this book. However, since the use of the Fourier series is fundamental to many of these techniques, the basic mathematics will be considered. To simplify matters, we shall only consider the application of the series to data which is sampled at regular intervals, also we shall treat the topic numerically rather than analytically. The method discussed follows closely that described by Harbaugh & Merriam (1968) and Davis (1973). Stephenson (1973, ch. 15, pp. 254ff.) provides an excellent, although mathematical, treatment of the topic, which is useful for students wishing further information, not usually found in geological texts.

In essence the Fourier series provides a means of breaking an oscillating time series (or related series) down into a number of simple harmonics which are represented numerically by a sequence of sine and cosine terms, one of each representing individual wavelengths, which in turn are related to the length of the series sampled. The series can be progressively decomposed into harmonics of progressively shorter wavelength, or can be built up by combining harmonics to create a series which approximates the original observed data. The importance of each harmonic in the series can be judged by the numerical value of a parameter calculated from the sine and cosine terms, and known as the *power spectrum.* As this value is related to the variance, it also provides a means of comparing a number of similar time series statistically.

One general form of the infinite Fourier series can be written as

$$z = \frac{a_0}{2} \sum_{n=1}^{\infty} \left[a_n \cos\left(\frac{n\pi x}{L}\right) + b_n \sin\left(\frac{n\pi x}{L}\right) \right]$$

The angular relationships are expressed in radians, and:

z = the dependent variable, i.e. the height of the measured parameter on a graph,

a_0 = the coefficient of the zeroth-degree cosine term,

a_n = the coefficients of the cosine terms, $n = 1, 2, \ldots, \infty$

b_n = the coefficients of the sine terms, $n = 1, 2, \ldots, \infty$

x = the points of equal interval along the horizontal axis (there must be an even number) and

L = half of the fundamental sampling length, i.e. if we have k points sampled, then $L = k\Delta x/2$, where $\Delta x = x_{n+1} - x_n$.

This series can be used to approximate certain types of mathematical functions of the form

$$z = f(x)$$

In this situation the coefficients of the sine (b_n) and cosine (a_n) terms can be approximated by

$$a_n = \frac{2}{k} \frac{z_0 + z_k}{2} + \sum_{i=1}^{k-1} z_i \cos\left(\frac{n\pi x_i}{L}\right) \qquad n = 0, 1, 2, \ldots, k/2$$

$$b_n = \frac{2}{k} \sum_{i=1}^{k-1} z_i \sin\left(\frac{n\pi x_i}{L}\right) \qquad n = 1, 2, 3, \ldots, k/2$$

where k = the maximum index for points at equal intervals (k should be an even number and the number of points is $k + 1$, as the index goes from 0 to k) and i = the index of points: $0, 1, 2, \ldots, k$. There is no zero-degree sine term.

The power spectrum values related to each harmonic are calculated as

$$PS = \sqrt{(a_n^2 + b_n^2)}$$

If we wish to retrace our steps we can do so, using the calculated coefficients a_n and b_n, and calculating the values of our original series, at each sampling point, using

$$z_i = F(x_i) = \frac{a_0}{2} \sum_{n=1}^{N} \left[a_n \cos \left(\frac{n\pi x_i}{L} \right) + b_n \sin \left(\frac{n\pi x_i}{L} \right) \right]$$

where z_i = the observed value at the ith sample point, $F(x_i)$ = the approximating function and N = the maximum degree of the series. Now this is extremely useful, particularly should we wish to filter our data, since we can use the equation to combine harmonics of our choice. Thus, we can use only those which, from inspection of the power spectrum values, are thought to be important, and can construct a smoothed version of the original sequence. One of the chief advantages of applying this method is that, unlike moving-averages and related methods, points are not lost at the beginning and end of the series. Before looking at a practical application, it is convenient to start with some artificially constructed series, made up of data of known amplitude and wavelength.

The series used were constructed using sine tables, the actual angular value in the range 0–360° being used to represent distance in metres and the sine value for each 5-m increment being used to calculate the amplitude of the wave at the corresponding depth. In its simplest form this gives a wavelength of 360 m and, by adding unity to each sine value, gives an amplitude of 1. Changes in wavelength were achieved by sampling the amplitude values already generated at constant intervals according to the wavelength chosen. For example, to generate a wavelength of 180 m the series is sampled at 10-m intervals. The amplitude, on the other hand, can be altered by multiplying each value by a constant. In this way three series were generated of 360-, 180- and 45-m wavelengths, the first of these having an amplitude of 1 m, the remainder an amplitude of 10 m. The series generated in this way are shown in Figures 5.5a and b and Figure 5.6b. By combining these fundamental series, two other sequences were formed as illustrated in Figures 5.5c and 5.6c.

The numerical data relating to these series (using 19 points) were analysed using the computer program given as Program 5.2, which

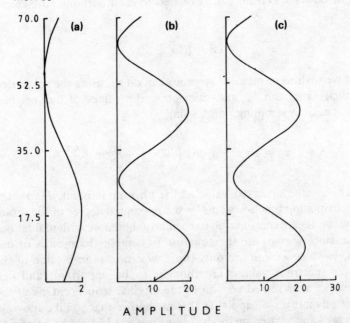

Figure 5.5 Artificially generated oscillating data series. (a) Wavelength 180 m; (b) wavelength 45 m; (c) combined 180 + 45 m. Amplitude constant 10 m.

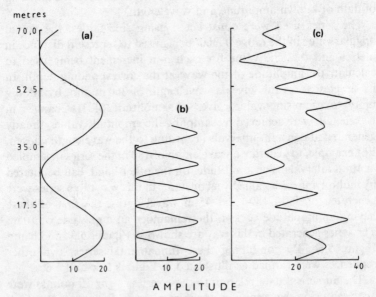

Figure 5.6 Artificially generated oscillating data series. (a) Wavelength 73 m, amplitude 1 m; (b) wavelength 36.5 m, amplitude 20 m; (c) combined.

Table 5.2 Power spectrum values for two artificial series of wavelength 360 and 180 m, and the combined values. The series are illustrated in Figure 5.5.

Harmonic	Power spectrum		
	360 m	180 m	Combined
0	0	0	0
1	1.003	0	0.996
2	0	10.014	10.024
3	0.004	0	0.014
4	0	0.020	0.029
5	0.001	0	0.010
6	0	0.021	0.028
7	0.001	0	0.011
8	0	0.01	0.018
9	0	0	0.010

has been written using the equations already discussed. The results of the analysis of this data are summarized in Tables 5.2 and 5.3, which give the power spectrum values related to each harmonic. Remember that since we started with 19 data points, the series will give rise to $(19 - 1)/2$ harmonics, plus the zeroth harmonic. Since the zeroth harmonic has no sine term, it does not have a corresponding power spectrum value.

Examination of the data in Table 5.2 shows that for the 360-m wavelength the dominant harmonic is the first, that for the 180-m

Table 5.3 Power spectrum values for two artificial series of wavelength 180 and 45 m, and combined values. The series are illustrated in Figure 5.6.

Harmonic	Power spectrum		
	180 m	45 m	Combined
0	0	0	0
1	0	0.044	0
2	10.014	0.038	10.040
3	0	0.044	0
4	0.020	0.045	0.029
5	0	0.044	0
6	0.021	0.023	0.056
7	0	0.044	0
8	0.010	10.030	10.004
9	0	0.044	0

wavelength the dominant harmonic is the second, and that the value of the power spectrum is equal to the amplitude of the series being analysed. The result of combining the two series shows that, as expected, the dominant harmonics are 1 and 2. Similarly, in Table 5.3 the dominant harmonic for the 45-m wavelength is 8, and in the combined data the second and eighth harmonics dominate. Finally, combining all three wavelengths gives the results shown in Table 5.4, where the dominant harmonics are 1, 2 and 8. In all of these examples the values for the other harmonics have values less than 1.0 and result from noise introduced by the inaccuracy of calculating the amplitude values, where only two significant figures were used.

Table 5.4 Power spectrum values for a combined series of 360-, 180- and 45-m wavelengths.

Harmonic	Power spectrum
0	0
1	0.908
2	10.137
3	0.111
4	0.129
5	0.111
6	0.131
7	0.110
8	10.100
9	0.111

Having looked at an example of the use of the Fourier series using artificially generated data, we shall now use some experimental data. These were generated during experiments designed to simulate the early diagenesis of carbonate ooids (Ferguson *et al.* 1984) by constantly monitoring and recording temperature and pressure at preset intervals. Data related to changes in sample thickness due to compaction effects were also recorded by monitoring the behaviour of a loaded piston which was in contact with the surface of the charge being treated. Recorded data relating to the period of 1 h, sampled at 2-min intervals for temperature, pressure and change in piston height, have been analysed using the Fourier analysis program. The results are given in Table 5.5, and the raw data are shown graphically in Figure 5.7. Note that the values measured are relative, not absolute.

There is a clear link between temperature and pressure in both the figures and the data analysis results. The dominant wavelength of

Table 5.5 Power spectrum values of data sampled at 2-min intervals over a period of 1 h, relating to temperature, pressure and the change in height (Δh) of a loaded piston resting on the top of the charge in the cell. The original data are shown in Figure 5.7.

	Power spectrum			Wavelength
Harmonic	Temperature	Pressure	Δh	(min)
0	0	0	0	
1	0.22	0.09	3.84	60
2	0.22	0.10	1.00	30
3	0.17	0.04	1.75	20
4	0.05	0.14	3.03	15
5	0.15	0.30	0.82	12
6	0.3	0.27	3.18	10
7	2.17	1.70	2.18	8.5
8	0.23	0.15	1.85	7.5
9	0.12	0.25	3.13	6.7
10	0.09	0.10	6.95	6
11	0.13	0.11	2.06	5.45
12	0.11	0.09	2.19	5
13	0.17	0.26	5.40	4.6
14	0.40	0.10	4.96	4.25
15	0.05	0.22	4.38	4

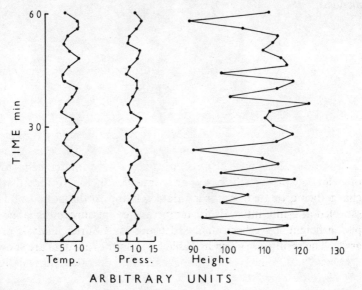

Figure 5.7 Experimental data sampled at regular intervals over a period of 60 min. See text and Table 5.5 for details.

8.5 min is controlled by the cutting in and out of the thermostat which is used to keep the equipment at a constant temperature (in this case 200°C). For the change in height of the piston there are many apparently significant harmonics, the largest of which (measured by the value of the power spectrum) is 6 min, with others at 4, 4.25 and 4.6 min. The 8.5-min harmonic related to temperature is still present, but is not dominant as in the case of temperature and pressure.

Although it is not immediately apparent why the piston oscillates as it does, this example illustrates the use of this type of analysis in simplifying large and complicated data sets. In the context of this particular analysis, it is easy to see the effect of the cutting in and out of the temperature control on other parameters, which will enable filtering to be carried out to remove the effect, making the subsequent analysis of the data set much less difficult. As mentioned at the beginning of this section, the theory of filters and its application is of fundamental importance in the interpretation of many forms of geophysical data.

For those interested in studying this field further, the classical text is Blackman and Tukey (1959). However, as a further introduction to the topic, at a more-advanced level than that given in this chapter, the discussion of the topic by Camina & Janacek (1984) is recommended.

6 Number arrays, the algebra of matrices

6.1 Introduction and definitions

If we consider the written representation of a number, we can see that it relies on the principle of position in one dimension only, the straight-line power series. Arithmetic operations, on the other hand, employ the same principle in a two-dimensional arrangement. So, for example, if we were to formalize the operation of multiplication in a two-dimensional set-up, it would be easy to demonstrate that the position of individual numbers within the layout has a specific meaning (Hogben 1967, p. 521). Such an arrangement is known as a **matrix**, and is an economic way of representing complex operations by assigning meaning to a number with reference to its cell position within the grid.

A geological illustration of the meaning of the above statement can be given using an example from stratigraphy. Figure 6.1 shows a typical diagrammatic method of recording stratigraphic data in one dimension in the form of a stratigraphic column. An alternative representation would be as a matrix recording the relationships within the data in terms of the number of transitions from one lithology to another. If we use the main lithologies in the sequence, then we can record the data as transition relationships in matrix form, as in Table 6.1. The matrix is compiled by starting at the bottom of the sequence and recording the number of times each lithology passes into another, recording the transition from row to column.

This has converted the conventional one-dimensional layout into two dimensions, achieving a considerable economy of notation by its use. Although this representation allows a quick appraisal of how lithologies relate to one another, we have lost important information in the form of the thickness of each recorded unit. This can be rectified by choosing an appropriate sample interval and recording transitions at each sample point for the chosen interval. The result of sampling Figure 6.1 at 50-cm intervals is given in Table 6.2. The significant differences between this and Table 6.1 are:

(a) we now have numbers in the principal diagonal which represent self-transitions, the actual numerical value representing

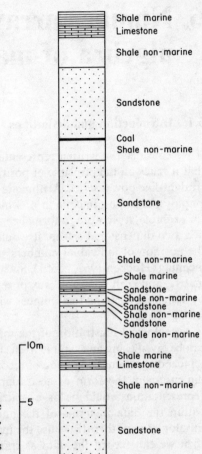

Figure 6.1 Stratigraphic sequence measured in the Lower Carboniferous, Weardale, Co. Durham. Used to compile the transition data matrix given as Tables 6.1 and 6.2.

Table 6.1 Data from Figure 6.1 recorded as a transition matrix.

	Shale (m)	Shale (nm)	Sandstone	Limestone	Coal
shale (m)	0	2	0	0	0
shale (nm)	0	0	4	2	0
sandstone	1	5	0	0	1
limestone	2	0	0	0	0
coal	0	0	1	0	0

m, marine; nm, non-marine.

Table 6.2 Data from Figure 6.1 sampled at 50-cm intervals.

	Shale (m)	Shale (nm)	Sandstone	Limestone	Coal
shale (m)	3	2	0	0	0
shale (nm)	0	27	2	2	0
sandstone	1	3	36	0	0
limestone	2	0	0	2	0
coal	0	0	1	0	0

m, marine; nm, non-marine.

the relationship between the sample interval and bed thickness; and

(b) there are differences in the transition numbers for shale (nm)/ sandstone and sandstone/shale (nm), again due to the relationship between bed thickness and sample interval.

From this, one of the principal difficulties in applying this method can be seen; that is, the problem of how to choose the sample interval. If the stratigraphic sequence to be sampled is made up of units which are generally similar in thickness, then there is no problem, but if, as in this example, there are wide differences in thickness between units, then problems can arise. As can be seen, if we reduce the sample interval so that it is small enough to include all recordable transitions, then the values in the principal diagonal will become extremely large. However, despite these limitations, matrix notation of stratigraphic data has received considerable attention from geologists, in their attempt to understand the underlying processes which control the deposition of stratigraphic sequences. A good introduction to this work, which includes the application of aspects of probability theory to stratigraphy, is given by Harbaugh & Bonham-Carter (1970, ch. 4).

Most algebraic and statistical methods have their equivalents in matrix algebra, which allows for great economy in both manipulation and representation of many problems. Also important is the fact that there is a very high degree of compatibility between matrix methods and the way in which computers can be most easily programmed to perform arithmetic operations on large arrays of data. Thus, stratigraphy is not the only field in geology where knowledge of matrix algebra is useful. Indeed, one can say that since the application of a wide variety of mathematical and statistical techniques in geology, matrix algebra has become an essential tool of the mathematical geologist. Before we consider specific applications, we need to establish the accepted conventions of notation and the basic rules of the algebra.

6.1.1 Scalars, vectors and matrices

In matrix algebra a **scalar** is a single number and is normally represented by a lower-case Greek letter, e.g. λ or a. A **matrix** is a rectangular array of numbers or symbols which represent numbers, which are known as its **elements**. Individual elements can normally have any finite numerical value, and can be negative, positive or zero. A matrix can have any number of *rows* and *columns* and is usually denoted by an upper-case letter in bold type, e.g. **M**. The **order** of a matrix is its size expressed in terms of the number of rows and columns: thus, a matrix of order $n \times m$ has n rows and m columns, in the case of a *square matrix* its order is simply the number of rows (or columns). A matrix with only one row is known as a **row vector**, and one with only one column is a **column vector**. It should be noted that a vector has magnitude and direction. If we have a vector with elements x and y, then, by Pythagoras' Theorem, the magnitude is given by

$$\sqrt{(x^2 + y^2)}$$

and its direction by

$$\tan^{-1}(x/y)$$

A vector is represented by a lower-case letter in bold type, e.g. **a**. Matrices are commonly square; other forms do exist, but because of the rules of the algebra they are not as easy to manipulate.

In general, an operation performed on a matrix will involve all of the elements of the matrix. However, to identify individual elements, subscripts are used. If **A** is a 3×3 matrix, then the elements are given as:

$$\mathbf{A}$$

$$
\begin{array}{ccc}
\text{col}_1 & \text{col}_2 & \text{col}_3
\end{array}
$$

$$
\begin{array}{c}
\text{row}_1 \\
\text{row}_2 \\
\text{row}_3
\end{array}
\begin{bmatrix}
a_{1,1} & a_{1,2} & a_{1,3} \\
a_{2,1} & a_{2,2} & a_{2,3} \\
a_{3,1} & a_{3,2} & a_{3,3}
\end{bmatrix}
$$

Table 6.3 Conventional symbols used in matrix notation.

Symbol	Meaning
A	any matrix
a	any vector (row or column)
λ	any scalar
$a_{i,j}$	an element of matrix **A**: the subscripts i and j give row and column position, respectively
I	the identity matrix
X′	the transpose of matrix **X**
|**M**|	the determinant of matrix **M**
A^{-1}	the inverse of matrix **A**

If **X** is a matrix of size $n \times n$, then each element can be denoted by $x_{i,j}$, where i and $j = 1, \ldots, n$ and i and j denote the row and column position, respectively. Elements whose subscripts are equal form the **principal diagonal** of the matrix. One important square matrix is the **identity** or **unit matrix**, denoted by **I**, whose elements are zero except for those of the principal diagonal, which are unity. As we shall see later, this matrix has special properties and uses.

The **transpose** of a matrix is the matrix written with its rows as columns. The transpose of matrix **A** is normally denoted by **A**′ (or A^T). A square matrix can be reduced to a simple form by calculating its **determinant**, a single number denoted by \|**A**\|. Finally, the **inverse** of a matrix is denoted by A^{-1} and, as will be shown later, a matrix whose determinant is zero has no inverse. The conventional matrix notation is summarized in Table 6.3.

6.2 Basic matrix operations

6.2.1 Addition and subtraction

Provided two matrices are of the same order, they can be added or subtracted simply by performing the required operation using each corresponding element

$$\mathbf{A} \quad + \quad \mathbf{B} \quad = \quad \mathbf{C}$$

$$\begin{bmatrix} 5 & 1 \\ 3 & 2 \end{bmatrix} + \begin{bmatrix} 2 & 7 \\ 4 & 1 \end{bmatrix} = \begin{bmatrix} 7 & 8 \\ 7 & 3 \end{bmatrix}$$

6.2.2   Transposition

Writing the rows of a matrix as columns and columns as rows:

$$\mathbf{M} \qquad = \qquad \mathbf{M}'$$

$$\begin{bmatrix} 1 & 2 \\ -1 & 4 \\ -3 & 3 \end{bmatrix} = \begin{bmatrix} 1 & -1 & -3 \\ 2 & 4 & 3 \end{bmatrix}$$

Row and column vectors can also be transposed.

6.2.3   Multiplication

(a) BY A SCALAR

To multiply a matrix by a scalar, each element is multiplied by the scalar. For example, we might need to convert a matrix of measurements in one scale to another, in which case we simply multiply each element of the matrix by the required constant:

$$\mathbf{A} \qquad \cdot \quad \lambda \quad = \qquad \mathbf{B}$$

$$\begin{bmatrix} 5 & 2 \\ 1 & 3 \end{bmatrix} \quad \cdot \quad 6 \quad = \quad \begin{bmatrix} 30 & 12 \\ 6 & 18 \end{bmatrix}$$

(b) BY A VECTOR

If we consider the algebraic equations

$$y_1 = a_1 x_1 + a_2 x_2$$

$$y_2 = a_3 x_1 + a_4 x_2$$

which can be written in matrix form as

$$\mathbf{y} = \mathbf{Ax}$$

this simply means that the vector of y-values, is equal to the matrix of the coefficients of the x-values (denoted by a_1, etc.), multiplied by the vector of the x-values. Thus, if we are given values for $a_1, \ldots, a_4$

and x_1 and x_2, we can calculate y_1 and y_2 simply by following the rules of number algebra. Translated into matrix form, this is the multiplication of the first row of the matrix by the values of the vector **x** and summation to give the first element of the unknown vector **y**, followed by multiplication of the second row of the matrix by the vector of **x** and summation to give the second element of the vector **y**. This is the **row-by-column rule** for matrix multiplication:

$$\begin{bmatrix} y_1 \\ y_2 \end{bmatrix} = \begin{bmatrix} a_1 & a_2 \\ a_3 & a_4 \end{bmatrix} \begin{bmatrix} x_1 \\ x_2 \end{bmatrix}$$

which is

$$y_1 = a_1 x_1 + a_2 x_2$$

$$y_2 = a_3 x_1 + a_4 x_2$$

In geometric terms we can consider the vector **x** as representing the co-ordinates of a point relative to a pair of axes, then the column vector **y** is the co-ordinates of the points after multiplication. The matrix **A** represents an operation which transforms the point P_1 to some new position P_2, as in Figure 6.2a.

Several common transformations are recognized.

(a) $\begin{bmatrix} 0 & 1 \\ 1 & 0 \end{bmatrix}$ A reflection of the plane in the line through the origin at 45° to the x-axis, see Figure 6.2b.

(b) $\begin{bmatrix} a & 0 \\ 0 & 1 \end{bmatrix}$ An elongation or compression parallel to the x-axis, see Figure 6.2c.

(c) $\begin{bmatrix} 1 & 0 \\ 0 & a \end{bmatrix}$ An elongation or compression parallel to the y-axis.

(d) $\begin{bmatrix} 1 & 0 \\ b & 1 \end{bmatrix}$ A shear parallel to the y-axis.

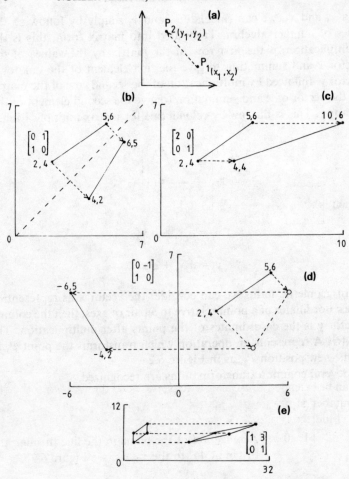

Figure 6.2 Graphical representation of some simple transformations.

(e) $\begin{bmatrix} 1 & b \\ 0 & 1 \end{bmatrix}$ A shear parallel to the *x*-axis, see Figure 6.2d.

A change in sign in any of these gives a reflection in the appropriate axis, as for example illustrated in Figure 6.2e. Figure 6.3 shows two examples of the transformation of the unit square, showing shear and reflection. It should be noted that these ideas can be extended into *n* dimensions, where *n* is the order of the matrix of transformation, and hence the number of rows in the vector. For most practical

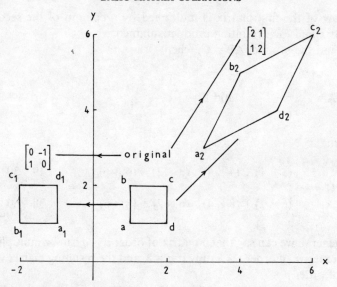

Figure 6.3 Transformation of the unit square *abcd*. Showing a reflection in the *y*-axis, $a_1b_1c_1d_1$ and shear, $a_2b_2c_2d_2$.

geological purposes three dimensions are sufficient, and higher-order matrices appear mainly in statistics.

The row-by-column rule for multiplication of a matrix by a vector can be extended to any size matrix, provided the vector has the same number of rows as the matrix has columns.

Find the product $\mathbf{Xy} = \mathbf{z}$, where

$$\mathbf{X} = \begin{bmatrix} -2 & 2 \\ 0 & 4 \\ 1 & 3 \end{bmatrix} \quad \text{and} \quad \mathbf{y} = \begin{bmatrix} 2 \\ 4 \end{bmatrix}$$

Then

$$\mathbf{z} = \begin{bmatrix} (-2 \times 2) + (2 \times 4) \\ (0 \times 2) + (4 \times 4) \\ (1 \times 2) + (3 \times 4) \end{bmatrix} = \begin{bmatrix} 4 \\ 16 \\ 14 \end{bmatrix}$$

(c) BY ANOTHER MATRIX

This operation also follows the row-by-column rule as above, where a row of the first matrix is multiplied by a column of the second matrix and each resulting product summed.

Find the product $\mathbf{AB} = \mathbf{C}$, where

$$\mathbf{A} = \begin{bmatrix} 3 & 4 \\ 6 & 8 \end{bmatrix} \quad \text{and} \quad \mathbf{B} = \begin{bmatrix} 1 & 2 \\ 4 & 6 \end{bmatrix}$$

Then

$$\mathbf{C} = \begin{bmatrix} (3 \times 1) + (4 \times 4) & (3 \times 2) + (4 \times 6) \\ (6 \times 1) + (8 \times 4) & (6 \times 2) + (8 \times 6) \end{bmatrix} = \begin{bmatrix} 19 & 30 \\ 38 & 60 \end{bmatrix}$$

In general, we can say that a matrix of order $p \times q$ can be multiplied by a matrix of order $r \times s$ only if $q = r$, and the resulting matrix will be of order $p \times s$.

In matrix algebra the product $\mathbf{AB}$ does not equal the product $\mathbf{BA}$, if either of these products exist – i.e. multiplication is not commutative as in number algebra. For this reason post-multiplication and pre-multiplication are distinguished. Thus, for the product $\mathbf{AB}$, $\mathbf{A}$ is post-multiplied by $\mathbf{B}$, and for the product $\mathbf{BA}$, $\mathbf{A}$ is pre-multiplied by $\mathbf{B}$. A computer program is listed as Program 6.1, which will multiply a matrix by a scalar, a vector or another matrix (within the rules of the algebra). The general case is given by

$$C_{i,j} = \sum_{k=1}^{n} A_{i,k} B_{k,j}$$

A matrix remains unchanged if it is multiplied by the identity matrix. This operation is equivalent to multiplying by unity in number algebra, thus

$$\mathbf{AI} = \mathbf{A}$$

Also, the following result holds:

$$\mathbf{AI} = \mathbf{IA} = \mathbf{A}$$

6.2.4 Matrix raised to any power

In some circumstances it is necessary to raise a matrix to some predetermined power. In this case the rules of matrix multiplication are obeyed as given above. Thus, if we take a simple example

$$\mathbf{AA} = \mathbf{B} \quad \text{or} \quad \mathbf{A}^2 = \mathbf{B}$$

where

$$\mathbf{A} = \begin{bmatrix} 3 & 4 \\ 5 & 1 \end{bmatrix}$$

then

$$\mathbf{B} = \begin{bmatrix} (3 \times 3) + (4 \times 5) & (3 \times 4) + (4 \times 1) \\ (4 \times 3) + (1 \times 5) & (4 \times 4) + (1 \times 1) \end{bmatrix} = \begin{bmatrix} 29 & 16 \\ 17 & 17 \end{bmatrix}$$

From the rules, it follows that only square matrices can be treated in this fashion.

6.2.5 Determinants

The determinant of a 2×2 square matrix is calculated as the product of the NW and SW elements minus the product of the other two:

$$\begin{array}{cc} \mathbf{A} & \quad\quad |\mathbf{A}| \end{array}$$

$$\begin{bmatrix} 4 & 2 \\ 6 & 5 \end{bmatrix} \quad |(4 \times 5) - (2 \times 6)| = 8$$

The determinant of a matrix is zero if any two rows or columns are identical, or if one row is a multiple of another row. A matrix with a zero determinant is said to be **singular**.

The determinant of a 3×3 matrix is found as in the following example.

$$\begin{array}{ccc} 5 & 4 & 2 \\ \hline 6 & 4 & 3 \\ 0 & 2 & 5 \end{array}$$

Stage 1. Multiply the determinant of the 2 × 2 **minor** formed by the four elements of the SE corner by the NW element of the top row:

$$5 \begin{vmatrix} 4 & 3 \\ 2 & 5 \end{vmatrix} = 5(20 - 6) = 70$$

Stage 2. Multiply the determinant of the 2 × 2 minor formed by the outer four elements by the central element of the top row, and reverse the sign:

$$-4 \begin{vmatrix} 6 & 3 \\ 0 & 5 \end{vmatrix} = -4(30 - 0) = -120$$

Stage 3. Multiply the determinant of the 2 × 2 minor formed by the four elements of the SW corner by the NE element of the top row:

$$2 \begin{vmatrix} 6 & 4 \\ 0 & 2 \end{vmatrix} = 2(12 - 0) = 24$$

Stage 4. Sum up the values resulting from the calculations of stages 1–3:

$$|\mathbf{D}_3| = 70 - 120 + 24 = -26$$

or

$$|\mathbf{D}_3| = \begin{vmatrix} 5 & 4 & 2 \\ 6 & 4 & 3 \\ 0 & 2 & 5 \end{vmatrix}$$

$$= 5 \begin{vmatrix} 4 & 3 \\ 2 & 5 \end{vmatrix} - 4 \begin{vmatrix} 6 & 3 \\ 0 & 5 \end{vmatrix} + 2 \begin{vmatrix} 6 & 4 \\ 0 & 2 \end{vmatrix}$$

$$= 70 - 120 + 24 = -26$$

The determinant of a 4 × 4 matrix:

$$\begin{matrix} + & - & + & - \\ a & b & c & d \\ \hline e & f & g & h \\ j & k & l & m \\ n & p & q & r \end{matrix}$$

$$|\mathbf{D_4}| = a\begin{vmatrix} f & g & h \\ k & l & m \\ p & q & r \end{vmatrix} - b\begin{vmatrix} e & g & h \\ j & l & m \\ n & q & r \end{vmatrix} + c\begin{vmatrix} e & f & h \\ j & k & m \\ n & p & r \end{vmatrix} - d\begin{vmatrix} e & f & g \\ j & k & l \\ n & p & q \end{vmatrix}$$

and the determinant of each 3 × 3 minor is calculated as outlined above. The determinants of higher-order matrices can be calculated by extension of the above method and, as can be seen, this is an extremely cumbersome and long-winded process. Fortunately, there are other methods for finding the determinant of a matrix, and one of these will be considered in the next section.

The determinant can be interpreted geometrically, as follows. Consider the matrix $\mathbf{R}$:

$$\begin{bmatrix} 0 & -1 \\ 1 & 0 \end{bmatrix}$$

whose determinant $|\mathbf{R}| = 0 - (-1) = 1$, and the matrix $\mathbf{S}$:

$$\begin{bmatrix} 2 & 1 \\ 1 & 2 \end{bmatrix}$$

whose determinant $|\mathbf{S}| = 4 - 1 = 3$. Use these to operate on the co-ordinates of a unit square a, b, c and d as in Figure 6.3, represented by the vectors

$$\mathbf{a} = \begin{bmatrix} 1 \\ 1 \end{bmatrix} \quad \mathbf{b} = \begin{bmatrix} 1 \\ 2 \end{bmatrix} \quad \mathbf{c} = \begin{bmatrix} 2 \\ 2 \end{bmatrix} \quad \mathbf{d} = \begin{bmatrix} 2 \\ 1 \end{bmatrix}$$

The multiplication operations are

$$\mathbf{Ra} = \begin{bmatrix} -1 \\ 1 \end{bmatrix} = a_1 \qquad \mathbf{Sa} = \begin{bmatrix} 3 \\ 3 \end{bmatrix} = a_2$$

$$\mathbf{Rb} = \begin{bmatrix} -2 \\ 1 \end{bmatrix} = b_1 \qquad \mathbf{Sb} = \begin{bmatrix} 4 \\ 5 \end{bmatrix} = b_2$$

and

$$\mathbf{Rc} = \begin{bmatrix} -2 \\ 2 \end{bmatrix} = c_1 \qquad \mathbf{Sc} = \begin{bmatrix} 6 \\ 6 \end{bmatrix} = c_2$$

$$\mathbf{Rd} = \begin{bmatrix} -1 \\ 2 \end{bmatrix} = d_1 \qquad \mathbf{Sd} = \begin{bmatrix} 5 \\ 4 \end{bmatrix} = d_2$$

and a, a_1 and a_2, etc., are as plotted in Figure 6.3. As noted earlier, the multiplication of the co-ordinates for each point by the matrix $\mathbf{R}$ represents a rotation and reflection in the y-axis, but without a change in area; while multiplication by the matrix $\mathbf{S}$ involves a shear to the right and a stretch, resulting in an increase in area. Measuring the area shows that there has been an increase, by a factor of 3, from the original. Thus, the ratio of the new area to the old is equal to the value of the determinant of the matrix used in the transformation. If a singular matrix had been used, then the transformation would be to a straight line; in other words, we would lose one dimension. This is not reversible, whereas transformations brought about by non-singular matrices are. These ideas can be extended to matrices of higher order. For example, in the case of a third-order matrix the vectors will represent the corners of a solid, and after multiplication by a singular matrix, the transformation will be from a volume to an area, i.e. again one dimension is lost.

Determinants are the basis of **Cramer's method** for the solution of simultaneous linear equations. We can write the equations in matrix form as demonstrated in Section 6.2.3:

$$[A][x] = [b]$$

In words, the matrix of the coefficients of the equations multiplied by the vector of unknowns, is equal to the vector of values on the right-hand side of the equation. Cramer's Rule states that

$$x_n = Z/|A|$$

where Z is the determinant of the matrix of coefficient values with the nth column replaced by the vector $[b]$, i.e. we replace the coefficients of the unknown, which we are determining, by the vector of values from the right-hand side of the equation, provided that $|A| \neq 0$.

This method will be dealt with in detail in Section 7.3.3, but is noted here since the idea of using determinants to solve simultaneous linear equations is used in Section 6.3.

6.2.6 Matrix inversion

The **inverse** (or **reciprocal**) of a square matrix is the matrix which when multiplied by the original, gives the identity or unit matrix:

$$AA^{-1} = I$$

For a 2×2 matrix:

Stage 1. Reverse the signs of the NE and SW elements.
Stage 2. Interchange the NW and SE elements.
Stage 3. Divide each element produced by the determinant of the original matrix.

Note that if the original matrix (of any order) is singular, i.e. has a determinant of zero, then there is no inverse. Let us now consider an example:

$$
A = \begin{bmatrix} a & b \\ c & d \end{bmatrix}
\qquad
A^{-1} = \begin{bmatrix} \dfrac{d}{|A|} & \dfrac{-b}{|A|} \\[2ex] \dfrac{-c}{|A|} & \dfrac{a}{|A|} \end{bmatrix}
$$

If

$$\mathbf{A} = \begin{bmatrix} 4 & 2 \\ 6 & 5 \end{bmatrix} \quad \text{and} \quad |\mathbf{A}| = 8$$

$$\mathbf{A}^{-1} = \begin{bmatrix} \dfrac{5}{8} & \dfrac{-1}{4} \\ \dfrac{-3}{4} & \dfrac{1}{2} \end{bmatrix} = \begin{bmatrix} 0.625 & -0.25 \\ -0.75 & 0.5 \end{bmatrix}$$

We can check our arithmetic:

$$\mathbf{A}\mathbf{A}^{-1} = \mathbf{I}$$

$$\begin{bmatrix} 4 & 2 \\ 6 & 5 \end{bmatrix} \begin{bmatrix} 0.625 & -0.25 \\ -0.75 & 0.5 \end{bmatrix} = \begin{bmatrix} 1 & 0 \\ 0 & 1 \end{bmatrix}$$

Another method, known as the method of synthetic elimination, will be described, as this can be extended to deal with square matrices of any order. It also allows the calculation of the determinant of the matrix at the same time. The method involves augmenting the matrix whose inverse is to be found by an identity matrix of the same order, and by simultaneous operations converting the former into the identity matrix and the latter into the inverse sought. We will now use the matrix of the last example to illustrate this method for the 2×2 case:

Stage 1. The matrix **A** is augmented by an identity matrix on the right:

$$\begin{bmatrix} 4 & 2 \\ 6 & 5 \end{bmatrix} \begin{bmatrix} 1 & 0 \\ 0 & 1 \end{bmatrix}$$

Stage 2. Row 1 is divided by the value of the first element (4), to give 1 at $a_{1,1}$:

$$\begin{bmatrix} 1 & \frac{1}{2} \\ 6 & 5 \end{bmatrix} \begin{bmatrix} \frac{1}{4} & 0 \\ 0 & 1 \end{bmatrix}$$

Stage 3. Row 1 is multiplied by a value (6) such that when it is subtracted from row 2, we get 0 at $a_{2,1}$:

$$\begin{bmatrix} 1 & \frac{1}{2} \\ 0 & 2 \end{bmatrix} \quad \begin{bmatrix} \frac{1}{4} & 0 \\ -\frac{3}{2} & 1 \end{bmatrix}$$

Stage 4. Row 2 is divided by a value (2) to give 1 at $a_{2,2}$:

$$\begin{bmatrix} 1 & \frac{1}{2} \\ 0 & 1 \end{bmatrix} \quad \begin{bmatrix} \frac{1}{4} & 0 \\ -\frac{3}{4} & \frac{1}{2} \end{bmatrix}$$

Stage 5. Row 2 is multiplied by a value ($\frac{1}{2}$) such that when it is subtracted from row 1, we get 0 at $a_{1,2}$:

$$\begin{bmatrix} 1 & 0 \\ 0 & 1 \end{bmatrix} \quad \begin{bmatrix} \frac{5}{8} & \frac{1}{4} \\ -\frac{3}{4} & \frac{1}{2} \end{bmatrix}$$

Thus, we have arrived at the same answer as before. We can, by using the transformation rules relating to determinants, calculate the determinant of the original matrix. The rules invoked are:

(a) if each element of any row i in a matrix $\mathbf{A}$ is multiplied by a constant a, then the determinant becomes $a\mathbf{A}$;
(b) if two rows of a matrix $\mathbf{A}$ are interchanged, then the determinant becomes $-\mathbf{A}$; and
(c) if a multiple of one row is added to another row, then the determinant remains $\mathbf{A}$.

Thus, the determinant is found as the product of the divisors used to reduce the pivots to unity at each stage. In the example above, the divisor at stage 2 used to reduce element $a_{1,1}$ to unity is multiplied by the divisor at stage 4, which was used to reduce element $a_{2,2}$ to unity. Thus

$$|\mathbf{A}| = 4 \times 2 = 8$$

This method can be applied to matrices of any size and, in practice, because of the large number of arithmetic operations involved, this is normally performed by computer. A suitable computer program based on the method is listed as Program 7.3, where it is used as the basis of a method for the solution of simultaneous linear equations. However, before leaving the topic we will work through an example using a 3×3 matrix.

Find the inverse of the matrix

$$\begin{bmatrix} 5 & 4 & 2 \\ 6 & 4 & 3 \\ 0 & 2 & 5 \end{bmatrix}$$

We start as before, augmenting the matrix:

$$\begin{bmatrix} 5 & 4 & 2 \\ 6 & 4 & 3 \\ 0 & 2 & 5 \end{bmatrix} \begin{bmatrix} 1 & 0 & 0 \\ 0 & 1 & 0 \\ 0 & 0 & 1 \end{bmatrix}$$

Divide row 1 by 5, to give 1 at $a_{1,1}$:

$$\begin{bmatrix} 1 & 0.8 & 0.4 \\ 6 & 4 & 3 \\ 0 & 2 & 5 \end{bmatrix} \begin{bmatrix} 0.2 & 0 & 0 \\ 0 & 1 & 0 \\ 0 & 0 & 1 \end{bmatrix}$$

Multiply row 1 by 6 and subtract from row 2, to give 0 at $a_{2,1}$:

row 2	6	4	3	0	1	0
$6 \times$ row 1	6	4.8	2.4	1.2	0	0
subtract	0	-0.8	0.6	-1.2	1	0

which gives

$$\begin{bmatrix} 1 & 0.8 & 0.4 \\ 0 & -0.8 & 0.6 \\ 0 & 2 & 5 \end{bmatrix} \begin{bmatrix} 0.2 & 0 & 0 \\ -1.2 & 1 & 0 \\ 0 & 0 & 0 \end{bmatrix}$$

Divide row 2 through by -0.8, to give 1 at $a_{2,2}$:

$$\begin{bmatrix} 1 & 0.8 & 0.4 \\ 0 & 1 & -0.75 \\ 0 & 2 & 5 \end{bmatrix} \quad \begin{bmatrix} 0.2 & 0 & 0 \\ 1.5 & -0.8 & 0 \\ 0 & 0 & 0 \end{bmatrix}$$

Multiply row 2 by 0.8 and subtract from row 1, to give 0 at $a_{1,2}$:

row 1	1	0.8	0.4	0.2	0	0
$0.8 \times$ row 2	0	0.8	-0.6	1.2	-0.64	0
subtract	1	0	1	-1	0.64	0

which gives

$$\begin{bmatrix} 1 & 0 & 1 \\ 0 & 1 & -0.75 \\ 0 & 2 & 5 \end{bmatrix} \quad \begin{bmatrix} -1 & 0.64 & 0 \\ 1.5 & -0.8 & 0 \\ 0 & 0 & 1 \end{bmatrix}$$

Divide row 3 through by 5, to give 1 at $a_{3,3}$:

$$\begin{bmatrix} 1 & 0 & 1 \\ 0 & 1 & -0.75 \\ 0 & 0.4 & 1 \end{bmatrix} \quad \begin{bmatrix} -1 & 0.64 & 0 \\ 1.5 & -0.8 & 0 \\ 0 & 0 & 0.2 \end{bmatrix}$$

Multiply row 3 by -0.75 and subtract from row 2, to give 0 at $a_{2,3}$:

row 2	0	1	-0.75	1.5	-0.8	0
$-0.75 \times$ row 3	0	-0.3	-0.75	0	0	-0.15
subtract	0	1.3	0	1.5	-0.8	0.15

which gives

$$\begin{bmatrix} 1 & 0 & 1 \\ 0 & 1.3 & 0 \\ 0 & 0.4 & 1 \end{bmatrix} \quad \begin{bmatrix} -1 & 0.64 & 0 \\ 1.5 & -0.8 & 0.15 \\ 0 & 0 & 0.2 \end{bmatrix}$$

Divide row 2 by 1.3, to give 1 at $a_{2,2}$:

$$\begin{bmatrix} 1 & 0 & 1 \\ 0 & 1 & 0 \\ 0 & 0.4 & 1 \end{bmatrix} \quad \begin{bmatrix} -1 & 0.64 & 0 \\ 1.15 & -0.6 & 0.115 \\ 0 & 0 & 0.2 \end{bmatrix}$$

Multiply row 2 by 0.4 and subtract from row 3, to give 0 at $a_{3,2}$:

row 3	0	0.4	1	0	0	0.2
0.4 × row 2	0	0.4	0	0.46	−0.24	0.046
subtract	0	0	1	−0.46	0.24	0.154

which gives

$$\begin{bmatrix} 1 & 0 & 1 \\ 0 & 1 & 0 \\ 0 & 0 & 1 \end{bmatrix} \quad \begin{bmatrix} -1 & 0.64 & 0 \\ 1.15 & -0.6 & 0.115 \\ -0.46 & 0.24 & 0.154 \end{bmatrix}$$

Subtract row 3 from row 1, to give 0 at $a_{1,3}$:

row 1	1	0	1	−1	0.64	0
row 3	0	0	1	−0.46	0.24	0.154
subtract	1	0	0	−0.54	0.4	−0.154

which gives, finally,

$$\begin{bmatrix} 1 & 0 & 0 \\ 0 & 1 & 0 \\ 0 & 0 & 1 \end{bmatrix} \begin{bmatrix} -0.54 & 0.4 & -0.154 \\ 1.15 & -0.6 & 0.115 \\ -0.46 & 0.24 & 0.154 \end{bmatrix}$$

The determinant is given, as before, by the product of the divisors:

$$|\mathbf{A}| = 5 \times (-0.8) \times 5 \times 1.3 = -26$$

The arithmetic can be checked by multiplication of the matrix by its inverse to give the identity matrix. Unfortunately, in this example, because only a maximum of three significant figures has been carried in the calculation, the result of this operation will not be as expected. The method of matrix inversion will be looked at later in the context of the solution of simultaneous linear equations (Section 7.3.3b), where the problem of accuracy will also be discussed.

6.2.7 Division in matrix algebra

We should note that there is no direct equivalent to the arithmetic operation of division in matrix algebra. Thus, if we need to perform this operation on two matrices, we multiply by the inverse of the divisor, the relationship is:

$$\mathbf{A}/\mathbf{S} = \mathbf{S}^{-1}\mathbf{A}$$

It is also worth noting that, since we can only find the inverse of square matrices, it is only possible to perform this particular operation if the divisor is a square matrix with the same number of rows as the other has columns.

6.3 Eigenvalues and eigenvectors

The topic of eigenvalues and eigenvectors is regarded by most authors as probably one of the most difficult in matrix algebra, a fact which is borne out by a quick check of the majority of textbooks. Fortunately for those who would like to understand and use these properties without becoming too involved in the detailed mathematics, a paper by Gould (1967) explains the topic in an extremely clear and understandable fashion. Thus, following the example of King (1969) and Davis (1973), the discussion of eigenvalues and eigenvectors which follows relies heavily on Gould's paper. For the student who would like a more mathematical treatment, Sawyer's *A path to modern mathematics* (1966, ch. 5) provides an excellent introduction.

First, we must establish the idea of the **characteristic equation** associated with a square matrix **A**, of order *n*. Consider a hypothetical simultaneous linear equations set

$$[A][x] = \lambda[x]$$

which is the same as

$$[A][x] = [b]$$

except that

$$[b] = \lambda[x]$$

What is now required is to find values of λ, which satisfy this relationship. We can rewrite the equation as

$$([A] - \lambda[I])[x] = [0]$$

This relationship can be written in the form of simultaneous linear equations. Suppose, for simplicity, that we have two unknowns. We rewrite as

$$(A_1 - \lambda)x_1 + B_1 x_2 + C_1 = 0$$

$$A_2 x_1 + (B_2 - \lambda)x_2 + C_2 = 0$$

A solution for the vector [x] is given by

$$[x] = \frac{[0]}{|A|}$$

This is Cramer's Rule, where the values of **x** are given as the ratio of two determinants; however, the determinant of the numerator is zero, since it has one row made up of zeros. We can rewrite the equation as

$$|\mathbf{A}|[\mathbf{x}] = 0$$

Now, if the vector $[\mathbf{x}]$ is not equal to zero, then it follows that the determinant $|\mathbf{A}|$ must be zero:

$$|[\mathbf{A}] - \lambda[\mathbf{I}]| = \begin{vmatrix} A_1 - \lambda & B_1 \\ A_2 & B_2 - \lambda \end{vmatrix} = 0$$

The equation

$$|\mathbf{A} - \lambda\mathbf{I}| = 0$$

is known as the characteristic equation for any square matrix $\mathbf{A}$ of order n, and the vector λ represents the **characteristic roots** or **eigenvalues** for that matrix.

We can expand the determinant, i.e. write it as we would calculate it (Section 6.2.5), hence

$$(A_1 - \lambda)(B_2 - \lambda) - A_2 B_1 = 0$$

Multiplying out,

$$\begin{array}{r} A_1 - \lambda \\ B_2 - \lambda \\ \hline A_1 B_2 - B_2\lambda \\ -A_1\lambda \qquad\qquad + \lambda^2 \\ \hline -A_1\lambda + A_1 B_2 - B_2\lambda + \lambda^2 \end{array}$$

which is

$$A_1 B_2 - A_2 B_1 - A_1\lambda - B_2\lambda + \lambda^2 = 0$$

Since in the practical situation we know the numerical values of A_1, B_1, etc., we can collect up the terms in the form of a quadratic

$$\lambda^2 + a\lambda + \beta = 0$$

Finding the roots of this equation will give the values of λ, the eigenvalues of the matrix.

The use of a simple example will help to clarify the calculation procedure. Consider the equation set

$$4x + 2y = a$$

$$6x + 5y = b$$

The coefficient matrix is

$$[\mathbf{A}] = \begin{bmatrix} 4 & 2 \\ 6 & 5 \end{bmatrix}$$

Subtracting λ times the identity matrix,

$$[\mathbf{A}] - \lambda[\mathbf{I}] = \begin{bmatrix} 4 - \lambda & 2 \\ 6 & 5 - \lambda \end{bmatrix}$$

Equating the determinant to zero,

$$\begin{bmatrix} 4 - \lambda & 2 \\ 6 & 5 - \lambda \end{bmatrix} = 0$$

Expanding the determinant,

$$|(4 - \lambda)(5 - \lambda) - (2)(6)| = 0$$

Multiplying out,

$$20 - 9\lambda + \lambda^2 - 12 = 0$$

Collecting terms,

$$\lambda^2 - 9\lambda + 8 = 0$$

Factorizing,

$$(\lambda - 8)(\lambda - 1) = 0$$

thus $\lambda = 8$ or 1, which are the eigenvalues of the matrix $\mathbf{A}$.

Several things should be noted at this stage. In the example just calculated there are two real roots, but for other matrices this is not the only possibility. Thus, going back to the problem of the solution of quadratic equations, it should be remembered that there are occasions when the roots are complex numbers (Section 2.1.3).

Although matrices with complex eigenvalues do occur, in most practical applications the matrix is symmetric, and symmetric matrices have real roots. Also, the number of roots will be equal to the order of the matrix. Finally, since the sum of the eigenvalues is equal to the sum of the elements in the principal diagonal, this can be used to check the arithmetic.

Returning to an earlier equation,

$$(\mathbf{A} - \lambda\mathbf{I})\mathbf{x} = \mathbf{0}$$

which can be rewritten more fully, as (for a 2 × 2 matrix)

$$\begin{bmatrix} a_{11} - \lambda & a_{12} \\ a_{21} & a_{22} - \lambda \end{bmatrix} \begin{bmatrix} x_1 \\ x_2 \end{bmatrix} = \begin{bmatrix} 0 \\ 0 \end{bmatrix}$$

Now, if the eigenvalues λ have been found, we can solve for x_1 and x_2, which are the **eigenvectors** associated with the particular eigenvalue substituted in the equation. There will be **one pair of eigenvectors for each eigenvalue.** Thus, for the example which we have been using:

for $\lambda = 8$

$$\begin{bmatrix} 4 - 8 & 2 \\ 6 & 5 - 8 \end{bmatrix} \begin{bmatrix} x_1 \\ x_2 \end{bmatrix} = \begin{bmatrix} 0 \\ 0 \end{bmatrix}$$

which is analogous to the simultaneous linear equation set

$$-4x_1 - 2x_2 = 0$$

$$6x_1 - 3x_2 = 0$$

whence $x_1 = 1$ and $x_2 = 2$

for $\lambda = 1$

$$\begin{bmatrix} 4 - 1 & 2 \\ 6 & 5 - 1 \end{bmatrix} \begin{bmatrix} x_1 \\ x_2 \end{bmatrix} = \begin{bmatrix} 0 \\ 0 \end{bmatrix}$$

which is

$$3x_1 + 2x_2 = 0$$

$$6x_1 + 4x_2 = 0$$

whence $x_1 = 2$ and $x_2 = -3$.

To summarize, we have now calculated:

(a) an eigenvalue of 8 with an associated eigenvector of (1,2); and
(b) an eigenvalue of 1 with an associated eigenvector of (2, -3).

In geometric terms we have reduced our matrix to two vectors whose magnitude is given by the eigenvalues, and whose directions are given by the eigenvectors. We are now in a position to consider a geological example, which we will interpret graphically after calculating the eigenvalues and their associated eigenvectors.

We start with the following matrix (the row and column labels are appended for clarity)

$$
\begin{array}{cc}
 & \text{Mg} \quad \text{K} \\
\begin{array}{c} \text{Mg} \\ \text{K} \end{array} &
\begin{bmatrix}
1.0 & 0.45 \\
0.45 & 1.0
\end{bmatrix}
\end{array}
$$

whose elements are the product moment correlation coefficients for the trace elements magnesium (Mg) and potassium (K), based on data from ten samples of Cretaceous flint, collected from Neolithic flint mines at Grimes Graves, Norfolk. The values of unity in the principal diagonal of the matrix represent self-correlation. The coefficient ranges from + 1.0 (perfect positive correlation) to 0.0 (complete disassociation) to - 1.0 (perfect negative correlation). Students who have not already met this coefficient are referred to either Cheeney (1983, pp. 87ff.) or Moroney (1951, pp. 286ff.), or any good statistics textbook for further details. Proceeding as in the previous example,

$$
[\mathbf{A}] - \lambda[\mathbf{I}] =
\begin{bmatrix}
1 - \lambda & 0.45 \\
0.45 & 1 - \lambda
\end{bmatrix}
$$

Equating the determinant to zero,

$$\begin{bmatrix} 1 - \lambda & 0.45 \\ 0.45 & 1 - \lambda \end{bmatrix} = 0$$

Expanding the determinant, multiplying out and collecting terms,

$$\lambda^2 - 2\lambda + 0.7975 = 0$$

Using the formula for the solution of a quadratic,

$$\lambda = 1.45 \quad \text{or} \quad 0.55$$

which are the eigenvalues of the correlation matrix.
   Substituting $\lambda = 1.45$, we get

$$\begin{bmatrix} 1 - 1.45 & 0.45 \\ 0.45 & 1 - 1.45 \end{bmatrix} \begin{bmatrix} x_1 \\ x_2 \end{bmatrix} = \begin{bmatrix} 0 \\ 0 \end{bmatrix}$$

which gives

$$-0.45x_1 + 0.45x_2 = 0$$

$$0.45x_1 - 0.45x_2 = 0$$

whence $x_1 = 1$ and $x_2 = 1$. Similarly, substituting $\lambda = 0.55$, we get

$$0.45x_1 + 0.45x_2 = 0$$

$$0.45x_1 + 0.45x_2 = 0$$

whence $x_1 = 1$ and $x_2 = -1$.
   The eigenvalues and eigenvectors can be plotted relative to a pair
of axes x_1 and x_2, where x_1 represents the element Mg and x_2
represents K, as in Figure 6.4. The eigenvalues define the lengths of
two vectors, whose slopes are defined by the eigenvectors. These are
mutually orthogonal (i.e. at right angles) and form the major and
minor axes of an ellipse (it should be noted that not all matrices give
vectors which are mutually orthogonal). From the figure it can be
seen that the vector represented by the eigenvalue 1.45 (plotted using

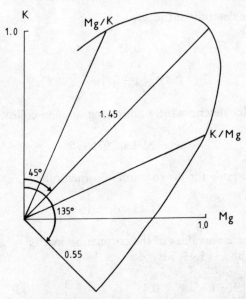

Figure 6.4 Diagrammatic representation of a correlation matrix for the elements potassium and magnesium, trace elements in Cretaceous flint from Grimes Graves, Norfolk. Showing the eigenvectors and eigenvalues. See text for details.

the same scale as the axes, which are of unit length), corresponds to half the length of the major axis of the ellipse and has a slope of 45°, while the vector represented by the eigenvalue 0.55 is half the length of the minor axis and has a slope of 135° (both slopes are measured from the vertical axis of the plot). The values of the correlation coefficients for the two metals represent the tangents of the angles which two vectors make with the appropriate axis, and can be represented by plotting on the perimeter of the ellipse as shown. The origin of the axes for this type of plot is always at the centre of the ellipse. To summarize, we have taken a matrix representing the correlation between two variables, and have reduced it to a pair of vectors whose magnitude and direction are given by the eigenvalues and eigenvectors of the correlation matrix. With more-complex data sets, where many variables are involved, the method can be extended. It is an extremely useful technique, and is the basis of a number of methods in multivariate statistics. Another application, as will be seen in Section 6.4.4, is in structural geology.

During the consideration of the problem of determining the eigenvalues and eigenvectors, the characteristic equation for a square matrix of order n has been defined, and a mathematical technique has been described for its solution. The method outlined can be used to solve square matrices of any order, but it proves to be too cumbersome for the solution of examples where the order is > 3. Several alternative methods of solution have been developed to facilitate the solution of higher-order matrices. One method, specifically designed to find the eigenvalues and eigenvectors for real symmetrical matrices, known as the Jacobi method, is described by Cheeney (1983, pp. 119ff.). This method is used as the basis of Program 6.2, which is a development of a Fortran program given by Davis (1973, pp. 168–9).

6.4 Geological applications and examples

6.4.1 Stratigraphic data analysis

In the introduction to this chapter the idea of recording stratigraphic data in matrix form was introduced. The particular matrix is known as a transition matrix, and has two principal uses in geological data processing. In one application the matrix is transformed into a transition probability matrix and used in simulation studies. In the other it is used without alteration in conjunction with its randomized form, to deduce cyclic associations. Armed with the basic techniques of matrix algebra, we can look at both of these applications.

(a) TRANSITION PROBABILITY MATRICES: CALCULATION AND
      USES

The calculation of a transition probability matrix is relatively simple once the transition matrix for the sequence has been compiled. The row sums for each lithology are found, and the individual transition frequency are divided by the appropriate row sum. This gives values for the probability of one lithology (row label) passing into another lithology (column label). Tables 6.4 and 6.5 show these operations

Table 6.4 Transition matrix for a sequence measured in the Jurassic, Blisworth Limestone. Sample interval 20 cm. Lithologies simplified.

	Limestone	Marl	Clay	Row sum
limestone	38	4	8	50
marl	4	9	2	15
clay	7	2	6	15

Table 6.5 Transition probability matrix for the data of Table 6.4.

	Limestone	Marl	Clay	Row sum
limestone	0.76	0.08	0.16	1.00
marl	0.27	0.60	0.13	1.00
clay	0.47	0.13	0.40	1.00

for data compiled from a sequence in the Blisworth Limestone (Jurassic, Bathonian). Thus,

$$p_{(i,j)} = \frac{T_{(i,j)}}{S_{(i)}}$$

where $p_{(i,j)}$ = the probability of lithology i passing into lithology j, $T_{(i,j)}$ = the transition frequency for lithology i passing into lithology j and $S_{(i)} = \sum_{j=1}^{n} T_{(i,j)}$, n being the number of lithologies.

Most uses of the transition probability matrix have been based on the idea that stratigraphic sequences are not random, and that each lithology deposited is in some way dependent on earlier events. Such sequences, which show some dependence on earlier events, occur in many natural time series and have been called *Markov processes*, after the Russian mathematician who was the first to make a comprehensive study of them. Thus, stratigraphic data can be said to exhibit a Markov property, which in the simplest case means that the lithology being deposited at any particular time is dependent on the immediately preceding depositional event (one-step dependence). However, in most cases it is likely that more-complicated relationships occur. The notion of the Markov property implies that the sequence has a 'memory' for previous events. One simple method of discovering the extent of the 'memory' is to find the probabilities associated with more than a single step.

Let us consider what happens if we use the data in Table 6.5, starting, for example, with the lithology marl. For step 1 the probabilities of going to any lithology will be as given by the values in the corresponding row. For subsequent steps the probabilities will be governed by the axioms of probability theory, as already discussed in Sections 2.3.1 and 2.3.2. The sequence starts

p (marl → limestone) = 0.27 (step 1)

p (limestone → clay) = 0.27 × 0.16 = 0.0432 (step 2)

this follows from the multiplication axiom.

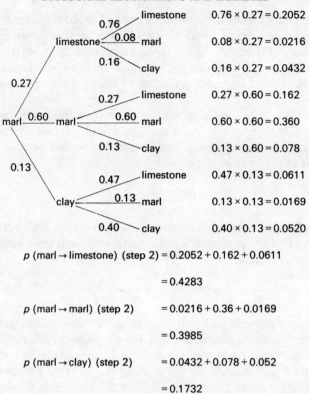

p (marl → limestone) (step 2) = 0.2052 + 0.162 + 0.0611

$\qquad\qquad\qquad\qquad\quad$ = 0.4283

p (marl → marl) (step 2) $\qquad$ = 0.0216 + 0.36 + 0.0169

$\qquad\qquad\qquad\qquad\quad$ = 0.3985

p (marl → clay) (step 2) $\qquad$ = 0.0432 + 0.078 + 0.052

$\qquad\qquad\qquad\qquad\quad$ = 0.1732

Figure 6.5 Tree diagram for the three-state transition probability matrix of Table 6.5, to show the successive probabilities of reaching a given lithology after two steps, starting with marl.

However, we can also get to clay at step 2 via either

$$p \text{ (marl} \rightarrow \text{marl)} = 0.60 \text{ (step 1)}$$

$$p \text{ (marl} \rightarrow \text{clay)} = 0.60 \times 0.13 = 0.078 \text{ (step 2)}$$

or

$$p \text{ (marl} \rightarrow \text{clay)} = 0.13 \text{ (step 1)}$$

$$p \text{ (clay} \rightarrow \text{clay)} = 0.13 \times 0.40 = 0.052 \text{ (step 2)}$$

Thus, the probability of being in lithology clay at step 2 is the sum of the probabilities for each possible path:

$$p \text{ (marl} \rightarrow \text{clay) (step 2)} = 0.0432 + 0.078 + 0.052 = 0.1732$$

which follows from the addition axiom of probability theory. The complete sequence of possible events for two steps is shown as a tree diagram in Figure 6.5. The diagram summarizes how, starting with the lithology marl, we can get to any of the three lithologies in the sequence in two steps, the probability values for each possible path are given.

If we complete similar calculations starting with each of the other lithologies, then we will find that the probability values are the same as those which would have been obtained if we had performed the matrix multiplication operation

$$\mathbf{MM} = \mathbf{M}^2 = \mathbf{P}_{(\text{step 2})}$$

where $\mathbf{M}$ is the original transition probability matrix. Similarly, if we wish to find the probabilities associated with each state after three steps, we calculate

$$\mathbf{MMM} = \mathbf{M}^3 = \mathbf{P}_{(\text{step 3})}$$

Successive powering of a transition probability matrix generally leads to a limiting matrix $\mathbf{T}$, where the elements of each column are equal; at which point the probability of passing from one state to another is independent of the starting state. Table 6.6 shows the result of powering the data of Table 6.5, from which we conclude that for the data set under consideration, transitions after step 8 will be independent of the starting state, i.e. the sequence has no 'memory' of the starting lithology after eight depositional events. Also, since the rows of the matrix are equal, this must represent the proportions of each lithology in the original sequence on which the matrix was based. To facilitate this calculation, Program 6.3 is given, which will power a transition probability matrix to any predetermined level.

The transition probability matrix is also used as a basis for the simulation of stratigraphic sequences. For this, the matrix is used in its cumulative form, where the probabilities in each row are cumulated from left to right. The two matrices in Table 6.7 show (a) the transition probability matrix and (b) the cumulative transition probability matrix for data taken from a sequence in the Jurassic, Blisworth Limestone, measured at Irchester in Northamptonshire. The sequence is illustrated in Figure 6.6a.

A simulation is started by choosing, at random, a starting lithology (say, limestone), picking a random number in the range 0–

Table 6.6 The result of powering the probability transition matrix of Table 6.5, correct to two decimal places. Row and column labels have been omitted, as well as some of the individual steps. Note that the probabilities recorded for row 2 of the step 2 matrix are the same as those calculated in Figure 6.5.

step 2	0.67	0.13	0.20
	0.43	0.40	0.17
	0.58	0.17	0.25
step 4	0.62	0.17	0.20
	0.56	0.24	0.20
	0.61	0.19	0.21
step 6	0.61	0.18	0.20
	0.59	0.20	0.20
	0.61	0.19	0.20
step 7	0.61	0.19	0.20
	0.60	0.19	0.20
	0.61	0.19	0.20
step 9	0.61	0.19	0.20
	0.61	0.19	0.20
	0.61	0.19	0.20

1.0 (using either random-number tables or a computer). Then, if the random number falls in the range 0–0.74, the original lithology is deemed to have passed into itself, if it falls in the range 0.74–0.84 then a marl follows. However, if it is in the range 0.84–1.0 a clay follows. Suppose our first random number was 0.82, then the sequence starts

$$\text{limestone} \rightarrow \text{marl}$$

Table 6.7 Transition probability and cumulative probability matrix for the sequence illustrated in Figure 6.6a. Sample interval 20 cm.

Lithology	(a) Transition probability			(b) Cumulative transition probability		
	Limestone	Marl	Clay	Limestone	Marl	Clay
limestone	0.74	0.10	0.16	0.74	0.84	1.00
marl	0.25	0.59	0.16	0.25	0.84	1.00
clay	0.43	0.43	0.14	0.43	0.86	1.00

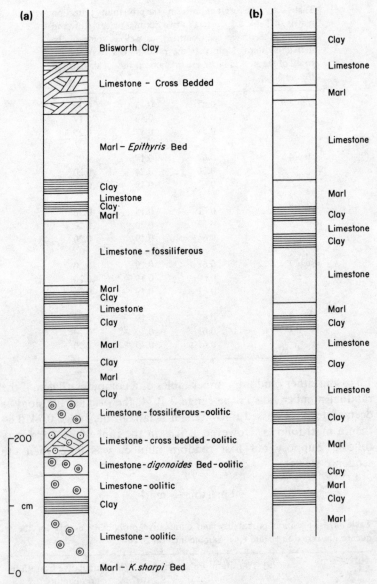

(a)

Blisworth Clay

Limestone – Cross Bedded

Marl – *Epithyris* Bed

Clay
Limestone
Clay
Marl

Limestone – fossiliferous

Marl
Clay
Limestone
Clay

Marl

Clay
Marl

Clay

Limestone – fossiliferous – oolitic

200

Limestone – cross bedded – oolitic

Limestone – *digonoides* Bed – oolitic

Limestone – oolitic

Clay

cm

Limestone – oolitic

0

Marl – *K. sharpi* Bed

(b)

Clay

Limestone

Marl

Limestone

Marl

Clay
Limestone
Clay

Limestone

Marl
Clay

Limestone

Clay

Limestone

Clay

Marl

Clay
Marl
Clay

Marl

Figure 6.6 (a) Sequence measured in the Bathonian, Blisworth Limestone at Irchester, Northamptonshire. (b) Simulated sequence using the Markov simulation method described in the text and the data of Table 6.7b.

We select a second random number, say 0.215. Going to the row giving the transition probabilities for marl, and since our number is in the range 0–0.25, the marl is followed by a limestone and the sequence becomes

$$\text{limestone} \rightarrow \text{marl} \rightarrow \text{limestone}$$

This process of picking (or generating) a random number and assigning a new lithology is repeated as many times as required, building up a simulated stratigraphic sequence.

As the probability transition matrix was based on a 20-cm sampling interval, it then follows that the lithology generated at each stage is equivalent to 20 cm thickness of rock. The resulting sequence will not be exactly the same as the original, but will show a close resemblance. Figure 6.6b shows part of a generated sequence using the data of Table 6.7b, alongside the original measured sequence, to illustrate this point. It must be remembered that there is no objective method of comparing a simulation of this nature with the real geological situation. One can only pose the question: is there any similarity between the two? If the answer is yes, then it is likely to imply that some of the ideas behind the model may be valid. On the other hand, a negative answer need not imply that the model is invalid.

In this section we have presented the notion of event dependence in the form of the Markov process as a method of analysing stratigraphic sequences, without recourse to statistical proof or verification of the hypothesis, but simply as an example of the use of matrix algebra. Those who would like to pursue these ideas further should consult the textbooks by Harbaugh & Bonham-Carter (1970) and Davis (1973), both of which deal in some detail with Markov models in geology, and contain numerous references to papers on the subject.

(b) ELUCIDATION OF CYCLICITY IN STRATIGRAPHIC DATA

The validity of the Markov Model as applied in stratigraphic analysis has been questioned by Selley (1970), who proposed a simple alternative. The model is designed to isolate and define cyclicity within a stratigraphic sequence starting with the transition matrix. Selley (1970, p. 559) suggests that the transition matrix will be objective and reproducible if the matrix is based on a record of bed transitions only. Having found the transition matrix (as shown in Section 6.1) for the sequence being studied, the next step is to calculate the equivalent expected random matrix, i.e. the transition matrix expected if the same number of beds had been deposited at random. This matrix will have the same total number of transitions as the original, as well as having the same row and column sums. Each element of the expected random matrix is found by calculating

$$E_{i,j} = \frac{\text{RSUM}_j \cdot \text{CSUM}_i}{\text{TSUM}}$$

where $E_{i,j}$ is the expected frequency for each element i,j, RSUM_j is the row sum of the jth row of the observed matrix, CSUM_i is the column sum of the ith column of the observed matrix, TSUM is the sum of all the elements in the observed matrix, and i and j range from 1 to n, n being the number of different lithologies in the sequence. In other words, if we wish to find the expected frequency for any element i,j we multiply the row total for row j by the column total for column i and divide by the total number of transitions. Having obtained the expected random matrix, this is then subtracted from the original to give the difference matrix. These calculations are shown in Table 6.8, which is based on a simple example, recording

Table 6.8 Calculation of an expected random matrix and difference matrix, based on a transition matrix relating to a sequence in the Lower Carboniferous (see text for details).

	Limestone	Sandstone	Shale	Row sum
(a) Observed transition matrix **O**				
limestone	0	3	4	7
sandstone	2	0	4	6
shale	5	3	0	8
column sum	7	6	8	$N = 21$
(b) Expected randomized matrix **E**				
	2.3	2.0	2.7	7
	2.0	1.7	2.3	6
	2.7	2.3	3.0	8
column sum	7	6	8	$N = 21$
(c) Difference matrix **D** = **O** − **E**				
	− 2.3	1.0	1.3	
	0	− 1.7	1.7	
	2.3	0.7	− 3.0	

transitions only, from a borehole core through strata in the Carboniferous, Visean of Upper Teesdale, Durham.

Selley's argument (Selley 1970, p. 560) is that we should pay particular attention to transitions which occur more frequently than we would expect if the sequence were random. Thus, by inspecting the difference matrix we should be able to construct a facies relationship diagram for the sequence being examined. Looking at the difference matrix in Table 6.8, the largest difference (numerically) is for the shale → limestone transition, if we now look at the row corresponding to limestone, the largest value is for limestone → shale transition. Thus, the transition

$$shale \rightarrow limestone \rightarrow shale$$

represents the major cyclic sequence in the data. Further minor cycles can be found by looking for the largest value which has not previously been accounted for. In this example we note that there is a minor cycle

$$sandstone \rightarrow shale \rightarrow sandstone$$

Although these ideas have not received universal acceptance, it is an easy method to apply, allowing the apparent cyclicity in data sets to be analysed objectively. Also, as Selley (1970) has shown, the results can be intriguingly different from those expected.

6.4.2 The matrix and its transpose in statistics

(a) THE DISPERSION MATRIX

In some multivariate statistical methods a matrix known as the dispersion matrix is used as a starting point in an analysis. The matrix for each population is made up as follows (in the simple two-variable case).

Element 1,1 is the sum of the squared deviations from the mean (the use of the unqualified mean in this section implies the arithmetic mean), for variable 1

$$d_{1,1} = \sum (x_{1,j} - \mu_1)^2$$

Elements 1,2 and 2,1 are the sum of the product of the differences of the means for each variable

$$d_{1,2} \text{ and } d_{2,1} = \sum (x_{1,j} - \mu_1)(x_{2,j} - \mu_2)$$

Element 2,2 is the sum of the squared deviations from the mean for variable 2

$$d_{2,2} = \sum(x_{2,j} - \mu_2)^2$$

which is

$$\mathbf{D} = \mathbf{MM'}$$

where $\mathbf{D}$ is the dispersion matrix which will be square and of order i, and i is the number of variables, $\mathbf{M}$ is the data matrix where each element is expressed as a deviation from the appropriate mean and $\mathbf{M'}$ is its transpose.

The matrix will have i columns (number of variables) and n rows (number of samples). Details of this calculation are set out in Table 6.10, using data for trace elements in ten samples of flint from the Neolithic flint mine site at Grimes Graves, Norfolk, as listed in Table 6.9.

Table 6.9 Raw data matrix $\mathbf{R}$, relating to trace element analysis of ten samples of flint, from Grimes Graves, Norfolk.

	\multicolumn{10}{c}{Sample no.}									Mean
	1	2	3	4	5	21	22	23	24	25	
aluminium (ppm)	636	616	605	586	495	668	648	512	635	503	590.4
magnesium (ppm)	29	24	26	26	90	21	21	19	28	18	30.2
potassium (ppm)	240	247	220	247	202	217	250	203	234	172	223.2

(b) THE CORRELATION MATRIX R

Another important matrix in multivariate statistics is the correlation matrix $\mathbf{R}$, where each element is the product moment correlation coefficient relating the variables. In this case the data are pretreated so that the measured variable for each sample has a mean of zero and a standard deviation of unity. Thus, if $\mathbf{N}$ is the normalized data matrix, then each element $n_{i,j}$, where i is the sample index and j is the variable index, is given by

$$n_{i,j} = x_{i,j} - \mu_j/\sigma_j$$

where $x_{i,j}$ is the ith sample of the jth variable, σ_j is the standard

Table 6.10 Calculation of the dispersion matrix, using the flint mine data of Table 6.9.

(a) The data expressed as the deviation from the mean for each element, matrix **M**

---

aluminium (ppm)	45.6	25.6	14.6	−4.4	−95.4	77.6	57.6	−78.4	44.6	−87.4
magnesium (ppm)	−1.2	−6.2	−4.2	−4.2	59.8	−9.2	−9.2	−11.2	−2.2	−12.2
potassium (ppm)	16.8	23.8	−3.2	23.8	−21.2	−6.2	26.8	−20.2	10.8	−51.2

(b) Data matrix **M** written as its transpose **M′**

Al	Mg	K
45.6	−1.2	16.8
25.6	−6.2	23.8
14.6	−4.2	−3.2
−4.4	−4.2	23.8
−95.4	59.8	−21.2
77.6	−9.2	26.8
−78.4	−11.2	−20.2
44.6	−2.2	10.8
−87.4	−12.2	−51.2

(c) Details of calculation of the dispersion matrix, where **MM′** = **D**

$D_{1,1} = (45.6 \times 45.6) + (25.6 \times 25.6) + \ldots + (-87.4 \times -87.4)$
$D_{1,2} = (-1.2 \times 45.6) + (-6.2 \times 25.6) + \ldots + (-12.2 \times -87.4)$
$D_{1,3} = (16.8 \times 45.6) + (23.8 \times 25.6) + \ldots + (-51.2 \times -87.4)$
$D_{2,1} = (45.6 \times -1.2) + (25.6 \times -6.2) + \ldots + (-87.4 \times -12.2)$

$D_{3,3} = (16.8 \times 16.8) + (23.8 \times 23.8) + \ldots + (-51.2 \times 51.2)$

(d) The dispersion matrix **D**

	Al	Mg	K
Al	37182.4	−5358.8	10849.2
Mg	−5358.8	4099.6	−884.4
K	10849.2	−884.4	5777.6

Table 6.11 Part of the raw data set from Table 6.9, and the calculated mean ;
standard deviation for each element.

	Sample no.					Mean	Standard deviation
	1	2	3	4	21		
aluminium (ppm)	636	616	605	586	668	622.2	28.1
magnesium (ppm)	29	24	26	26	21	25.2	2.6
potassium (ppm)	240	247	220	247	217	234.2	13.1

deviation of the jth variable and x_j is the mean of the jth variable.
The correlation matrix $\mathbf{R}$ is given by

$$\mathbf{R} = (1/n)(\mathbf{N}\mathbf{N}')$$

where $\mathbf{N}$ is the normalized data matrix, $\mathbf{N}'$ is its transpose and n is the
number of samples. The matrix $\mathbf{R}$ will be square and of order m,
where m is the number of variables. Details of this calculation, using
the data set given in Table 6.11, are given in Table 6.12 as an
example.

   In both of the example calculations given, only three variables
have been used. However, the method can be extended to take into
account any number of variables. For details of the use of these
matrices in multivariate statistics, the reader is referred to a statistical text such as that of Davis (1973). Program 6.4 is a computer
program which allows the multiplication of a matrix by its transpose
and, if required, will also calculate either the dispersion matrix $\mathbf{D}$ or
the correlation matrix $\mathbf{R}$.

6.4.3   Vectors and matrices in structural geology

If we consider the case of simple shear in two dimensions, as
illustrated in Figure 6.7, then the vector joining an initial point with
co-ordinates x,y to its final position x',y' can be resolved into
components u, which is parallel to the x-axis, and v, which is parallel
to the y-axis:

$$u = x' - x \qquad v = y' - y$$

which leads to the displacement equations

Table 6.12 Details of calculation of the correlation matrix **R**.

(a) The normalized data matrix **N** (each value has a mean of zero and standard deviation of unity)

	Sample no.				
	1	2	3	4	21
aluminium (ppm)	0.49	− 0.22	− 0.61	− 1.29	1.63
magnesium (ppm)	1.46	− 0.46	0.31	0.31	− 1.62
potassium (ppm)	0.44	0.98	− 1.08	0.98	− 1.31

(b) The transpose matrix **N′**

Al	Mg	K
0.49	1.46	0.44
− 0.22	− 0.46	0.98
− 0.61	0.31	− 1.08
− 1.29	0.31	0.98
1.63	− 1.62	− 1.31

(c) Multiplication of **N** by its transpose, where **NN′** = **R**n

5.0	− 2.422	− 2.741
− 2.422	5.0	2.283
2.741	2.283	5.0

(d) The correlation matrix **R**, where **R** = $(1/n)$(**NN′**)

	Al	Mg	K
Al	1.00	0.48	− 0.55
Mg	0.48	1.00	0.46
K	− 0.55	0.46	1.00

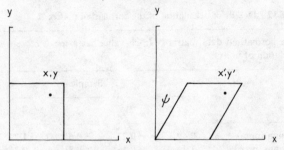

Figure 6.7 Simple shear showing the transformation of the point (x,y) to the new position (x',y') and the angular shear strain ψ.

$$u = -\gamma y \qquad v = 0$$

where $\gamma = \tan \psi$. ψ is the **angular shear strain**, and is negative.

The co-ordinate transform equations are

$$x' = x - \gamma y \qquad y' = y$$

or

$$x' = x - \gamma y \qquad y' = 0x + y$$

which is the strain matrix:

$$\begin{bmatrix} x' \\ y' \end{bmatrix} = \begin{bmatrix} 1 & -\gamma \\ 0 & 1 \end{bmatrix} \begin{bmatrix} x \\ y \end{bmatrix}$$

Strain equations can be written either relating the final position to the original or vice versa. Thus, for body translation we have the following.

(a) Lagrangian specification

$$x' = ax + by \qquad y' = cx + dy$$

in matrix form

$$\begin{bmatrix} x' \\ y' \end{bmatrix} = \begin{bmatrix} a & b \\ c & d \end{bmatrix} \begin{bmatrix} x \\ y \end{bmatrix}$$

(b) Eulerian equation

$$x = Ax' + By' \qquad y = Cx' + Dy'$$

in matrix form

$$\begin{bmatrix} x \\ y \end{bmatrix} = \begin{bmatrix} A & B \\ C & D \end{bmatrix} \begin{bmatrix} x' \\ y' \end{bmatrix}$$

If the values for the coefficients of the matrix for the Lagrangian specification are known, then the values of the coefficients of the Eulerian form can be calculated as follows:

$$A = d/(ad - bc)$$

$$B = -b/(ad - bc)$$

$$C = -c/(ad - bc)$$

$$D = a/(ad - bc)$$

Then, applying the rules of matrix algebra and remembering that the above equations represent the inverse of a 2×2 matrix (Section 6.2.6),

$$\begin{bmatrix} A & B \\ C & D \end{bmatrix} = \begin{bmatrix} a & b \\ c & d \end{bmatrix}^{-1}$$

The displacement vector field is given by

$$u = x' - x = (a - 1)x + by$$

$$v = y' - y = cx + (d - 1)y$$

which is

$$\begin{bmatrix} u \\ v \end{bmatrix} = \begin{bmatrix} a - 1 & b \\ c & d - 1 \end{bmatrix} \begin{bmatrix} x \\ y \end{bmatrix}$$

If the transformation equations are linear, then homogeneous strain results. One important property of homogeneous strain can be derived from calculating the effect of distorting a circle of unit radius

$$x^2 + y^2 = 1$$

with its centre at the origin of the linear displacement equation. It is deformed into a new shape, an ellipse, and the x', y' co-ordinate pairs representing the perimeter of the deformed circle are given by

$$\begin{bmatrix} a & b \\ c & d \end{bmatrix} \begin{bmatrix} x \\ y \end{bmatrix} = \begin{bmatrix} x' \\ y' \end{bmatrix}$$

and the lengths of the major and minor semi-axes of the ellipse are given by the eigenvalues of the shear matrix, and the principal finite extensions e_1 and e_2, by the lengths of the eigenvalues minus one. That is, since the lengths of the major and minor semi-axes are given by $(1 + e_1)$ and $(1 + e_2)$, respectively (Ramsay & Huber 1983, p. 31), then $e_1 = $ (largest eigenvalue $-$ 1.0) and $e_2 = $ (smallest eigenvalue $-$ 1.0). Also, since the eigenvectors associated with each eigenvalue give the vector direction, we can use them to define the orientation of the strain ellipse. Any area change or dilatation is given by the determinant of the matrix and the ellipticity by the square root of the ratio of the largest to smallest eigenvalues. It should be noted that the strain ellipse concept is a Lagrangian concept. Students wishing more information on this application of matrix algebra are referred to the textbook *Strain analysis applied to structural geology* by Ramsay & Huber (1983).

Before leaving this topic, it is worthwhile considering two simple examples. Table 6.13 lists co-ordinate pairs defining the simplified outline of the Palaeozoic brachiopod genus *Spirifer* and the resulting pairs after shear represented by the two matrices

$$\begin{bmatrix} 1 & 1.5 \\ 0 & 1 \end{bmatrix} \quad \text{and} \quad \begin{bmatrix} 2 & 1 \\ 1 & 2 \end{bmatrix}$$

new co-ordinate pairs being calculated as outlined in Section 6.2.3.

For the first of these matrices, which represents simple shear, the angular shear strain is given by

$$\tan^{-1} 1.5 \approx 56°$$

Table 6.13 Co-ordinates (x,y) representing points on the perimeter of a simplified outline of a spiriferid brachiopod, and the corresponding pairs $(x'_1,y'_1$ and $x'_2,y'_2)$ after shear represented by the two matrices given in the text. These data are plotted in Figure 6.8.

x	1	3	5	6	7	9	11	3	9	6	5.5	6.5
y	4	4	4	4.5	4	4	4	2	2	1.5	1	1
x'_1	7	9	11	12.75	13	15	17	6	12	8.25	7	8
y'_1	4	4	4	4.5	4	4	4	2	2	1.5	1	1
x'_2	6	10	14	16.5	18	22	26	8	20	13.5	12	14
y'_2	9	11	13	15	15	17	19	7	13	9	7.5	8.5

We can verify this by reference to Figure 6.8, where a line joining the point representing the umbo of the shell (a) and the sulcus (b) is parallel to the y-axis in the original undeformed shape. However, in the deformed shape (outline at lower right on figure) a line joining the same two points in their transformed positions (a_1,b_1) makes an angle of about 55° with the y-axis. Also, since the determinant is unity there is no area change. This can also be verified by reference to the figure.

The second matrix represents homogeneous shear, and it follows

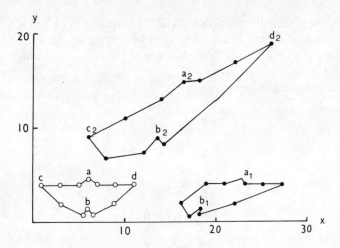

Figure 6.8 An illustration of the effect of shear on the outline of a spiriferid brachiopod. The lower figure shows the effect of simple shear (it has been moved to the right in the figure for clarity of illustration), while the upper shows homogeneous shear.

that the changes will be more complex for this transformation. First
we calculate the determinant of the matrix, which is

$$\begin{vmatrix} 2 & 1 \\ 1 & 2 \end{vmatrix} = |(2 \times 2) - (1 \times 1)| = 3$$

There will therefore be an area change. The transformed figure will
be three times greater than the original, which can again be verified
by reference to the upper figure in Figure 6.8. The eigenvalues are
given by

$$\begin{bmatrix} 2 - \lambda & 1 \\ 1 & 2 - \lambda \end{bmatrix} = 0$$

Expanding,

$$\lambda^2 - 4\lambda + 3 = 0$$

$$(\lambda - 3)(\lambda - 1) = 0$$

$$\lambda = 3 \text{ or } 1$$

Thus, the principal extension is 2 and the ellipticity is $\sqrt{(3/1)} = 1.73$.
The principal extension can be verified by comparing the horizontal
distance c–d (Fig. 6.8) with the horizontal distance c_2–d_2, which are
10 and 20 units, respectively.

The eigenvectors are given by

$$2 - \lambda x + \qquad y = 0$$

$$x + 2 - \lambda y = 0$$

For the eigenvalue $\lambda = 3$ we get

$$-x + y = 0$$

$$x - y = 0$$

whence $x = 1$ and $y = 1$.

For the eigenvalue $\lambda = 1$ we get

$$x + y = 0$$

$$x + y = 0$$

whence $x = 1$ and $y = -1$.

The eigenvectors show that the principal axis of the strain ellipse for this matrix is at 45° to the x-axis, whereas the minor axis is at right angles to this. Returning to Figure 6.8 we can verify this by observing that lines joining corresponding points, for example a,a_2 or b,b_2 will also be at 45° to the x-axis, i.e. parallel to the principal axis of the strain ellipse.

So far we have only considered simple examples of the shear matrix order 2, dealing with changes in two dimensions; we can, however, take into account the third dimension, and more-complex shear matrices of order 3 and vectors of the same order locating points in three dimensions can be used. The mathematical procedures are the same as those outlined above, only the interpretation will be slightly different. The determinant will give the change in volume (if any), while the eigenvalues (3) of the shear matrix will give the lengths of the principal axes of the ellipsoid. Students should also be aware of the existence and uses of other matrices in structural geology, often referred to as tensors. These matrices provide a convenient method of specifying completely the three-dimensional state of stress at a point. In the context of structural geology, simple tensors are square matrices of order 3, with the elements representing the nine stress vectors acting across the positive faces of a small cube whose edges are parallel to the co-ordinate axis as:

x-axis	y-axis	z-axis
$\sigma_{x,y}$	$\sigma_{x,y}$	$\sigma_{x,y}$
$\sigma_{y,x}$	$\sigma_{y,y}$	$\sigma_{y,z}$
$\sigma_{z,y}$	$\sigma_{z,y}$	$\sigma_{z,z}$

The rules of tensor algebra are the same as those of matrix algebra, and for their application to problems in structural geology students are referred to texts such as that of Means (1976).

7 Introduction to numerical methods

7.1 The need for numerical methods

Implicit in much elementary mathematics is the idea that to a particular mathematical problem there exists a solution which is exact, and which can be found by algebraic manipulation. Thus, for example, an equation of the form

$$aX^2 + bX + c = 0$$

can be solved if the factors can be found; or by the application of the formula

$$X = \frac{-b \pm \sqrt{(b^2 - 4ac)}}{2a}$$

as explained in Section 2.1.3. Unfortunately, such simple algebraic manipulation is not always possible, and many authors have classified equations according to the difficulties encountered in solving them (Harbaugh & Bonham-Carter 1970, p. 170). Thus, even ordinary linear differential equations are relatively easy to solve, whereas many partial differentials are difficult and, in the case of non-linear equations, solution may be impossible by traditional algebraic techniques.

Another difficulty which can arise is that of writing down an exact decimal representation of the answer to a particular problem. Because of the need to overcome these difficulties, a branch of mathematics known as numerical analysis has developed. Thus, as Noble (1964, p. 1) has commented, 'the aim of numerical methods is to provide practical procedures for calculating solutions of problems in applied mathematics to a specified degree of accuracy'. In geology, since many of the problems which can be tackled using mathematical methods are complex, often involving 'difficult' equations, it is important to have some knowledge of basic numerical techniques. What follows is an introduction to the most commonly used numerical methods in mathematical geology. Before getting involved in the methods themselves, it is worth while looking in some detail at the various problems involved in obtaining numerical solutions.

7.1.1 Accuracy and error

The accuracy to which an answer needs to be known will depend on the nature of the problem being tackled. Thus, for example, it would not normally be acceptable to calculate the value of a particular parameter to 3 decimal places if that value is going to be involved in further calculations requiring that it be multiplied by a large number (say, in excess of 10^3). On the other hand, common sense suggests that, if for one reason or another, errors accumulate during a calculation which cannot reasonably be avoided, then it may not be worth while carrying out the calculation to a high degree of accuracy. In general, errors are usually under the control of the operator, and as the theory relating to how errors accumulate is well understood, necessary action can be taken.

There are four sources of error.

(a) *Round-off error*. This is due to the need to represent a number in decimal notation, using a finite number of significant figures, and will be dependent on the facilities available for calculation. Thus, we may be required to find $\sqrt{2}$, which can be represented by the series of fractions: 1/1, 3/2, 7/5, etc., as in Table 7.1, each subsequent term becoming closer to the true value of $\sqrt{2}$, but never quite reaching it. If we evaluate each successive term of this series, using a hand-held calculator (Table 7.1), the following is apparent: if we require an answer accurate to 1 decimal place, then the value given by the third term is sufficiently accurate; for 3 decimal place accuracy, rounding-off the fifth term suffices, and so on. However, on evaluating the ninth and subsequent terms, we have come to the limit of the accuracy of our calculator. Therefore, if we require more significant figures, we will require a more accurate calculating machine or a computer.

As was noted in Section 1.3.1, it is important to remember that different computers will give answers to different degrees of accuracy, since accuracy depends on the word-length of the machine, and occasionally on the particular compiler being used. It has been known for two different compilers on the same computer to give different answers in complex calculations, due

Table 7.1 Evaluation of the series for $\sqrt{2}$, using a hand-held calculator. Numerators and denominators of successive terms are evaluated by doubling those of the previous terms and adding the term before that: e.g. term 4 numerator = (2 × term 3 numerator) + term 2 numerator = (2 × 7) + 3 = 17; similarly, term 4 denominator = (2 × 5) + 2 = 12.

Fraction	Decimal
1/1	1.0
3/2	1.5
7/5	1.4
17/12	1.416666
41/29	1.413793
99/70	1.414285
239/169	1.414201
577/408	1.414215
1393/985	1.414213
3363/2378	1.414213

to the way in which round-off error is handled. In general, mainframe computers have a larger word-length than micros, and the latest generation of micros have a larger word-length than older models. In this context one must be particularly careful when adapting programs to run on different machines.

(b) *Mistakes.* We are all prone to making these. There is only one way to prevent them; by checking and rechecking. It cannot be overemphasized how essential it is when developing computer programs, to have ready a test data set for which the *correct* answer is known, to the degree of accuracy required, so that the program can be thoroughly checked. Also, it is good practice, when developing a program, to include sufficient PRINT or WRITE statements throughout the program to ensure that you know exactly what the machine is doing while it is carrying out the instructions you have given it.

(c) *Errors arising because of the nature of the formulae being used.* For example, a continuous function may have to be represented by a series of discrete numbers of limited accuracy.

(d) *Error inherent in constants.* It may be that constants which are being used have their own inherent error, or are only known approximately.

It must be emphasized that it is extremely important, in numerical work, to bear in mind all of the sources of error during a particular computation, to make every effort to minimize them and to take note how they accumulate and affect the final results. It is also good practice to make a statement of the maximum or probable error when presenting the results of a calculation. Most good textbooks contain a statement on error theory; a useful summary for those requiring an introduction to the subject is given by Cheeney (1983), or in a more mathematical text by Atkinson (1985, ch. 3, pp. 33ff.).

7.1.2 Speed of calculation

The speed of calculation can be very important, particularly since the advent of microcomputers. For example, a program designed to perform calculations solving the Laplace equation for two-dimensional potential flow, originally developed and operated on a mainframe computer requiring only a few minutes of execution time, took $1\frac{1}{2}$ h when programmed to run on a micro. This particular program, which depends on the use of an iterative method, points to a problem which is common to all such methods: they may require long execution times because of the large number of iterations required to produce solutions which converge to an acceptable value. Techniques for speeding up calculations are therefore of paramount importance. Sadly, most methods of speeding up calculations on microcomputers, such as using the resident integer variables or integer arithmetic, lead to severe restrictions in accuracy. In general terms, we can say that as the number of unknowns increases, or as the complexity of the equations to be solved increases, then the time required to solve them also increases. Frequently these times increase exponentially.

The speed of computation for a particular machine or compiler can be checked relatively easily using one of the many published bench tests. These are frequently published in popular computer magazines, and allow timings to be made in a variety of circumstances.

7.1.3 Suitability of method

Care must be exercised in the choice of method, not only because of the factors discussed earlier, but simply because the methods are not universal in their application. Many instances could be quoted to illustrate this problem; one example will suffice at this stage.

We are asked to solve:

$$10X_1 + 7X_2 + 8X_3 + 7X_4 = 32$$

$$7X_1 + 5X_2 + 6X_3 + 5X_4 = 23$$

$$8X_1 + 6X_2 + 10X_3 + 9X_4 = 33$$

$$7X_1 + 5X_2 + 9X_3 + 10X_4 = 31$$

which, on solution using the method of Gaussian elimination (see Section 7.3.1) gives

$$X_1 = 3.5 \quad X_2 = -3.25 \quad X_3 = 2.25 \quad X_4 = 0.25$$

By back-substitution using the calculated values in the original equations, we can calculate new values for the right-hand sides of the equations, which should tally with those given originally. This operation, which will be explained later, is often referred to as calculating the residuals, and can be written in matrix form as

$$
\mathbf{R} =
\begin{bmatrix} 32 \\ 23 \\ 33 \\ 31 \end{bmatrix}
-
\begin{bmatrix} 10 & 7 & 8 & 7 \\ 7 & 5 & 6 & 5 \\ 8 & 6 & 10 & 9 \\ 7 & 5 & 9 & 10 \end{bmatrix}
\begin{bmatrix} 3.5 \\ -3.25 \\ 2.25 \\ 0.25 \end{bmatrix}
=
\begin{bmatrix} 0 \\ 0 \\ -0.25 \\ 0 \end{bmatrix}
$$

These residual values do not appear too bad, but it is easy to verify that

$$X_1 = X_2 = X_3 = X_4 = 1.0$$

using, for example, the Gauss–Seidel iteration method (Section 7.3.2). This particular example emphasizes the difficulties encountered during the solution of some problems of this type. As in this case, the fact that the answer is incorrect is not always apparent at first sight.

7.2   Iterative methods for the solution of equations

This section introduces one of the most important classes of numerical method, that of **iteration**. The basic technique is best illustrated by describing the procedure for solving an algebraic equation $x^2 - 5x + 2 = 0$ and a **transcendental equation** $\ln x = 1 + 1/x$ (transcendental equations are those containing transcendental functions such as ln or tan, for example).

7.2.1   Simple iteration

(a) We are asked to solve the equation

$$x^2 = 5x + 2 = 0$$

by a simple iterative method.

Step 1. Rewrite the equation in the form $x = f(x)$:

$$x = 0.2x^2 + 0.4$$

Step 2. Make initial guesses of the values of x:

$$x = 0 \quad \text{and} \quad x = 10$$

Step 3. Putting $x = 0$ on the right-hand side of the equation,

$$x = 0.4$$

Putting this value on the right-hand side of the equation,

$$x = 0.2(0.4^2) + 0.4 = 0.432$$

This process is repeated until, on the fourth occasion, we find that

$$x = 0.43825 \quad \text{(1st root)}$$

Step 4. Putting $x = 10$ on the right-hand side of the equation,

$$x_1 = 20.4$$

$$x_2 = 83.6$$

$$x_3 = 1398.2$$

etc.

Step 5. Make another guess at the value of the second root: say $x = 5$, then put this value on the right-hand side of the equation:

$$x_1 = 5.4$$

$$x_2 = 6.232$$

$$x_3 = 8.1676$$

etc.

The value of the roots of the equation can be evaluated by an exact analytical method, and are

$$x = 0.438447 \quad \text{and} \quad 4.561553$$

In this example, any choice of value for x which is just lower than the value of the largest root, will give answers which will *converge* on the lowest root. A choice of x which is higher than the largest root will always *diverge*. This illustrates one of the fundamental problems of iteration, that of convergence.

(b) Find the positive root of the equation (correct to 4 decimal places),

$$\ln x = 1 + 1/x$$

First we need to find an approximation x_0 to the positive root of the equation. The simplest way of achieving this is to sketch the curves, by plotting the two functions

$$y = \ln x \quad \text{and} \quad y = 1 + (1/x)$$

on the same axis, as in Figure 7.1. The point of intersection of the two curves will give the root of the equation. Inspection of Figure 7.1 indicates that the point of intersection lies somewhere just to the right of $x = 3$

$$x_0 = 3.0$$

We now rewrite our equation in the form

$$x = f(x)$$

which is

$$x = \exp[1 + (1/x)]$$

and set up the recurrence relationship

$$x_{n+1} = \exp[1 + (1/x_n)]$$

In other words, having written the function with the unknown required on both sides of the equation, we attach subscripts to the unknown such that an estimated value can be inserted on the right-

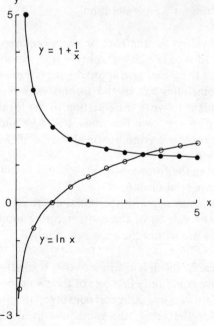

Figure 7.1 Sketch of the curves of the two functions $y = \ln x$ and $y = 1 + 1/x$. The point where the two curves cut, near $x = 3$, represents an approximation to the value of the root near 3, of the equation $\ln x = 1 + 1/x$.

hand side of the equation and an updated estimate calculated. This new value can then be used to produce further updates until successive estimates differ by less than some preset tolerance. Students should note that it is not normally necessary to calculate values for the initial steps, using this method, to the accuracy required in the final answer.

Setting $x_0 = 3.0$, we get

$$x_1 = \exp[1 = (1/3.0)] = \exp(1.3) = 3.7$$

$$x_2 = \exp[1 + (1/3.7)] = \exp(1.27) = 3.56$$

.
.
.

$$x_8 = \exp[1 + (1/3.5913)] = 3.59107$$

$$x_9 = \exp[1 + (1/3.59107)] = 3.59114$$

Since the successive approximations are alternatively above and below the root, the root lies between 3.59107 and 3.59114. Hence, $x = 3.5911$, correct to 4 decimal places.

We can now summarize the method as used in the two examples, to arrive at a general procedure for simple iteration.

Step 1. Find approximate values for the root or roots required. The simplest method is to sketch a graph $y = f(x)$, points where the curve cuts the x-axis give approximate values of the real roots. Sometimes (as in the second example, above) it is convenient to write the equation in the form $f_1(x) = f_2(x)$ and plot the two functions $y = f_1(x)$ and $y = f_2(x)$. Any real roots are given by the abscissae of the points of intersection.

Step 2. Write the equation in the form $x = f(x)$.

Step 3. Set up the recurrence relationship.

Step 4. Solve the equations, starting with the initial approximation of the value (or values) of the root, iterating until successive estimates are within the accuracy required.

(c) Testing for convergence. In the first example above, using the method of simple iteration, we could only find one of the two roots for the equation. For one root successive estimates converged to give the correct answer, while for the other, the estimates diverged, successive estimates becoming larger (i.e. x_r tends to infinity as r increases). From a practical standpoint it is important that convergence should occur, and that it should happen as rapidly as possible. To test for convergence, it can be shown that an equation will converge if the following result holds:

$$f'(x_0) < 1$$

In other words, if, after differentiating the equation and putting into the differential the initial guess for the unknown root, the result is less than unity, then the iteration will converge, giving a real root of the equation. Returning to our two examples:

For the quadratic $\qquad x = 0.2x^2 + 0.4,$

$$f'(x) = 0.4x$$

when $\quad x = 0, f'(x) = 0 \quad$ will converge

when $\quad x = 4, f'(x) = 1.6 \quad$ will not converge

For the equation $\qquad x = \exp[1 + (1/x)],$

$$f'(x) = -(1/x^2)\exp[1 + (1/x)]$$

$$f'(x_0) = -(1/9)\exp[1 + 1/3]$$

$$\approx -0.4$$

therefore the equation will converge. This test can be extended to include higher-order equations, as required.

In the simple cases considered, convergence has been quite rapid, but this is not always the case. However, it can be said that if a real root or roots exist and the iteration converges, then an answer will eventually be obtained using the method as outlined. It is also true that a correct answer will eventually be obtained, even though there are arithmetic errors in the intermediate calculation.

7.2.2   The Newton–Raphson iteration formula

The Newton–Raphson iteration formula states that if x_n is an approximation to the root a of the equation

$$f(x) = 0$$

then a better approximation is generally given by x_{n+1}, where

$$x_{n+1} = x_n - f(x_n)/f'(x_n)$$

Also, convergence will tend to be faster by this method than by the simple iterative procedure just described.

We are asked to find, correct to 4 decimal places, the root near 0.5 of the equation

$$e^{-x} - \sin x = 0$$

$$f(x) = e^{-x} - \sin x$$

$$f'(x) = -(e^{-x} + \cos x)$$

Hence the Newton–Raphson formula becomes

$$x_{n+1} = x_n + \frac{e^{-x_n} - \sin x_n}{e^{-x_n} + \cos x_n}$$

If $x_0 = 0.5$, then

$$x_1 = 0.5 + 0.128/1.485 \qquad = 0.586$$

$$x_2 = 0.586 + 0.0035/1.3897 = 0.5885$$

$$x_3 = 0.5885 + 0.0005/1.3693 = 0.5885$$

Hence

$$x = 0.5885 \text{ correct to 4 decimal places}$$

This is also an excellent method for calculating the nth root of a number. For example, calculate $\sqrt{11}$ correct to 4 decimal places:

$$f(x) = x^2 - a$$

$$f'(x) = 2x$$

The Newton–Raphson formula becomes

$$x_{n+1} = x_n - \frac{x_n^2 - a}{2x_n}$$

Choosing $x_0 = 3.0$,

$$x_1 = 3 - [(9 - 11)/6] \qquad\qquad = 3.33$$

.
.
.

$$x_4 = 3.31667 - [(3.31667^2 - 11)/6.63334] = 3.31662$$

Hence $\sqrt{11} = 3.3166$, correct to 4 decimal places.

Unfortunately, space does not permit a more extensive treatment of iterative procedures, and students requiring further information should consult a text on numerical analysis, such as Noble (1964) or Atkinson (1985). The iterative solution of simultaneous linear equations will be discussed in the next section.

7.3 The solution of simultaneous linear equations

The solution of simultaneous linear equations is a problem of great practical importance in many fields of science, particularly since many problems in applied mathematics can be reduced to such a set of equations. In geology a number of applications spring to mind: in optimizing problems using linear programming; in contour mapping using trend surface analysis; in problems involving the solution of the Laplace equation for modelling the flow of liquids or gases in rock; in a number of multivariate statistical methods; etc. Many of these we have either already considered, or will consider later. Thus, in general, we are required to find

$$x_1, x_2, \ldots, x_n$$

when

$$a_1 x_1 + b_1 x_2 + c_1 x_3 + \ldots + n_1 x_n = z_1$$

$$a_2 x_1 + b_2 x_2 + c_2 x_3 + \ldots + n_2 x_n = z_2$$

.
.
.

$$a_m x_1 + b_m x_2 + c_m x_3 + \ldots + n_m x_n = z_m$$

Given values for

$$a_1, a_2, \ldots, a_m$$

$$b_1, b_2, \ldots, b_m$$

$$c_1, c_2, \ldots, c_m$$

$$n_1, n_2, \ldots, n_m$$

$$z_1, z_2, \ldots, z_m$$

The methods of solution can be divided into three separate groups.

(a) Developments of traditional algebraic techniques:

   (i) Gauss–Jordan elimination; and
   (ii) Gaussian elimination.

(b) Iterative methods – the Gauss–Seidel method.
(c) Matrix methods:

   (i) determinants – Cramer's Rule; and
   (ii) matrix inversion.

The choice of method will depend on a number of factors, including how large the system of equations is and what type of calculating equipment is available. Both of these factors lead back to the problems mentioned earlier, those of speed and accuracy. For instance, suppose we were to use Cramer's Rule in a situation where the number of unknowns was 100: we would need 1.6×10^{160} operations and, if our computer does 1 million operations per second, it would take 5×10^{146} years to complete the calculation! We have already shown that although it is possible to test the accuracy of a solution by back-substitution and calculating residual values (the difference between the given and calculated values from the right-hand side of the equation), the small numerical size of the values does not guarantee the accuracy of the solution. It may also transpire that a particular problem may not be soluble using the technique chosen, if at all. As an example, we are asked to solve

$$55x_1 + \qquad 89x_2 = 144$$

$$89x_1 + (144 + a)x_2 = 233$$

when $a = 0.018$ and $a = 0.02$. On solving, we find
  (a) When $a = 0.018$,

$$x_1 = -159.2 \quad \text{and} \quad x_2 = 100$$

  (b) When $a = 0.02$,

$$x_1 = 18.8 \quad \text{and} \quad x_2 = -10.0$$

Also, if we are asked to solve these equations when $a = 0.01818$, there is no solution, the reason for this being that the first equation is almost exactly a multiple of the second. An example such as this serves to illustrate the problem of *conditioning*, in which the matrix of coefficient values is said to be 'ill-conditioned'. This is actually a misnomer, as it is the problem which is ill-conditioned, not the matrix. Since problems of this nature arise frequently in many practical situations, the matter will be discussed more fully in Section 7.3.4.

7.3.1   Methods of solution based on algebraic techniques

(a) GAUSS–JORDAN ELIMINATION

In Gauss–Jordan elimination we systematically eliminate unknowns from the left-hand side of the equation to leave the **pivots**, or principal diagonal, of $x_1, x_2, \ldots, x_n$. We are asked to solve

$$2x_1 - x_2 + 3x_3 - x_4 = \quad 7 \qquad (1)$$

$$x_1 - x_2 + 4x_3 - 2x_4 = \quad 5 \qquad (2)$$

$$3x_1 + 2x_2 + x_3 + 4x_4 = \quad 31 \qquad (3)$$

$$4x_1 - 3x_2 + 3x_3 - 3x_4 = -5 \qquad (4)$$

First we need to find multiples of Eqn 1 which will eliminate x_1, from Eqns 2, 3 and 4. Appropriate values are $-\frac{1}{2}$, $-\frac{3}{2}$ and $-\frac{4}{2}$.

For convenience we can note these **multipliers**, denoted by m, in the left-hand column. Also, for clarity we can leave out x_1, x_2, etc., and tabulate:

m	x_1	x_2	x_3	x_4	b	
	2	-1	3	-1	7	(1)
$-\frac{1}{2}$	1	-1	4	-2	5	(2)
$-\frac{3}{2}$	3	2	1	4	31	(3)
$-\frac{4}{2}$	4	-3	3	-3	-3	(4)

To calculate these multipliers the coefficient (2) of x_1 in Eqn 1, is used as a divisor; this is known as the **1st pivot** and Eqn 1 is known as the **1st pivotal equation**. Therefore, to find the multiplier we divide the value we are eliminating by the pivot and reverse the sign. We then multiply Eqn 1 by the appropriate multiplier, and subtract from this the equation which contains the value we wish to eliminate, as shown below:

	x_1	x_2	x_3	x_4	b	
	2	-1	3	-1	7	(1)
					$-\frac{1}{2}$	
	-1	$\frac{1}{2}$	$-\frac{3}{2}$	$\frac{1}{2}$	$-\frac{7}{2}$	
add	1	-1	4	-2	5	(2)
	$-\frac{1}{2}$	$\frac{5}{2}$	$-\frac{3}{2}$	$\frac{3}{2}$		(6)

By repeating this operation, using Eqns 3 and 4 and the appropriate multipliers, we get

x_1	x_2	x_3	x_4	b	
2	-1	3	-1	7	(5)
	$-\frac{1}{2}$	$\frac{5}{2}$	$-\frac{3}{2}$	$\frac{3}{2}$	(6)
		$\frac{7}{2}$	$-\frac{7}{2}$	$\frac{11}{2}$	$\frac{41}{2}$	(7)
		-1	-3	-1	-19	(8)

Note that we have recorded the pivotal equation (now labelled Eqn 5), unchanged after these operations. The next step is to eliminate the x_2 coefficients from Eqns 5, 7 and 8. In this process the x_2 value of $-\frac{1}{2}$ in Eqn 6 is used; this is the **2nd pivot** and Eqn 6 is known as the **2nd pivotal equation**. The multipliers are calculated using $-\frac{1}{2}$ as the divisor:

m	x_1	x_2	x_3	x_4	b	
-2	2	-1	3	-1	7	(5)
		$-\frac{1}{2}$	$\frac{5}{2}$	$-\frac{3}{2}$	$\frac{3}{2}$	(6)
7	$\frac{7}{2}$	$-\frac{7}{2}$	$\frac{11}{2}$		$\frac{41}{2}$	(7)
-2		-1	-3	-1	-19	(8)

and, performing the operations as before, using the new set of multipliers, we get

x_1	x_2	x_3	x_4	b	
2		-2	3	6	(9)
	$-\frac{1}{2}$	$\frac{5}{2}$	$\frac{3}{2}$	$\frac{3}{2}$	(10)
		14	-5	31	(11)
		-8	2	-22	(12)

We now need to eliminate the x_3 coefficients from Eqns 9, 10 and 12. The **3rd pivot** is x_3 in Eqn 11, and Eqn 11 is the **3rd pivotal equation**. The multipliers are calculated as before, using the coefficient 14 as the divisor:

m	x_1	x_2	x_3	x_4	b	
$\frac{1}{7}$	2		-2	3	4	(9)
$-\frac{5}{2}$		$-\frac{1}{2}$	$\frac{5}{2}$	$\frac{3}{2}$	$\frac{3}{2}$	(10)
			14	-5	31	(11)
$\frac{4}{7}$			-8	2	-22	(12)

So we have

x_1	x_2	x_3	x_4	b	
2			$\frac{9}{7}$	$\frac{59}{7}$	(13)
	$-\frac{1}{2}$		$-\frac{17}{28}$	$-\frac{113}{28}$	(14)
		14	-5	31	(15)
			$-\frac{6}{7}$	$-\frac{30}{7}$	(16)

By back-substitution we can eliminate the x_4-values from Eqns 13, 14 and 15, and find that

$$x_1 = 1 \quad x_2 = 2 \quad x_3 = 4 \quad x_4 = 5$$

For this method, if n is the number of unknowns, then the number of operations N is given by

$$N = \tfrac{1}{2}n^3 + n^2 - \tfrac{3}{2}n$$

(b) GAUSSIAN ELIMINATION

The Gaussian elimination method is similar to the Gauss–Jordan method just described, but instead of eliminating all terms except the pivots, leaving the principal diagonal, only the bottom half of the matrix is eliminated.

We are asked to solve

$$2x_1 - x_2 + 3x_3 - x_4 = \quad 7 \qquad (1)$$

$$x_1 - x_2 + 4x_3 - 2x_4 = \quad 5 \qquad (2)$$

$$3x_1 + 2x_2 + x_3 + 4x_4 = \quad 31 \qquad (3)$$

$$4x_1 - 3x_2 + 3x_3 - 3x_4 = -5 \qquad (4)$$

We start as before, by eliminating x^1 from Eqns 2, 3 and 4, to give

x_1	x_2	x_3	x_4	b	
2	-1	3	-1	7	(5)
	$-\frac{1}{2}$	$\frac{5}{2}$	$-\frac{3}{2}$	$\frac{3}{2}$	(6)
	$\frac{7}{2}$	$-\frac{7}{2}$	$\frac{11}{2}$	$\frac{41}{2}$	(7)
	-1	-3	-1	-19	(8)

Next we eliminate x_2 from Eqns 7 and 8 only, leaving the 1st pivotal equation unchanged:

m	x_1	x_2	x_3	x_4	b	
	2	-1	3	-1	7	(5)
		$-\frac{1}{2}$	$\frac{5}{2}$	$-\frac{3}{2}$	$\frac{3}{2}$	(6)
7		$\frac{7}{2}$	$-\frac{7}{2}$	$\frac{11}{2}$	$\frac{41}{2}$	(7)
-2		-1	-3	-1	-19	(8)

to give

x_1	x_2	x_3	x_4	b	
2	-1	3	-1	7	(9)
	$-\frac{1}{2}$	$\frac{5}{2}$	$-\frac{3}{2}$	$\frac{3}{2}$	(10)
		14	-5	31	(11)
		-8	2	-22	(12)

Finally, we eliminate x_3 from Eqn 12, leaving the other equations unchanged:

m	x_1	x_2	x_3	x_4	b	
	2	-1	3	-1	7	(9)
		$-\frac{1}{2}$	$\frac{5}{2}$	$-\frac{3}{2}$	$\frac{3}{2}$	(10)
			14	-5	31	(11)
$\frac{8}{14}$			-8	2	-22	(12)

to leave

x_1	x_2	x_3	x_4	b	
2	-1	3	-1	7	(13)
	$-\frac{1}{2}$	$\frac{5}{2}$	$-\frac{3}{2}$	$\frac{3}{2}$	(14)
		14	-5	31	(15)
			$-\frac{6}{7}$	$-\frac{30}{7}$	(16)

By back-substitution we find that

$$x_1 = 1 \quad x_2 = 2 \quad x_3 = 4 \quad x_4 = 5$$

For this method, if n is the number of unknowns, then the number of operations N is given by

$$N = \tfrac{1}{3}n^3 + n^2 - \tfrac{1}{3}n$$

We can compare the two methods as shown in Table 7.2.

(c) GAUSSIAN ELIMINATION WHERE THE COEFFICIENTS ARE INEXACT

In the previous examples, *exact* coefficients obviated the necessity of checking the calculation for accuracy at each stage. When the coefficients are *inexact* it is necessary to check the calculation, to ensure that errors do not accumulate, and that the final answer will be sufficiently accurate.

We are asked to solve the following sets of equations by Gaussian elimination:

Table 7.2 Comparison of Gauss–Jordan and Gaussian elimination in diagrammatic form. In the Gauss–Jordan method we reduce the matrix of coefficients to the elements of the principal diagonal, whereas in Gaussian elimination we reduce it to the upper triangular form.

	Gauss–Jordan				Gaussian elimination			
stage 1	X	x	x	x	X	x	x	x
	x	x	x	x	x	x	x	x
	x	x	x	x	x	x	x	x
	x	x	x	x	x	x	x	x
stage 2	X	x	x	x	X	x	x	x
		X	x	x		X	x	x
		x	x	x		x	x	x
		x	x	x		x	x	x
stage 3	X		x	x	X	x	x	x
		X	x	x		X	x	x
			X	x			X	x
			x	x			x	x
stage 4	X			x	X	x	x	x
		X		x		X	x	x
			X	x			X	x
				X				X
stage 5	X							
		X						
			X					
				X				

$$2.4759x_1 + 1.6235x_2 + 4.6231x_3 = 0.0647 \qquad (1)$$

$$1.4725x_1 + 0.9589x_2 - 1.3253x_3 = 1.0475 \qquad (2)$$

$$2.6951x_1 + 2.8965x_2 - 1.4794x_3 = -0.6789 \qquad (3)$$

First we set out the equations as follows:

m	x_1	x_2	x_3	b	$\sum$	
	2.4759	1.6235	4.6231	0.0647		(1)
	1.4725	0.9589	-1.3253	1.0475		(2)
	2.6951	2.8965	-1.4794	-0.6789		(3)

Notice that we now have one extra column in our layout, the *check-sum* column, labelled $\sum$, this will contain the sum of the numerical values for each equation:

$$\sum = x_1 + x_2 + \ldots x_n + b$$

We form our multipliers as before, dividing the coefficient that we are eliminating by the pivot, and reversing the sign. We perform this operation to at least one more decimal place than the original coefficients:

m	x_1	x_2	x_3	b	$\sum$	
	2.4759	1.6235	4.6231	0.0647	8.7872	(1)
-0.59473	1.4725	0.9589	-1.3253	1.0475	2.1536	(2)
-1.08853	2.6951	2.8965	-1.4794	-0.6789	3.4333	(3)

which gives

m	x_1	x_2	x_3	b	$\sum$	
	2.4759	1.6235	4.6231	0.0647	8.7872	(4)
		-0.00664	-4.07480	1.00902	-3.07241	(5)
		1.12927	-6.51178	-0.74933	-6.13183	(6)

Notice that we have two new check-sum values for Eqns 5 and 6. We can now check our calculation as follows.

Take the check-sum value for the 1st pivotal equation, multiply by one of the row multipliers as in (a) below. Add this to the check sum for the row chosen as in (b) below. This value should agree with the new check-sum value for that row, i.e. subtraction should give a zero value, as in (c) below.

For example, to check Eqns 2 and 5:

(a) $8.7872 \times -0.59473 = -5.226011$
(b) $-5.226011 + 2.1536 = -3.072011$
(c) $-3.07241 - (-3.072011) = 0.000399$

Again, to check Eqns 3 and 6:

(a) $8.7872 \times -1.08853 = -9.56513$
(b) $-9.56513 + 3.4333 = -6.13183$
(c) $-6.13183 - (-6.13183) = 0$

We now eliminate the x_2-value from Eqn 6:

m	x_1	x_2	x_3	b	$\sum$	
	2.4759	1.6235	4.6231	0.0647	8.7872	(4)
		-0.00664	-4.0748	1.00902	-3.07241	(5)
170.07078		1.12927	-6.51178	-0.74933	-6.13183	(6)

to give

x_1	x_2	x_3	b	$\sum$	
2.4759	1.6235	4.6231	0.0647	8.7872	(7)
	-0.00664	-4.0748	1.00902	-3.07241	(8)
		-699.51619	170.85548	-528.6588	(9)

Back-substitution leads to

$$x_1 = 1.8408 \quad x_2 = -2.072 \quad x_3 = -0.2442$$

Now, since we are dealing with inexact coefficients, it is wise to check our calculations by calculating a **vector of residual values r**. Using matrix notation, we can write

$$\mathbf{r} = \mathbf{b} - \mathbf{d}$$

where **b** is the vector containing the original values from the right-hand sides of the equations and **d** is the vector containing calculated values for the right-hand sides of the equations, calculated as:

$$\mathbf{d} = \mathbf{A}_x \mathbf{c}$$

where $\mathbf{A}_x$ is the matrix of coefficients for the x-values and $\mathbf{c}$ is the vector of x-values:

$$(2.4579 \times 1.8408) + (1.6235 \times (-2.072)) + \\ (4.6231 \times (-0.2442)) = 0.0648$$

$$(1.4725 \times 1.8408) + (0.9589 \times (-2.072)) - \\ (1.3253 \times (-0.2442)) = 1.0467$$

$$(2.6951 \times 1.8408) + (2.8965 \times (-2.072)) - \\ (1.4794 \times (-0.2442)) = -0.6821$$

$$\mathbf{b} \qquad - \qquad \mathbf{d} \qquad = \qquad \mathbf{r}$$

$$
\begin{bmatrix} 0.0647 \\ 1.0475 \\ -0.6789 \end{bmatrix}
-
\begin{bmatrix} 0.0648 \\ 1.0467 \\ -0.6821 \end{bmatrix}
=
\begin{bmatrix} -0.0001 \\ 0.0008 \\ -0.0032 \end{bmatrix}
$$

The size of the third residual is probably due to the loss of significant figures during the formation of the 2nd pivot and its use in subsequent calculations. This suggests that the equations may be ill-conditioned, and it may be that we would only be justified in quoting our answer correct to 2 decimal places.

In the methods described we have been systematic in our choice of pivots, and have also used the values in the order given and without any attempt at scaling. However, there are variants of the methods discussed which involve scaling where it is practicable, and involve choosing pivots according to their numerical value. This last method has the advantage that, if we use the numerically largest element in each row as the pivot, then inaccuracies in calculation due to using excessively small pivots, as in the last example, can be avoided.

A suitable computer program for the solution of simultaneous linear equations is listed as Program 7.1. It is based on the Gaussian elimination method as described in the text, except that the pivots are chosen on the basis of the largest element in each row. Results from the program include the value of the determinant of the coefficient matrix and the values of the pivots used in the calculation.

7.3.2 *Methods of solution based on an iterative technique*

Algebraic methods of the solution of simultaneous linear equations and those based on matrix algebra are *direct methods*, whereas the iterative method, known as the Gauss–Seidel method, is an *indirect method*.

For example, we are asked to solve the equations

$$3x_1 + 2x_2 = 2$$

$$2x_1 + 3x_2 = 4$$

We can rewrite the equations in terms of x_1 and x_2:

$$x_1 = (2 - 2x_2)/3 \qquad (1)$$

$$x_2 = (4 - 2x_1)/3 \qquad (2)$$

We can now guess a value for x_2, say 3, and solve Eqn 1:

$$x_1 = [2 - (2)(3)]/3 = -1.33$$

This value can be used in Eqn 2:

$$x_2 = [4 - (2)(-1.33)]/3 = 2.22$$

Putting the new value of x_2 into Eqn 1,

$$x_1 = -0.81$$

Putting this value into Eqn 2,

$$x_2 = 1.87$$

We can repeat this procedure as many times as we wish, to give an answer to any required degree of accuracy. The results for this problem are tabulated below, for seven iterations.

	\multicolumn{7}{c}{Iteration number}						
	1	2	3	4	5	6	7
x_1	−1.33	−0.81	−0.58	−0.51	−0.44	−0.41	−0.41
x_2	2.22	1.87	1.72	1.67	1.62	1.61	1.60

The true values are

$$x_1 = -0.40 \qquad x_2 = 1.60$$

The solution of a pair of simultaneous linear equations by this method is shown graphically in Figure 7.2. Note that the solution of the equation set is where the two curves intersect, and the iterative solution is indicated as a path between the lines representing the equations.

In general we have

$$x_1 = (1/a_1)(Z_1 - b_1x_2 - c_1x_3 - \ldots - n_1x_n)$$

$$x_2 = (1/b_2)(Z_2 - a_2x_1 - c_2x_3 - \ldots - n_2x_n)$$

.
.
.

$$x_n = (1/n_m)(Z_m - a_mx_1 - b_mx_2 - \ldots - n_mx_n)$$

If there are more than two unknowns, then we can proceed by one of several different methods, only two of which we need to consider here.

(a) The method of *simultaneous corrections*, where the estimates of $x_1, \ldots, x_n$ remain constant during each cycle of iteration, only

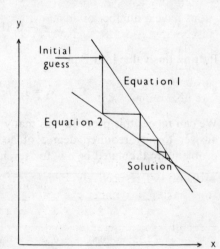

Figure 7.2 Graphical illustration of the iterative solution of simultaneous linear equations. Each successive iteration produces values of x and y which converge on the true value as indicated.

being updated at the end of the cycle. The recurrence relationships for the case of three unknowns are

$$x_1^{(l+1)} = (1/a_1)(\qquad\quad - b_1 x_2^{(l)} - c_1 x_3^{(l)} + z_1)$$

$$x_2^{(l+1)} = (1/b_2)(- a_2 x_1^{(l)} \qquad\quad - c_2 x_3^{(l)} + z_2)$$

$$x_3^{(l+1)} = (1/c_3)(- a_3 x_1^{(l)} - b_3 x_2^{(l)} \qquad\quad + z_3)$$

(b) The method of *successive corrections*, where the estimates of x_1, ..., x_n are updated as each new estimate is available. In the situation where three equations are involved the recurrence relationships are

$$x_1^{(l+1)} = (1/a_1)(\qquad\quad - b_1 x_2^{(l)} \quad - c_1 x_3^{(l)} + z_1)$$

$$x_2^{(l+1)} = (1/b_2)(- a_2 x_1^{(l+1)} \qquad\quad - c_2 x_3^{(l)} + z_2)$$

$$x_3^{(l+1)} = (1/c_3)(- a_3 x_1^{(l+1)} - b_3 x_2^{(l+1)} \qquad\quad + z_3)$$

Either method is satisfactory, although the second generally converges much quicker than the first. The starting estimates for $x_1^{(l)}$, etc., can be set to zero or equal to the value from the right-hand side of the equation divided by the coefficient corresponding to the x-value being estimated.

Iterative methods for the solution of simultaneous linear equations have a number of advantages over others. They are relatively fast computationally, and are particularly useful where the matrix of coefficients is diagonally dominant. In the specific situation where there are a large number of zero values among the coefficients, it is probably the best method to use, since problems of ill-conditioning are not so important.

A computer program based on the method of successive corrections is listed as Program 7.2. This program allows a maximum of 1000 iterations with the tolerance for an acceptable solution being set at 0.0001, both of these can be altered by changing statements 410 and 190, respectively. If an acceptable solution is not found after the maximum number of iterations, then the current estimates $x_1^{(l)}$, ..., $x_n^{(l)}$ are listed. Also, the initial guesses are set at zero in this version; again alteration of statement 220 can change this assignment. No specific test has been included to ascertain whether the solution will converge and execution will be terminated by the program error 'TOO LARGE', if the solution is divergent.

7.3.3 *Methods of solution based on matrix algebra*

There are two principal methods for the solution of simultaneous equations based on matrix algebra, using determinants and matrix inversion. The first of these, known as *Cramer's Rule*, which we have already noted in passing (Section 6.2.5), is extremely time-consuming when large numbers of unknowns are involved, and is not recommended for large systems of equations. The other method, *matrix inversion*, is much less cumbersome, but it can be affected by ill-conditioning induced by problems of round-off error. Both techniques will be discussed.

(a) THE METHOD OF DETERMINANTS: CRAMER'S RULE

Taking as a starting point two general equations:

$$a_1 x_1 + b_1 x_2 = z_1$$

$$a_2 x_1 + b_2 x_2 = z_2$$

We can rewrite as

$$x_1 = \frac{z_1 b_1 - z_2 b_2}{a_1 b_2 - a_2 b_1}$$

and

$$x_2 = \frac{a_1 z_2 - a_2 z_1}{a_1 b_2 - a_2 b_1}$$

provided that

$$a_1 b_2 - a_2 b_1 \neq 0$$

Now, from our earlier consideration of matrices (Section 6.2.5), the determinant of a 2×2 matrix is

$$|\mathbf{A}| = ad - cb$$

where

$$\mathbf{A} = \begin{bmatrix} a & b \\ c & d \end{bmatrix}$$

Therefore we can write our equations in matrix form as

$$x_1 = \frac{\begin{vmatrix} z_1 & b_1 \\ z_2 & b_2 \end{vmatrix}}{\begin{vmatrix} a_1 & b_1 \\ a_2 & b_2 \end{vmatrix}} \qquad x_2 = \frac{\begin{vmatrix} a_1 & z_1 \\ a_2 & z_2 \end{vmatrix}}{\begin{vmatrix} a_1 & b_1 \\ a_2 & b_2 \end{vmatrix}}$$

provided that

$$\begin{vmatrix} a_1 & b_1 \\ a_2 & b_2 \end{vmatrix} \neq 0$$

The method can be extended to solve sets of equations with as many unknowns as required. We proceed as follows:

(1) Calculate the determinant of the coefficient matrix. If this is not zero, proceed as below.
(2) To find x_n, replace the vector containing the x_n coefficients with the vector containing the values from the right-hand side of the equation, calculate the determinant and divide by the determinant of the coefficient matrix.
(3) Repeat (2) until all x_n have been determined.

For example, solve the following:

$$3x + y + 4z = 12$$

$$2x + 4y + 2z = 8$$

$$y + 3z = 16$$

First, find the determinant of the 3×3 coefficient matrix (Section 6.2.5):

$$|\mathbf{D}| = \begin{vmatrix} 3 & 1 & 4 \\ 2 & 4 & 2 \\ 0 & 1 & 3 \end{vmatrix} = 1 \begin{vmatrix} 4 & 2 \\ 1 & 3 \end{vmatrix} - 1 \begin{vmatrix} 2 & 2 \\ 0 & 3 \end{vmatrix} + 4 \begin{vmatrix} 2 & 4 \\ 0 & 1 \end{vmatrix}$$

$$= 32$$

Since $\mathbf{D} \neq 0$, we can continue

$$x = \tfrac{1}{32} \begin{vmatrix} 12 & 1 & 4 \\ 8 & 4 & 2 \\ 16 & 1 & 3 \end{vmatrix} = \frac{-96}{32} = -3$$

$$y = \tfrac{1}{32} \begin{vmatrix} 3 & 12 & 4 \\ 2 & 8 & 2 \\ 0 & 16 & 3 \end{vmatrix} = \frac{32}{32} = 1$$

$$z = \tfrac{1}{32} \begin{vmatrix} 3 & 1 & 12 \\ 2 & 4 & 8 \\ 0 & 1 & 16 \end{vmatrix} = \frac{160}{32} = 5$$

The principal drawback to this method is the amount of simple arithmetic which has to be carried out, so it is not a method recommended for the solution of systems of equations with more than three unknowns for hand-calculation, or more than six unknowns using a micro.

(b) SOLUTION BY MATRIX INVERSION

It is possible to take our original general form of the equations and rewrite them in matrix form:

$$\mathbf{A} = \begin{bmatrix} a_1 & b_1 & c_1 & \dots & n_1 \\ a_2 & b_2 & c_2 & \dots & n_2 \\ \cdot & \cdot & \cdot & & \cdot \\ \cdot & \cdot & \cdot & & \cdot \\ \cdot & \cdot & \cdot & & \cdot \\ a_m & b_m & c_m & \dots & n_m \end{bmatrix}$$

$$\mathbf{x} = \begin{bmatrix} x_1 \\ x_2 \\ \cdot \\ \cdot \\ \cdot \\ x_n \end{bmatrix} \qquad \mathbf{b} = \begin{bmatrix} z_1 \\ z_2 \\ \cdot \\ \cdot \\ \cdot \\ z_m \end{bmatrix}$$

An exact analytical solution is given provided that $|\mathbf{A}| \neq 0$, using

$$\mathbf{x} = \mathbf{A}^{-1}\mathbf{b}$$

If we consider the previous example, then the inverse of the coefficient matrix is calculated using the method of synthetic elimination outlined in Section 6.2.6, to give

$$\mathbf{A}^{-1} = \begin{bmatrix} 0.3125 & 3.125 \times 10^{-2} & -0.4375 \\ -0.1875 & 0.28125 & -6.25 \times 10^{-2} \\ 6.25 \times 10^{-2} & -9.375 \times 10^{-2} & 0.3125 \end{bmatrix}$$

and

$$[\mathbf{A}^{-1}] \begin{bmatrix} 12 \\ 8 \\ 16 \end{bmatrix} = \begin{bmatrix} -3 \\ 1 \\ 5 \end{bmatrix}$$

A program using this method is listed as Program 7.3, and is based on a matrix-inversion program given by Davis (1973, p. 142). Some indication of the condition of the original equations can be gained by comparing the size of the individual terms of the inverse matrix with the roots of the equations. If these terms appear large compared with the roots, then it is likely that the equations were ill-conditioned.

7.3.4 Ill-conditioned equations

It is important to be able to recognize whether a particular set of simultaneous linear equations is ill-conditioned, particularly since, if they are, it may be that the solution obtained using a particular method is not correct and that any subsequent calculations based on the answers obtained may be misleading. There are no formal, simple tests for conditioning, and therefore the following notes are for guidance only. There is no guarantee that they will always work.

(a) If one equation is nearly a multiple of the other, then the system of equations will be ill-conditioned and problems of round-off error will become very important. Small changes in the coefficients lead to large changes in the roots of the equations (cf. example in general discussion at start of Section 7.3). Test by calculating the determinant which should be small compared with the expansion of the terms that make up the determinant. Also note that if the determinant is small in the sense just described: it is likely that an iterative procedure will take a long time to converge. Thus, the rate of convergence can be taken as a rough guide to condition.

(b) If the determinant is zero, then the equations are exact multiples and plot graphically as parallel lines.

(c) Estimates of roots which differ appreciably from the true roots can produce small residuals (cf. earlier comment on small residuals not guaranteeing good solutions, Section 7.3.1c).

(d) If individual terms of the inverse of the coefficient matrix are large compared with the roots of the equation.

(e) If the ratio of the largest to the smallest eigenvalue is large.

The opposite to ill-conditioned is well-conditioned, and occurs when the values of the diagonal elements of the coefficient matrix are large relative to the others. When all of the non-diagonal elements are zero, then the equations are perfectly conditioned. Some graphical representations of these problems where ill-conditioning can arise, are shown in Figure 7.3. Although systems of equations involving only two unknowns are shown, because of the limitations of graphical illustration, the principles involved are the same no matter how many unknowns are involved. It is hoped that the above guidelines will enable the problem to be identified and, in most cases, overcome if at all possible.

As was seen in Section 4.5.2, one practical use of the solution of simultaneous linear equations, which has been extensively used by geologists, is trend surface analysis. This is a technique based on the method of multiple regression; unfortunately, it is particularly prone to problems of ill-conditioning. There are three principal causes:

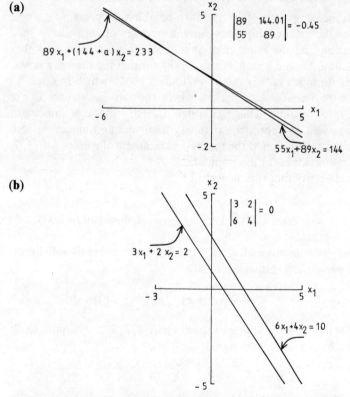

Figure 7.3 Examples of ill-conditioned equations. (a) Graph of the equations $89x_1 + (144 + a)x_2 = 233$ and $55x_1 + 89x_2 = 144$, where a is a small increment. The two equations plot almost exactly on top of one another. (b) Graph of the pair of equations $3x_1 + 2x_2 = 2$ and $6x_1 + 4x_2 = 10$, which plot as two parallel lines.

(a) round-off error during the calculation of the coefficient matrix;
(b) badly distributed data (in the geographical sense) and
(c) rogue values.

Of these, the most common is the first and, in practice, it often proves to be the easiest to overcome. In most cases it is simply a matter of recalculating the geographical co-ordinates with their origin at the centre of the area being studied.

7.4   Geological applications

7.4.1   Iterative methods

(a)   THE CALCULATION OF THE DIVERSITY INDEX, FISHER'S a

In palaeoecology it is often useful to be able to express by a single number the relationship between the number of individuals in a population and the number of species which go to make up that population. Such a number is generally termed the **diversity index**. One useful index is 'Fisher's a' (Williams 1964), which is a special case of the Poisson distribution, where the zero occurrence is not taken into account. This particular diversity index is important since, as well as expressing diversity as a unique number, it also allows the calculation of the theoretical numbers of species with 1, 2, 3 . . ., n individuals in the population.

The diversity index, a, is given by

$$S = a \ln\left(1 + \frac{N}{a}\right) \qquad (1)$$

where S = the number of species and N = the number of individuals in the population. Now, if

$$x = N/(N + a) \qquad (2)$$

then the theoretical number of species with 1, 2, 3, . . ., N individuals is given by the successive terms

$$ax, ax^2/2, ax^3/3, \ldots, ax^n/N \qquad (3)$$

Suppose we wish to calculate a (correct to 1 decimal place), when the sample size (representing the population), is 350 individuals and the number of species in the population is 30.

(a) Notice that Eqn 1 cannot be solved analytically.
(b) Rewrite Eqn 1 as a recurrence relationship:

$$a_i = S/\ln[1 + N/a_{i-1}]$$

(c) Make an initial guess of $a = 0.1$

$$a_1 = 30/\ln[1 + 350/0.1] \qquad = 3.676$$

$$a_2 = 30/\ln[1 + 350/3.676] = 6.5695$$

$$a_3 = 30/\ln[1 + 350/6.5695] = 7.5111$$

$$a_4 = 30/\ln[1 + 350/7.5111] = 7.7664$$

$$a_5 = 30/\ln[1 + 350/7.7664] = 7.8327$$

Therefore the value of a required = 7.8

Having calculated the required value for a, we can now find the number of species represented by 1, 2, 3, 4 and 5 individuals. We now have to calculate the value of x in Eqn 2 above. Substituting the required values, we get

$$x = 350/(350 + 7.8) = 0.978$$

and, from Eqn 3,

no. of species represented by 1 individual
$$= 7.8 \times 0.978 \quad = 8$$

no. of species represented by 2 individuals
$$= 7.8 \times 0.957/2 = 4$$

no. of species represented by 3 individuals
$$= 7.8 \times 0.935/3 = 2$$

no. of species represented by 4 individuals
$$= 7.8 \times 0.915/4 = 2$$

no. of species represented by 5 individuals
$$= 7.8 \times 0.895/5 = 1$$

Generalizing from the results obtained, we can say that Fisher's a distribution tells us that, in a sample of a population, there are normally more species represented by a small number of individuals than are represented by a large number. In the example above, just over 50 per cent of the species are represented by four or less individuals, forming about 8.5 per cent of the total sample size. It is instructive to compare these generalizations, based on this hypothetical example, with the data plotted on Figure 7.4. This shows a plot of number of individuals against number of species, for a collection of invertebrate fossils, from the Visean, Scar Limestone, at its outcrop in Swinhope Burn, Nr Stanhope, Co. Durham. This collection, which is assumed to represent a living population, contained 304 individuals of 33 species. The figure shows both actual and calculated distributions, which match quite closely. Also, the distribution is similar in pattern to the example calculated.

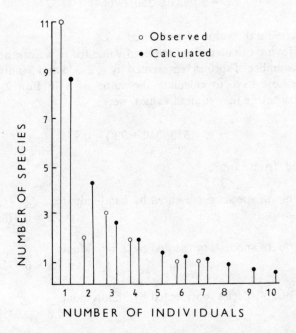

Figure 7.4 Plot of palaeoecological data showing the number of individuals representing a species against the number of species represented by that number of individuals; (○) observed; (●) calculated. For a community collected from the Lower Carboniferous of Weardale, Co. Durham. Fisher's $\alpha = 8.802$; no. of species $= 33$; no. of individuals $= 304$. See text for details.

(b) CALCULATION OF THE DISSOLUTION RATE OF ANHYDRITE

The problem of the dissolution of gypsum and anhydrite in the foundations of dams and other large hydraulic structures is extremely important. A study by James & Lupton (1978) has shown that, although both materials are relatively insoluble, significantly large amounts of them can be removed by dissolution in periods of between 50 and 100 years. Such a process, if unchecked, can lead to structural failure, perhaps of catastrophic proportions. The mathematical solution of one particular equation involved in the calculation provides a good example of the use of simple iteration. If we consider the dissolution of anhydrite, then the amount dissolved is governed by a second-order kinetic reaction, where

$$\frac{dM}{dt} = K(S - c)$$

This equation can be interpreted as meaning that the rate of dissolution (dM/dt) is equal to the difference between the concentration of a saturated solution (S) less the concentration of the final solution (c), after time t, multiplied by the solubility constant (K). Integration of this equation gives

$$\frac{KAt}{V} = \frac{c}{S(S - c)}$$

where M is the mass (kg), K is the solubility rate constant $(m^4 \, kg^{-1} \, s^{-1})$, A is the area of mineral exposed (m^2), t is the time (s), V is the volume of solution (m^3), S is the concentration of a saturated solution of the mineral $(kg \, m^{-3})$ and c is the concentration of the final solution $(kg \, m^{-3})$.

Suppose we let $KAt/V = x$, and a typical value of x could be 0.12, then

$$x = c/S(S - c)$$

and the recurrence relationship is

$$c_i = x[S(S - c_{i-1})]$$

If the solubility of anhydrite is 3.5 kg m^{-3} and the required accuracy of the calculation is 0.0001, and if we make an initial guess for $c_0 = 0$, then

$$c_1 = 0.12[3.5(3.5 - 0)] \qquad = 1.47$$

$$c_2 = 0.12[3.5(3.5 - 1.47)] \qquad = 0.8526$$

$$c_3 = 0.12[3.5(3.5 - 0.8526)] \quad = 1.1119$$

$$\cdot$$
$$\cdot$$
$$\cdot$$

$$c_{11} = 0.12[3.5(3.5 - 1.03503)] = 1.03529$$

$$c_{12} = 0.12[3.5(3.5 - 1.03529)] = 1.03518$$

$$c_{13} = 0.12[3.5(3.5 - 1.03518)] = 1.03522$$

i.e. the concentration of the final solution is $1.0352 \times 10^{-4} \, \text{kg m}^{-3}$.

The result as calculated, although small numerically, is highly significant, since the constants used to calculate the rate x were based on relatively small values derived from experimental data. In particular, because of limitations in acquiring the data, the time factor is small. Hence, extrapolating to a 'real-life' situation where the volumes of water circulating are very large and time is measured in years, the result implies that small fractures in the anhydrite will be enlarged by dissolution relatively quickly, leaving sizeable voids.

7.4.2 Solution of simultaneous linear equations

It has already been noted that the solution of simultaneous linear equations is basic to many numerical techniques of interest to geologists, and a number of examples appear elsewhere in this book. In Section 4.5.2 we developed the basic mathematics for multiple regression applied to trend surface analysis and, because the topic of simultaneous linear equation solution had not been tackled, we left the matter without looking at an example. We are now in a position to tackle a simple example.

The data for this problem are presented in Table 7.3, and relate to the percentage of methane relative to two other light hydrocarbon gases, ethane and propane, detected in a number of samples of limestone. These are from the Carboniferous, Lower Namurian, Great Limestone, in Newlandside Quarry, Nr Stanhope, Co. Dur-

Table 7.3 Percentage methane in samples of limestone collected on a regular grid from a quarry face at Newlandside Quarry, Nr Stanhope, Co. Durham.

Vertical, x	Horizontal, y	Percentage methane $\times 10^{-2}$, z
0.5	4.5	0.61
0.6	3.6	0.64
0.7	2.9	0.47
1.6	4.5	0.46
1.5	3.6	0.59
1.5	2.8	0.41
2.5	4.4	0.78
2.3	3.6	0.84
3.2	3.6	0.87
3.1	2.8	0.95
3.2	2.0	0.87
3.2	1.4	0.80
4.2	1.2	0.78
4.3	2.0	0.71
4.5	3.8	0.76

ham. They were collected on an approximate 1-m grid on either side of a vertical joint which has been mineralized. By using the technique of trend surface analysis and fitting a linear surface to the data, it is hoped to show the existence of a relationship between the mineralization and the percentage of methane in the rock. The hypothesis is that, if any relationship exists, then the linear trend of the data will be parallel to the joint plane.

The sums, sums of products and sums of squares required to solve the partial differentials calculated for the data, are

$$\sum x = 36.9 \qquad\qquad \sum y = 46.7$$

$$\sum z = 10.54 \qquad\qquad \sum x^2 = 116.41$$

$$\sum y^2 = 161.63 \qquad\qquad \sum xy = 104.34$$

$$\sum zx = 27.958 \qquad\qquad \sum zy = 32.106$$

with $n = 15$ (the number of data points), we can substitute in the appropriate equations to give:

$$15.0A + 36.9B + 46.7C = 10.54$$

$$36.9A + 116.41B + 104.34C = 27.958$$

$$46.7A + 104.34B + 161.63C = 32.106$$

The solution of these, using Gaussian elimination, is

$$C = 0.0105928$$

$$B = 0.0835258$$

$$A = 0.4633817$$

Back-substitution into the original equations gives the residual vector, which is

$$\mathbf{R} = \begin{bmatrix} 0.04379 \\ 0.03072 \\ 0.03888 \end{bmatrix}$$

The equations were solved by hand-calculation following the method outlined in Section 7.3.1c (for inexact coefficients). Checking the solutions obtained, using either Program 7.2 or Program 7.3, gives closely comparable results, except for the value for A, which differs by 0.00083; this difference is probably due to using a value of 46.7/15, which cannot be expressed exactly, for one of the second multipliers. However, since the residuals are small and the determinant large (Program 7.3 gives a value of 4576), the solutions found are acceptable and can be used to calculate values for the required surface.

Substituting the values for A, B and C into the equation:

$$z_{(calc)} = A + Bx + Cy$$

we can calculate values for $z_{(calc)}$ for any pair of co-ordinate values x and y. The results are presented as a linear trend map in Figure 7.5.

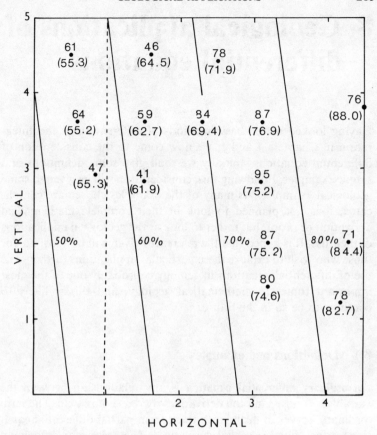

Figure 7.5 Linear trend surface map, calculated using the multiple regression method discussed in Section 4.5.2. The map represents a small section of a quarry face, showing a contoured plot of percentage methane (data from Table 7.4). Each marked sample location gives the original data value and the calculated trend value. The trend value is in parentheses. —————, Linear-trend contour line, values are percentage methane; — — — — —, mineralized joint plane.

From this map it can be seen that although there are discrepancies between the original data and the surface, the linear trend is almost parallel to the mineralized joint plane, which fits in with the hypothesis that there may be a relationship between the mineralization and the occurrence of light hydrocarbons in these samples.

8 Geological applications of differential equations

Having looked at the basic methods of differentiation and integration in Chapters 4 and 5, we now come to the consideration of differential equations. Initially we shall give some definitions and simple examples. Following this, consideration will be given to some geological examples. As many of the examples chosen are complicated, it is not planned to look at their complete mathematical derivation or proof, but rather to look at the geological implications of their use. It is hoped that the references given will be adequate for those who wish to explore these particular applications further. The use of differential equations in geology is probably one of the most important topics in mathematical geology, and this is likely to continue to be so in the future.

8.1 Definitions and examples

An **ordinary differential equation** is any relationship between the variables x and y, and the derivatives dy/dx, d^2y/dx^2, etc. The term 'ordinary' serves to distinguish them from partial differential equations, which involve partial derivatives. The **order** of a differential equation is that of the highest-order derivative occurring, so

$$\frac{dy}{dx} = f(x) \quad \text{is a first-order differential equation}$$

$$\frac{d^2y}{dx^2} + \frac{dy}{dx} = f(x) \quad \text{is a second-order differential equation}$$

The solution of a differential equation is an equation relating the variables involved which does not contain any differential coefficients. In other words, we integrate to eliminate the differentials:

$$\frac{dy}{dx} = 3x$$

$$f(x) = \int 3x \, dx = \frac{3}{2}x^2 + C$$

Note that here we include the constant of integration, which leads to the **general solution.** Thus, the equation gives rise to a family of curves, which will have the same slope for a particular value of x, as shown in Figure 8.1. If a **particular solution** is required, then an x- and corresponding y-value must be given. These are referred to as **boundary conditions,** and enable the constant of integration to be calculated. Thus, in the example we have just considered, if $x = 0$ when $y = 2$, then

$$y = \frac{3}{2}x^2 + 2$$

We have already seen that if the equation is in the form

$$\frac{\mathrm{d}y}{\mathrm{d}x} = f(x)$$

then we integrate directly, so

$$y = \int f(x)\mathrm{d}x$$

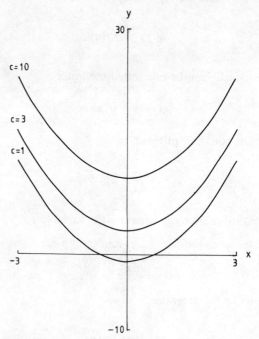

Figure 8.1 The family of curves of the differential equation $\mathrm{d}y/\mathrm{d}x = 3x$, i.e. $f(x) = \frac{3}{2}x^2 + c$ for $c = -1$, 3 and 10.

However, if the equation is of the form

$$\frac{dx}{dy} = f(y)$$

then the equation is rewritten in the form

$$\frac{1}{f(y)}\frac{dy}{dx} = 1$$

and then integrated

$$\int \frac{1}{f(y)} dy = \int dx$$

Another possibility is the form

$$\frac{dy}{dx} = \frac{f(x)}{g(x)}$$

In this, the variables are separable, so we can rewrite it in the form

$$g(y)\frac{dy}{dx} = f(x)$$

in which each side can be integrated separately:

$$\int g(y) dy = \int f(x) dx$$

An important equation of this type is

$$\frac{dy}{dx} = ky$$

k being a constant. We can separate the variables:

$$\frac{1}{y}\frac{dy}{dx} = k$$

which allows us to integrate:

$$\int \frac{1}{y} dy = \int k \, dx$$

which leads to

$$\ln y = kx + C$$

or

$$y = \exp(kx + C)$$

$$= \exp kx \exp C$$

8.2 Numerical solution: the method of finite differences

8.2.1 Differential equations with one independent variable

Starting with basic differentiation, it should be remembered that the first derivative of a function at any point on the curve is given by

$$\frac{dy}{dx} = \lim_{\Delta x \to 0} \frac{f(x + \Delta x) - f(x)}{\Delta x}$$

The derivative at any point $x = P$, is given by

$$\Delta \left(\frac{dy}{dx} \right)_P = f(x_0 + \Delta x) - f(x_0) + E\Delta x$$

where E is an error term which approaches zero as, in the limit, $\Delta x \to 0$. Therefore, in the limit we can write

$$\Delta \left(\frac{dy}{dx} \right)_P \approx f(x_0 + \Delta x) - f(x_0)$$

which can be rewritten as:

$$\left(\frac{dy}{dx} \right)_P \approx \frac{f(x_0 + \Delta x) - f(x_0)}{\Delta x}$$

If $x_1 = x_0 + \Delta x$, $x_2 = x_0 + 2\Delta x$ and $f(x_1)$ represents the value of the function at x_1, etc., then we can rewrite the equation as

$$\left(\frac{dy}{dx} \right)_P \approx \frac{f(x_1) - f(x_0)}{\Delta x}$$

This equation can be expressed in words as meaning that the slope of the tangent to the curve at a point P half-way between x_0 and x_1 is equal to the difference in value of the function at these points divided by Δx. In the limit, as $\Delta x \to 0$, the **finite-difference quotient** (the right-hand side of the equation) becomes equal to the derivative. It is more usual to express the derivative in the form of the difference between points separated by a distance of $2\Delta x$. Thus, we can write, for the derivative at x_0:

$$\left(\frac{dy}{dx}\right)_0 = \frac{f(x_1) - f(x_{-1})}{2\Delta x}$$

If we wish to obtain the finite-difference quotient for the second derivative, we proceed similarly. First we introduce a second point on the curve, Q. Then, as before, the approximation to the first derivative is

$$\left(\frac{dy}{dx}\right)_Q \approx \frac{f(x_0) - f(x_{-1})}{\Delta x}$$

The second derivative can be written as

$$\frac{d^2 y}{dx^2} = \frac{d}{dx}\left(\frac{dy}{dx}\right)$$

Thus, we can express the second derivative as an approximation to the difference between the first derivative at points P and Q:

$$\left(\frac{d^2 y}{dx^2}\right)_0 \approx \frac{(dy/dx)_Q - (dy/dx)_P}{\Delta x}$$

We replace the derivatives on the right-hand side of the equation by their finite-difference quotients:

$$\left(\frac{d^2 y}{dx^2}\right)_0 \approx \frac{[f(x_1) - f(x_0)]/\Delta x - [f(x_0) - f(x_{-1})]/\Delta x}{(\Delta x)^2}$$

Thus,

$$\left(\frac{d^2 y}{dx^2}\right)_0 \approx \frac{f(x_1) - 2f(x_0) + f(x_{-1})}{(\Delta x)^2}$$

We can derive the finite-difference quotients for higher-order derivatives similarly.

To use the finite-difference approximation we can drop the $y = f(x)$ notation and use values of y themselves. The finite-difference approximations with the $y = f(x)$ notation replaced by the corresponding y-values, for differential equations up to order four, are

$$\left(\frac{dy}{dx}\right)_j \approx \frac{y_{j+1} - y_{j-1}}{2\Delta}$$

$$\left(\frac{d^2y}{dx^2}\right)_j \approx \frac{y_{j+1} - 2y_j + y_{j-1}}{(\Delta x)^2}$$

$$\left(\frac{d^3y}{dx^3}\right)_j \approx \frac{y_{j+2} - 2y_{j+1} + 2y_{j-1} - y_{j-2}}{2(\Delta x)^3}$$

$$\left(\frac{d^4y}{dx^4}\right)_j \approx \frac{y_{j+2} - 4y_{j+1} + 6y_j - 4y_{j-1} + y_{j-2}}{(\Delta x)^4}$$

Having developed our general finite-difference approximations, how can we use them to solve any particular differential equation? The method illustrated has three steps.

(1) Translate the derivative into a finite-difference quotient.
(2) Formulate a set of simultaneous linear equations which will enable the unknowns to be evaluated. The number of equations will equal the number of unknowns.
(3) Solve the simultaneous equations.

We shall now tackle an example. Consider the linear differential equation

$$\frac{d^2y}{dx^2} = 5x$$

We translate this into a finite-difference quotient:

$$y_{j+1} - 2y_j + y_{j-1} = 5x(\Delta x)^2$$

We are asked to evaluate the differential for the range of values

$x = 0\text{–}0.5$. If we choose an interval of $\Delta x = 0.05$, we will have 11 values of x indexed with j, as follows:

$$x_0 = 0.0 \quad x_1 = 0.05 \quad x_2 = 0.10 \quad \cdots \quad x_{10} = 0.50$$

These values can now be inserted into the finite-difference equation, using the same index for y:

$$y_0 - 2y_1 + y_2 = 0.000625$$

$$y_1 - 2y_2 + y_3 = 0.00125$$

$$y_2 - 2y_3 + y_4 = 0.001875$$

$$\cdot$$
$$\cdot$$
$$\cdot$$

$$y_8 - 2y_9 + y_{10} = 0.005625$$

which are a set of nine equations with 11 unknowns (y-values). In order to solve these equations, we need to set boundary conditions. This will provide two values of y, y_0 and y_{10}, which will make the number of unknowns nine. For the present purpose we will set $y_0 = 0$ and $y_{10} = 10.0$. The equations will now be

$$-2y_1 + y_2 = 0.000625$$

$$y_1 - 2y_2 + y_3 = 0.00125$$

$$y_2 - 2y_3 + y_4 = 0.001875$$

$$\cdot$$
$$\cdot$$
$$\cdot$$

$$y_8 - 2y_9 \quad\quad = -9.994375$$

These equations can be solved iteratively using Gauss–Seidel iteration (Section 7.3.2), where the general form is

$$y_j = \frac{1}{2}(y_{j-1} + y_{j+1} - 0.000625j)$$

To illustrate the computer solution of the finite-difference equations, Program 8.1 is given. It should be noted that the boundary conditions are set in statements 80 and 90, and the general form of the equation for iteration is in statement 230. Similar examples could be run by changing these statements appropriately. The results are summarized in Table 8.1.

Table 8.1 Values obtained for the finite-difference solution of the equation $d^2y/dx^2 = 5x$ after 99 iterations using Program 8.1. Values marked with an asterisk are the boundary values.

$x_{(i)}$	$y_{(i)}$	$x_{(i)}$	$y_{(i)}$
0.00	0.0000*	0.30	5.9596
0.05	0.9895	0.35	6.9625
0.10	1.9797	0.40	7.9698
0.15	2.9712	0.45	8.9820
0.20	3.9646	0.50	10.0000*
0.25	4.9605		

8.2.2 Finite-difference solution with more than one independent variable

In many practical applications there is more than one independent variable. For example, the flow of a liquid through a porous medium can be considered in either a two- or a three-dimensional context. There will, accordingly, be two or three independent variables. Suppose we have an arbitrary grid, each cell being defined by an easting of size Δx and a northing of size Δy, and denote easting by the index i and northing by j. In each cell some parameter of interest is measured, which we can call z. This value can be represented on a third axis, and the resulting surface is described by the function

$$z = f(x,y)$$

x and y being the independent variables and z the dependent one. Now, the derivatives of z will be partial derivatives with respect to either x or y, written as

$$\frac{\partial z}{\partial x} \quad \text{and} \quad \frac{\partial z}{\partial y}$$

Higher-order partial derivatives can be denoted in the usual way. Following from Section 8.2.1, we get

$$\frac{\partial z}{\partial x} = \frac{z_{i+1,j} - z_{i-1,j}}{2\Delta x}$$

and

$$\frac{\partial z}{\partial y} = \frac{z_{i,j+1} - z_{i,j-1}}{2\Delta y}$$

Also, the second partial derivatives are

$$\frac{\partial^2 z}{\partial y^2} = \frac{z_{i+1,j} - 2z_{i,j} + z_{i-1,j}}{\Delta x^2}$$

and

$$\frac{\partial^2 z}{\partial y^2} = \frac{z_{i,j+1} - 2z_{i,j} + z_{i,j-1}}{\Delta y^2}$$

It should be noted that there are now two indices in the equations; when we hold y constant the index j remains constant and, conversely, when x is constant i remains constant.

Now consider the partial differential

$$\frac{\partial^2 z}{\partial x^2} + \frac{\partial^2 z}{\partial y^2} = C$$

where C is some numerical constant. Using our finite-difference quotients we have

$$\frac{z_{i+1,j} - 2z_{i,j} + z_{i-1,j}}{\Delta x^2} + \frac{z_{i,j+1} - 2z_{i,j} + z_{i,j-1}}{\Delta y^2} = C$$

If we use a regular grid where $\Delta x = \Delta y$, then this equation becomes

$$z_{i+1,j} + z_{i-1,j} + z_{i,j+1} + z_{i,j-1} - 4z_{i,j} = c(\Delta x)^2$$

Inspection of Figure 8.2 shows that there are 25 cells involved, nine of which are internal (i.e. have no external boundary), four have external corners and 12 contain an external edge.

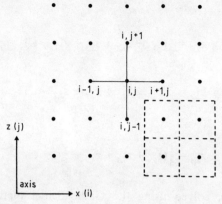

Figure 8.2 Method of indexing points for the finite-difference quotients, with two independent variables. Points are at the centre of a regular grid of $\Delta x = \Delta y$.

We can arbitrarily set our boundary condition at zero, in which case all cells containing external edges or corners have the boundary value

$$z_{1,1} = z_{1,2} = z_{1,3} = \ldots = 0.0$$

and we have to find values for the nine internal cells:

$$z_{2,2} \quad z_{2,3} \quad z_{2,4} \quad z_{3,2} \quad z_{3,3} \quad z_{3,4} \quad z_{4,2} \quad z_{4,3} \quad z_{4,4}$$

The equations are

$$z_{3,2} + z_{1,2} + z_{2,3} + z_{2,1} - 4z_{2,2} - C = 0$$

$$z_{3,3} + z_{1,3} + z_{2,4} + z_{2,2} - 4z_{2,3} - C = 0$$

$$z_{3,4} + z_{1,4} + z_{2,5} + z_{2,3} - 4z_{2,4} - C = 0$$

$$z_{4,2} + z_{2,2} + z_{3,3} + z_{3,1} - 4z_{3,2} - C = 0$$

$$z_{4,3} + z_{2,3} + z_{3,4} + z_{3,2} - 4z_{3,3} - C = 0$$

$$z_{4,4} + z_{2,4} + z_{3,5} + z_{3,3} - 4z_{3,4} - C = 0$$

$$z_{5,2} + z_{3,2} + z_{4,3} + z_{4,1} - 4z_{4,2} - C = 0$$

$$z_{5,3} + z_{3,3} + z_{4,4} + z_{4,2} - 4z_{4,3} - C = 0$$

$$z_{5,4} + z_{3,4} + z_{4,5} + z_{4,3} - 4z_{4,4} - C = 0$$

Rearranging,

$$z_{2,2} = \frac{1}{4}(z_{3,2} + z_{1,2} + z_{2,3} + z_{2,1} - C)$$

$$z_{2,3} = \frac{1}{4}(z_{3,3} + z_{1,3} + z_{2,4} + z_{2,2} - C)$$

.
.
.

$$z_{4,4} = \frac{1}{4}(z_{5,4} + z_{3,4} + z_{4,5} + z_{4,3} - C)$$

which can be solved using the Gauss–Seidel method. A good exposition of this method, which is commonly applied to problems of groundwater flow and associated areas is given in a number of books. These include Harbaugh & Bonham-Carter (1970), Verruijt (1970) and Wang & Anderson (1982).

8.3 Geological applications

As mentioned at the end of the previous section, differential equations in geology are commonly in use in the study of groundwater flow. Therefore, since there are a number of good texts on this application (see references at end of last section), the applications to be considered now are taken from other areas.

8.3.1 The exponential-growth equation

The exponential-growth equation is one of the simplest differential equations, yet has had the widest application throughout science. Geology is no exception, and in this section only a few of its many applications are reviewed.

There are two forms of the equation, one relating to growth

$$\frac{dN}{dt} = rN$$

and the other, relating to decay

$$\frac{dN}{dt} = -rN$$

where N = the population size, t = time and r = constant. Both equations can be solved analytically, and lead to

$$N_t = N_0 e^{rt}$$

and

$$N_t = N_0 e^{-rt}$$

where N_t = the size of the population at time t and N_0 = the size of population at time zero. The equations may also be written as

$$\ln N_t = \ln N_0 + rt$$

and

$$\ln N_t = \ln N_0 - rt$$

As we saw in Section 2.1.4, a graph of population size against time, according to these equations, has a characteristic exponential form.

(a) THE RATE LAW FOR FIRST-ORDER CHEMICAL REACTIONS

The exponential equation is used to describe the rate of change in the amounts of reactants in first-order chemical reactions. The equations are either

$$\frac{dC}{dt} = -kC$$

$$C = C_0 e^{-kt}$$

$$\ln C = \ln C_0 - kt$$

where C_0 = the concentration at the start of the reaction, k = the reaction rate constant, C = the concentration at time t, during the reaction, and t = time

or

$$\frac{dC}{dt} = k(C_s - C)$$

$$\frac{C_s - C}{C_s - C_0} = e^{-kt}$$

$$\ln\left(\frac{C_s - C}{C_s - C_0}\right) = -kt$$

where C_s = the steady-state concentration, other symbols as above (Lasaga 1981, p. 28).

In a laboratory study of the thermal conversion of lipids extracted from sedimentary rocks into a kerogen-like substance, Shioya and Ishiwatari (1983, p. 11) give the following in the interpretation of their results:

> In order to estimate the rate of conversion of soluble lipids into a kerogen-like substance, the lipids were heated at 6 different temperatures, in the range 125–200°C for periods ranging from 1 to 7 days. At the end of each experiment the residual lipids, any gases generated and the kerogen-like substance formed, were measured. Assuming a first order reaction:
>
> $$\frac{dA}{dt} = kS$$
>
> where A = ratio of the percentage kerogen-like substance to original lipids
> S = ratio of the percentage residual lipids to original lipids
>
> Since no gases were generated for the range of temperatures chosen, the amount of kerogen generated equals the amount of lipids which disappeared. Therefore:
>
> $$\frac{dA}{dt} = -\frac{dS}{dt}$$
>
> combining the two equations:
>
> $$\ln S = -kt + \ln 100$$
>
> The value of k, the rate constant for each of the 6 different temperatures used in the experiments, were estimated from plots of $\ln S$ against time. By plotting these constants against tempera-

ture, they concluded that the half-life of lipids in sediments is about 10^4–10^5 years at 0–30°C.

(b) DISTRIBUTION OF SEDIMENTARY ROCK MASSES

Garrels and Mackenzie (1971, pp. 255ff.) developed two simple mass balance models which can be used to help describe the distribution through time of sedimentary rock masses preserved in the Earth's crust. These are the constant-mass model and the linear-accumulation model (Garrels and Mackenzie 1972, p. 262). The two models have different starting points. The first assumes that the total mass of sediment has remained constant throughout geological time, and that there has been a balance between the metamorphism of sediments and the erosion of igneous rock, whether of primary or secondary origin. The implication of the constant-mass model is that at some time early in the Earth's history a large mass of sediment was formed almost instantaneously. The linear-accumulation model, on the other hand, assumes that the erosion of igneous rock has exceeded the rate of incorporation of sediments into the igneous mass. For the present purposes, only the constant-mass model will be considered.

If we start with a large mass of sediment M, at time t_0, then the processes of erosion and the incorporation of material back into the igneous mass will commence, so that by time t_1 the original mass will have decreased by an amount ΔM_e. However, since the process of deposition will also be taking place, a 'new' set of sediments will be deposited, equal in amount to ΔM_d. At time t_2 both 'old' and 'new' sediments will be affected by the processes in operation, giving rise to 'new' igneous rock and 'new' sediments. However, throughout the whole process, the total amount of sedimentary rock (of all ages) remains the same.

Harbaugh & Bonham-Carter (1970, p. 367) have formalized this model, suggesting that the amount of material lost by erosion, etc., per unit time can be described by the exponential decay equation

$$-\frac{dM}{dt} = \alpha M$$

where M = the mass of sediment, t = time and α = a constant controlling the loss of sediment. This gives

$$M_t = M_0 e^{-\alpha t}$$

where M_0 = the starting mass and M_t = the mass remaining at time t. Now, since the amount of sediment deposited is equal to the mass removed, the amount deposited is given by

$$M_d = M_0 - M_t$$

$$= M_0 - Me^{-at}$$

where M_d = the amount deposited.

If we divide geological time into a number of equal intervals, each Δt long, then this equation becomes

$$M_d = M - Me^{-a\Delta t}$$

$$= M(1 - e^{-a\Delta t})$$

where M = the total mass of sediment.

If geological time is divided into N equal parts, and we use the subscript i to label each increment, with $i = 1$ being the oldest, then the age of rocks being deposited during the ith time increment is

$$(N - i)\Delta t$$

The mass deposited during any time increment is M_d. The mass remaining today M_r, from sediments deposited at time i, is

$$M_r = M_d e^{-a(N - i)\Delta t}$$

$$= M(1 - e^{-a\Delta t})e^{a(i - N)\Delta t}$$

Thus, given values for M, a, N and Δt, we can calculate the mass remaining for values of i, where i goes from 1 to N. A Fortran program based on both of the Garrels and Mackenzie models is given by Harbaugh & Bonham-Carter (1970, pp. 367ff.). They also include a comprehensive discussion of the mathematics of the two models.

8.3.2   *Gravity measurement*

In geophysics the use of the torsion balance to measure gravity is of interest, since, although its use has been superseded by more-modern instruments, its theory is important. The torsion balance measures the distortion of the gravitational field, by measuring the rotation of a torsion balance beam, due to the gravitational forces acting on two masses at the ends of the beam. Since these forces which produce the torque in the beam are first derivatives of gravity, their rates of change must be second derivatives of the potential (Nettleton 1976, pp. 67ff.). The torque is given by

$$T = mhl\left[\left(\frac{\partial^2 u}{\partial y \partial z}\right)\cos\alpha - \left(\frac{\partial^2 u}{\partial x \partial z}\right)\sin\alpha\right]$$

$$+ ml^2\left[2\left(\frac{\partial^2 u}{\partial x \partial y}\right)\cos 2\alpha + \left(\frac{\partial^2 u}{\partial y^2} - \frac{\partial^2 u}{\partial x^2}\right)\sin 2\alpha\right]$$

where m = the mass of weights on the beam, h = the vertical distance between the weights, $2l$ = the horizontal distance between the weights, T = the torque, α = the angle between the beam and the x-axis (usually north) and $\partial^2 u/\partial y \partial z$, etc. = the 2nd partial derivatives of the gravitational potential u.

Since the torque produces a rotation of the balance, and if the deflected position is n and the undisturbed position is n_0, then the equation becomes

$$n - n_0 = P(u_{yz}\cos\alpha - u_{zx}\sin\alpha) + Q(2u_{xy}\cos 2\alpha + u\Delta \sin 2\alpha)$$

where $P = 2NDmhl/\tau$ and $Q = 2NDml^2/\tau$. P and Q are constants, and depend on the physical parameters of the instrument,

$$u_{yz} = \frac{\partial^2 u}{\partial x \partial z}, \qquad u_{xy} = \frac{\partial^2 u}{\partial x \partial y}, \text{ etc.}$$

and $u\Delta = u_{yy} - u_{xx}$.

There are four unknown quantities in the equation, which are the four second derivatives. Also, as there is no way of measuring n_0, so that is also an unknown. In this application it is not necessary to solve the differentials and, in practice, readings are taken in five different directions (i.e. five values of α), which reduces the problem to solving five simultaneous linear equations in five unknowns.

8.3.3 Diffusion of gases through rock

The use of organic geochemistry as a method of oil exploration depends on locating anomalous amounts of the light hydrocarbon gases methane, ethane and propane in samples of subsoil or near-surface rock. The occurrence of such anomalous amounts of light hydrocarbon gases are assumed to be caused by the diffusion of the gases from gas or oil reservoirs. The model is based on the premise that the gases 'leak' through the reservoir cap rock and diffuse upward, and are approximately at equilibrium, at a depth of 2–3 m from the surface. They enhance the naturally occurring gases already present in the rock, and form an anomaly significantly above the regional background (Horvitz 1939).

Subsequent to Horvitz's paper, there has been much discussion on the assumptions behind the model, and consequently on its validity as an exploration technique. A paper by Stegna (1961) tested the validity of the assumption that gases could diffuse through the overlying rock by developing a theoretical model. This model quantifies the process of diffusion to see, under what conditions of depth and time, steady-state diffusion could occur when taking into account the nature of the rocks likely to be found above a reservoir.

Stegna (1961, p. 447), started by taking the Fick's Law equation for diffusion as:

$$\frac{\partial c}{\partial t} = D \nabla C$$

which simply states that the change of concentration C with time t at any given point is equal to the Laplacian of the concentration, ∇C, times the coefficient of diffusion, D. To solve the differential equation, so that values for the concentration at a given depth z at time t could be found, boundary conditions are set using the following assumptions.

(a) Reservoir formation was instantaneous, at

$$\text{time } t = 0$$

$$\text{depth } z = h$$

(b) The gas concentration in the reservoir remains constant during time, i.e. the amount of gas lost by diffusion is very small compared with the amount present.
(c) At the surface $z = 0$ and the concentration of gas from diffusion is small enough to be neglected.
(d) The reservoir has a sedimentary cover of average diffusion coefficient D.

(e) The lateral extent of the reservoir is significantly greater than its depth. This means that the one-dimensional equation

$$\frac{\partial C}{\partial t} = D\frac{\partial^2 c}{\partial z^2}$$

can be used.

These assumptions, which are reasonably realistic, give the boundary conditions

$$C_{(0,z)} = 0$$

$$C_{(t,h)} = C_0$$

$$C_{(t,0)} = 0$$

The equation and boundary conditions are satisfied oy the function

$$C'_{(t,z)} = C_0 z/h$$

This does not, however, satisfy the first boundary condition. Therefore Stegna (1961, p. 448), assumed that the concentration at time t and depth z consisted of two parts:

$$C_{(t,z)} = C'_{(t,z)} + C''_{(t,z)}$$

and the boundary conditions for the function $C''_{(t,z)}$, are

$$C''_{(0,z)} = -C_{0,z/h}$$

$$C''_{(t,h)} = 0$$

$$C''_{(t,0)} = 0$$

and a particular solution is

$$C''_{(t,z)} = A_n e^{-a2Dt} \sin az$$

which will satisfy the third of the above boundary conditions, but not the second, unless

$$a = n\pi/h$$

where n is an integer. To satisfy the first condition, the constants A_n are chosen so that

$$\sum_{n=1}^{\infty} A_n \sin\left(\frac{n\pi}{h}\right) z = -C_0\left(\frac{z}{h}\right)$$

This leads to an equation which allows the calculation of the gas concentration C at a depth z and at time t, which is

$$C_{(t,z)} = C_0 \left(\frac{z}{h} + \frac{2}{\pi}\sum_{n=1}^{\infty} \frac{(-1)^n}{n} e^{-(n2\pi z/h^2)Dt} \sin\frac{n\pi z}{h}\right)$$

where C_0 = the concentration of absorbed gas (methane) in the immediate vicinity of the reservoir, and is taken to be 0.1 (Stegna 1961) and D = the diffusion coefficient, and is taken as being between 10^{-6} and 10^{-5} cm^{2}s^{-1}.

An average diffusion coefficient can be calculated from

$$\frac{1}{D} = \sum_{i=1}^{n} \frac{a_i}{D_i}$$

where a_i = the thickness of the ith lithology and D_i = the diffusion coefficient of the ith lithology.

It is interesting to note that Stegna concluded that in some situations sufficient time could not have elapsed from the formation of the reservoir to the present for steady-state diffusion to occur. Also, he argued that since the time required to reach steady-state diffusion varies with the square of the depth 'the geochemical method is a structure-prospecting rather than a direct oil-prospecting method' (Stegna 1961, p. 450).

This example is only one of many ways of solving the differential equation for Fick's Law. Harbaugh & Bonham-Carter (1970, pp. 238–58) look at several examples with different objectives, and hence different boundary conditions. Thus, if the material through which diffusion takes place is anisotropic then the diffusion coefficients k_x, k_y and k_z, for each direction x, y and z is

$$\frac{\partial c}{\partial t} = k_x\frac{\partial^2 c}{\partial x^2} + k_y\frac{\partial^2 c}{\partial y^2} + k_z\frac{\partial^2 c}{\partial z^2}$$

which can be solved by finite differences.

8.3.4 Formation of crenulation cleavage

This example follows closely the arguments and discussion of Cosgrove (1976), with some reference to the earlier work of Cobbold *et al.* (1971). There have been two proposed origins for crenulation cleavage (Cosgrove 1976, p. 157): either it is the result of microfaulting or the result of microfolding. Both types are well represented geologically, along with a third type – crenulation cleavage in conjugate sets. This last type has been considered as a consequence of microfaulting. Cosgrove (1976) demonstrated that these three types of crenulation cleavage are different expressions of buckling instabilities developed in anisotropic materials.

Certain assumptions were made:

(a) the material is linearly elastic or Newtonian viscous;
(b) it is anisotropic and homogeneous;
(c) it deforms by plane strain;
(d) deformation is not accompanied by a volume change;
(e) the maximum principal compressive stress is parallel to the mineral fabric; and
(f) it is in a uniform state of initial stress which gives rise to homogeneous flattening within the material.

The co-ordinate directions x and y are chosen to coincide with the symmetry axes of the material, as shown in Figure 8.3.

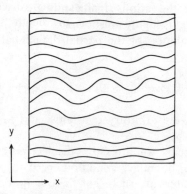

Figure 8.3 The relationship between foliation and the co-ordinate axes x and y chosen for the mathematical analysis of the formation of crenulation cleavage (after Cosgrove 1976, fig. 4).

The aim of Cosgrove's analysis is to investigate the types of instability which might disrupt the initial state. The displacement patterns which result are ordered and non-uniform, and are described by displacement vectors **U** and **V** which are in the x- and y-directions, respectively. By restating the above conditions mathematically a single equation has been developed, solutions to which satisfy the conditions specified. The buckling equation is a partial differential equation of fourth order:

$$(Q - P/2)\frac{\partial^4\varphi}{\partial x^4} + 2(2N - Q)\frac{\partial^4\varphi}{\partial x^2\partial y^2} + (Q + P/2) + \frac{\partial^4\varphi}{\partial y^4} = 0$$

where φ is a displacement function related to **U** and **V**:

$$\mathbf{U} = \frac{\partial\varphi_{xy}}{\partial y} \qquad \mathbf{V} = \frac{\partial\varphi_{xy}}{\partial x}$$

where $P =$ the differential stress $(\sigma_1 - \sigma_3)$, $Q =$ a measure of the resistance to shear and $N =$ a measure of the resistance to compression in the direction of the maximum compressive stress σ_1.

The shear and compressive moduli M and L for any stress condition can be given in terms of Q and N, as

$$M = N + P/4 \qquad L = Q + P/2$$

Their ratio M/L is a measure of anisotropy, and when M and L are very different, i.e. the ratio is significantly greater than or less than unity, the material is highly anisotropic.

The general solution of the partial differential (Cobbold *et al.* 1971, p. 29) is

$$\varphi = f_1(x + \xi_1 y) + f_2(x + \xi_1 y) + f_3(x + \xi_2 y) + f_4(x + \xi_2 y)$$

where ξ_1 and ξ_2 are arbitrary constants, and f_1, f_2, f_3 and f_4 are arbitrary functions.

To obtain specific solutions (i.e. displacement patterns) of the general equation, boundary conditions need to be defined. These boundary conditions are such that there is no deflection of shear stress at the edges of the material, which implies that buckling disturbances are restricted to the central part of the material. As Cosgrove (1976, p. 158) notes, in geological situations buckling is not restricted to these boundary conditions. However, the simplification is valid, and leads to the three types of the displacement function φ which are of geological interest. Cosgrove (1976, p. 159) has designated these as types 1, 2 and 3, as follows

type 1 $\qquad\qquad 2M > L$

where the stress conditions are

$$P > L$$

type 2 $\qquad\qquad 2M < L$

where the stress conditions are such that

$$4(M/L)(L - M) < P < L$$

type 3 $\qquad\qquad 2M < L$

where the stress conditions are

$$P > L$$

From these it is easy to see that the type of buckling which develops depends on the material properties, M and L, and the size of the differential stress, P. It should be noted that:

(a) type 3 buckling solutions develop in the same types of materials as type 2, but with a higher stress;
(b) structures associated with type 2 will develop before P is large enough to develop type 3 structures: the previous development of type 2 structures will generally inhibit the development of type 3 structures; and
(c) the displacement pattern for type 1 and type 3 solutions is the same.

In general, type 1 structures develop in materials with low anisotropy, whereas type 2 structures develop in materials with high anisotropy.

9 Beyond traditional mathematics

In common with most other subjects, mathematics is making advances in many areas, some of which are totally new or are new developments of traditional mathematics. In the case of such advancements, those involved may have applications in mind beyond the theoretical, but as in many fields of human activity there is frequently a marked time-lag between theoretical development and application. In this final chapter two topics have been chosen which have had some application in geology. They are here as a reflection of the author's interest, rather than their importance in absolute terms.

The advantage of both is that they provide a framework within which to re-think some old problems, rather than producing immediate new answers. With this in mind, it is interesting to speculate on what might have happened if, for example, one of the topics, catastrophe theory, had been around when Darwin was developing his theory of evolution. Catastrophe theory is concerned with the mathematics of systems which, although they can show gradual changes from one state to another, can also jump 'catastrophically', without going through the intermediate stages. Such ideas give credence to a theory of evolution in which change is not always continuous, a factor which might explain why palaeontologists have had so little success in their search for the so-called missing links.

In a book such as this it is not possible to go into the theory of the methods in great detail. It is possible, though, to give sufficient background to stimulate interest in the topics that the developments already made, toward their application to the study of geology, are not neglected. It is also worth bearing in mind that they are not the only possibilities which the new mathematics has to offer.

9.1 Catastrophe theory

Catastrophe theory has been principally developed by Thom (1972), with notable contributions by Zeeman (see, for example, Zeeman 1976, for a readable and comprehensive account of the development of the topic to that date). The subject concerns the study of sudden changes in a system, from a state of equilibrium. The theory derives from differential topology, which is concerned with the properties of surfaces in many dimensions. Topology allows the qualitative constructions of models which closely mirror the behaviour of many natural systems. When such surfaces are smooth, they are reflecting a state of equilibrium, when they are not smooth it indicates that the state of equilibrium has broken down, and catastrophes occur. At present the model is qualitative rather than quantitative.

Since it is difficult to describe all possible equilibrium surfaces and their associated catastrophes, matters have been simplified by the recognition of elementary forms. For processes where there are no more than four controlling factors, it has been shown that there are seven elementary catastrophes. These can be understood and applied to problems in sciences such as geology. In geology two papers are of note, those by Henley (1976) and Cubitt & Shaw (1976); in other branches of science notable contributions to the theory of evolution have been made by Waddington (1974) and Woodcock & Poston (1974). The discussion which follows is largely based on the references already cited, with the addition of Saunders (1980).

9.1.1 General theory

Considering catastrophe theory in its simplest form, we can say that it will relate to any system which can be described by an energy function of the form

$$V(Q_i, \lambda^j)$$

where V = the energy (or potential) function, Q_i = the finite set of state variables a, b, c, ...; i ranges from 1 to n: these control the system in the form of generalized co-ordinates and λ^j = the finite set of state variables x, y, z, ... ; j ranges from 1 to k: these are externally controlled parameters which describe the behaviour of the system.

Stationary values of V with respect to Q_i will give rise to equilibrium, maximum values giving unstable equilibria whereas minimum values give rise to stability. In other words, maximum energy represents unstable equilibrium and minimum energy represents stable equilibrium. In general the positions and number of equilibria are affected by variation of the control variables a, b, c, etc. If we limit the control space to four dimensions (a, b, c, d), then a smooth reversible change in the co-ordinates in the neighbourhood of a given point, will produce only one of seven possible elementary catastrophes. The number of elementary catastrophes is dependent only on the number of dimensions of the control space (e.g. for two dimensions only two are possible), whereas the type of catastrophe is controlled by the energy function.

The simple 'cusp' catastrophe, described by Zeeman (1971), requires a two-dimensional control space a and b, and the energy function is

$$V = \tfrac{1}{4}x^4 + \tfrac{1}{2}ax^2 + bx$$

Since the first derivative with respect to x is a cubic, i.e.

$$\mathrm{d}v/\mathrm{d}x = x^3 + ax + b$$

which will have either one or three real roots, it follows that there will be either one or three equilibrium positions for any given pair of values a, b. If for any position in the control space there is only one equilibrium position which is stable, there will be an energy minimum. Where there are three positions, the upper and lower are minima and the intermediate will be a maxima. The maxima will give rise to an unstable equilibrium.

The state of equilibrium is maintained on a topological surface either by smooth changes or by catastrophic jumps. The theory can be used to model and predict features of stable and unstable equilibrium. Zeeman (1971) has suggested that the catastrophe model could be appropriate if the system exhibits one or more of the following:

(a) bimodality;
(b) divergence;
(c) catastrophic jumps; or
(d) hysteresis delays.

Before considering some geological applications of the theory, we shall look at a simple physical model or machine, which shows all of the phenomena associated with the theory, known as Zeeman's catastrophe machine, and is illustrated in Figure 9.1. Most authors who have written on this topic have suggested that the machine, which is easily constructed, should be made and used to carry out the experiments described. This view is iterated here.

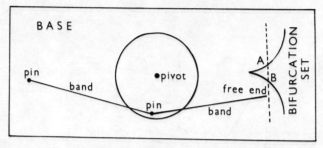

Figure 9.1 A diagrammatic representation of Zeeman's catastrophe machine.

The machine consists of a cardboard disc whose diameter is equal to the unstretched length of a rubber band. The disc is fixed to a suitable base, with a pin acting as a pivot at its centre, so that it is free to rotate. The rubber band which was used to establish the diameter of the disc and another band of equal length are attached at some point near the perimeter of the disc as in Figure 9.1. The free end of one band is fixed to the base at a distance of two diameters from the disc pivot and in line with it. The machine is operated by using the free end of the other band as the control point and moving it in the plane of the disc. Movements of the control point generally cause a smooth rotation of the disc, but in some situations the disc jumps. If all of the positions at which sudden jumps occur are marked on the base, a diamond shaped outline is generated (only half the area is shown on the figure). The outline or curve has four cusps, which form the bifurcation set of the cusp catastrophe equilibrium position. If the control point lies inside the curve there are two stable equilibria, if it is outside there is only one. The sudden movement of the disc relates to movement from one equilibrium position to another. This movement occurs at the point B if the control point moves from A to B as in the diagram; or at A, if the movement is in the opposite sense.

The phenomena exhibited by this machine can be visualized by means of a three-dimensional diagram, as illustrated in Figure 9.2. This model represents the cusp catastrophe, the simplest of the seven elementary catastrophes. The diagram is produced, constructing a behaviour surface over one segment of the bifurcation set, by plotting the points for which the first derivative $dV/dx = 0$. Every point on the top and bottom sheets of the behaviour surface (i.e. the part of the surface directly over the bifurcation set) represents a position of the disc where energy is a minimum, for the corresponding position of the control point. Therefore, if the control point is outside the bifurcation set only one mode of behaviour is possible,

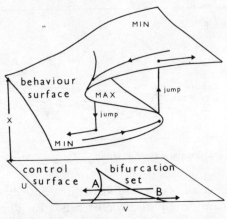

Figure 9.2 The cusp catastrophe model for Zeeman's catastrophe machine.

whereas inside the bifurcation set two modes are possible. These correspond to the two stable positions of the disc with two local minima (one on the top sheet and one on the bottom), even though the behaviour surface at this point is overfolded and has three sheets. This follows since the middle sheet, corresponding to a local maximum, is made up of points representing the least probable behaviour of the system. These factors can be more easily understood by plotting the energy function $V(x)$ for values of $u < 0$ for different values of v (the position of the control point). A set of plots of the energy state are shown in Figure 9.3. The position of the ball in the diagram shows, in a pictorial manner, how the catastrophe occurs.

Returning to our discussion of Figure 9.2, the inclusion of the middle sheet ensures that the behaviour surface is smooth and continuous; however, it should be noted that the control point is never represented on the middle sheet. Whenever the control point crosses the fold, either at A or at B, the point jumps between the top and bottom sheets catastrophically, since the middle sheet is inaccessible. The fold curve, marking the boundary between sheets, represents the inflection points. This sort of behaviour is characteristic of physical systems in which friction is important, as it allows them to assume a state of minimum energy. In the case of Zeeman's catastrophe machine, the energy is the potential energy stored in the rubber bands, so the disc will rotate until the tension of the rubber bands is minimized. Unless energy is added to the system, the machine will remain in a position of stable equilibrium. The process that keeps it there is called the dynamic.

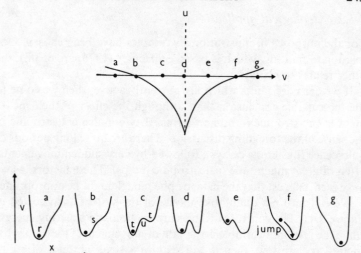

Figure 9.3 Energy states across the bifurcation set for Zeeman's catastrophe machine ($u < 0$ is fixed, values of v vary: a, b, c, etc.).

The behaviour associated with the cusp farthest away from the disc can be explained in a similar fashion, except that the energy is inverted, i.e. there are two points with maximum energy and only one where there is a minimum. As before, the dynamic compels the machine to remain in the single stable position of minimum energy. Also, on the behaviour surface the positions of maxima and minima are reversed and, as the maxima are unstable, the behaviour point can only lie on the middle sheet. This phenomena is known as a dual-cusp catastrophe.

Features of this system, which are common to all systems that follow the cusp model, are:

(a) bimodality over part of the range,
(b) hysteresis since the transition from one sheet to the other occurs at two positions, and does not occur in the middle of the cusp and
(c) divergence due to a small perturbation in the initial state of the system can lead to large differences in the final state.

Since each of these characteristics is present in a number of important geological systems, we are now in a position to look at some applications.

9.1.2   *Geological applications*

For the purposes of illustration, two topics have been chosen. One relating to faulting, which is based on Henley (1976, pp. 653ff.); the other relates to evolution.

If we consider faults which are currently active, then we come to the inescapable conclusion that, although the effect of their movement is catastrophic in human terms, they are also catastrophic in the sense of the foregoing discussion. There are quite long periods of quiescence (hysteresis delays), followed by very sudden movements, often of great magnitude (catastrophic jumps). These factors, as we have seen, suggest that the catastrophe model might be appropriate.

We can set up a qualitative model of the system as indicated in Figure 9.4a. The control variables are friction and shearing energy, while the response variable is the rate of movement. If the values for friction remain low, then it will require a small amount of strain energy to initiate movement. Also, if the strain energy increases, so will the movement. At high friction levels, which presumably occur in nature, increased energy will not cause movement until some threshold is reached, at which point there will be sudden jump to high rates of movement, following the path ABCD on the figure. Since the energy is released, due to the movement, there will be a second jump, back to quiescence, as indicated by the path DEB. Analysing the behaviour of a fault in this fashion shows that the catastrophe model provides a reasonable quantitative interpretation of reality.

To model evolution we can use as our control variables the increase in variability of the organism and the increase in environmental pressure. These factors are plotted as cusp catastrophe in Figure 9.4b, the interaction surface being used to define the relationship between the two control variables. Thus, at point A variability is low but the environmental pressure is high. At point B variability is high and environmental pressure is low. Now, Darwin's Theory in its simplest form tells us that evolution occurs as a response to environmental pressure, and that those organisms which can adapt quickly can be expected to survive.

Using Figure 9.4b let us explore what might happen using the model. Starting at a point A, where both environmental pressure and variability is low, and moving toward B, since there is only an increase in the potential toward variability, there will be a tendency to remain the same. If, on the other hand, variability remains low and environmental pressure increases, movement will be towards C

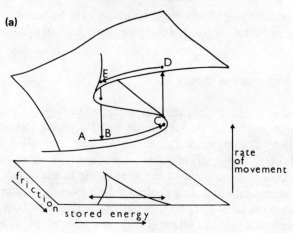

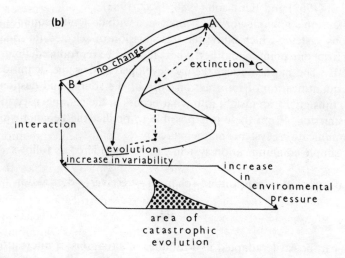

Figure 9.4 (a) The cusp catastrophe model applied to fault dynamics (after Henley 1976). (b) The cusp catastrophe model applied to evolution. The model relates variability of the organism to environmental pressure.

and possible extinction. The remaining option is that as environmental pressure increases, variability also increases, then there is the possibility that the path will lead smoothly toward evolution (solid line in figure), or with a small perturbation, the path will be diagonal across the surface to a point where a catastrophic jump is possible (broken line on figure). Thus, the analysis seems to indicate the possibility of evolution occurring as an almost continuous process or as catastrophic jumps, these jumps perhaps being the reason why no intermediate forms are found for some lines of evolution.

9.2 Information theory

The basic tenets of information theory were largely developed by Shannon and his co-workers in the Bell Telephone Laboratories in the USA. The mathematical theory of communication was published by Shannon (1948), and subsequently a large number of applications of the theory have been made in many fields outside communications, including geology. More recently a number of text books on the topic have been published, perhaps the most comprehensive being that of Guiasu (1977). In geology, applications have been published by Pelto (1954), Tasch (1965, 1980), Beerbower & Jordan (1960) and Ferguson (1980, 1982, 1983).

Shannon's original work was concerned with designing communications systems which allow the transmission of selected information from one point to another, where it could be reproduced almost exactly. The mathematical theory developed allows the definition and quantification of information both at the source and destination, thus giving an insight into what occurs in the channel used for transmission. From these it is possible to predict the behaviour of communications systems mathematically.

A simple communication system can be considered as follows:

$$\text{information} \rightarrow \text{transmitter} \rightarrow \text{channel} \rightarrow \text{receiver} \rightarrow \text{destination}$$
$$\uparrow$$
$$\text{noise}$$

This can be easily adapted in a number of situations of interest to geologists. Let us consider, for example, the process of fossilization. The following schematic is after Tasch (1965):

$$\text{living organism} \xrightarrow{\text{fossilization}} \text{fossil} \xrightarrow{\text{collection}} \text{interpretation}$$
$$\uparrow \qquad\qquad \uparrow$$
$$\text{noise} \qquad\qquad \text{noise}$$

In this, the information source is the living organism and the received message is the fossil. Noise is added in many parts of the system; for example, the effects of tectonism or poor collection (i.e.

the fossil is damaged during its extraction from the rock). These factors can produce distortion of the information, while the loss of soft parts and damage can cause an irretrievable loss of information.

Another example is given by considering the problem of producing a map on the basis of limited data. In this case the use of either a statistical or mathematical model is resorted to. We can use the following schematic to represent the process:

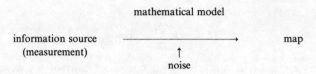

Here the information is transmitted via the mathematical model which, by its very nature, will impose its own characteristic structure on the data, which can be considered as noise. The destination is the map which is interpreted by the geologist.

Other concepts of information theory have also been applied in geology. Pelto (1954) used the concept of redundancy in the mapping of multi-component lithological systems. Beerbower & Jordan (1960) also used the same concept in an attempt to produce a taxonomic diversity index. In the next section we will consider the basic mathematics of the theory before exploring some of the applications in more detail.

9.2.1 General theory

The measure of information proposed by Shannon (1948, p. 380) is the bit or binary digit. Thus, if we have a device such as a switch, which has two stable positions, on or off, then

$$\log_2 2 = 1.0 \text{ bit}$$

Any number of such devices can store N bits of information and, as the total number of possible states is $2N$, then

$$\log_2 2N = n \text{ bits}$$

There is a close relationship between information and uncertainty, so the more uncertain an answer is, then the more information is passed when the answer is given. If there are a number of alternatives, then the amount of information is maximized when each is likely to occur. In other words, we have maximum uncertainty.

If we consider a system with N alternatives, and the probabilities of each alternative is given by

$$p_1, p_2, p_3 \ldots, p_n$$

then the information H, is given by

$$H = -K \sum_{i=1}^{n} p_i \log_2 p_i$$

In this equation K amounts to a choice of unit of measurement (Shannon 1948, p. 393, Guiasu 1977, pp. 1ff.). The equation is central to information theory, and relates information to choice and uncertainty. H is the entropy of the system.

If we consider the case of two alternatives, each being equally likely, then

$$p_1 = p_2 = 0.5$$

$$H = -0.5 \log_2 0.5 + 0.5 \log_2 0.5$$

$$= -1.0$$

If $p_1 = 1$ and $p_2 = 0$ (or vice versa), then

$$H = 0$$

or, if $p_1 = 0.25$ and $p_2 = 0.75$ (or vice versa), then

$$H = 0.8$$

Thus, H is maximized when $p_1 = p_2 = p_3 = \ldots = p_n$ and H is equal to $\log_2 n$

The ratio

$$\frac{\sum_{i=1}^{n} p_i \log_2 p_i}{\log_2 n}$$

is known as the **relative entropy** (RE) (Shannon 1948, p. 398).

In information theory the idea of redundancy is simply concerned with the repetition of the same message. Thus, if we have n possible messages and only one is transmitted, say 10 times, then assuming the channel is noiseless, only the first transmission of the message has any meaning, the remainder merely repeat the first and are therefore redundant. **Redundancy** (R), is measured as

$$R = 1 - RE$$

or, as a percentage,

$$R\% = (1 - RE) \times 100$$

The concept of redundancy is of considerable importance in the study of languages; written English has a redundancy of about 50 per cent, which means that when English is written half is determined by the structure of the language and half is freely chosen. There is a close link between redundancy and crossword puzzles. If the redundancy is low, then large crosswords become difficult to construct. A language with a redundancy of 33 per cent should theoretically enable the construction of three-dimensional puzzles (Shannon 1948, p. 399, Guiasu 1977, p. 130).

So far we have only considered single, discrete sources of information. Let us suppose we have two dependent events x and y, with m possibilities for x and n for y. If the joint probability of occurrence is $p(i,j)$, where i refers to the first and j to the second event, then

$$H(x,y) = -\sum_{i,j} p(i,j) \log_2 p(i,j)$$

(Shannon 1948, pp. 394ff.) and

$$H(x) = -\sum_{i,j} p(i,j) \log_2 \sum_j p(i,j)$$

$$H(y) = -\sum_{i,j} p(i,j) \log_2 \sum_i p(i,j)$$

Then

$$H(x,y) \leqslant H(x) + H(y)$$

It can also be shown (Shannon 1948, p. 395) that, if the two events are independent, then

$$H(x,y) = H(x) + H(y)$$

In other words, for two or more dependent events, the information content of the joint event is less than or equal to the sum of the individual information contents, while for two or more independent events the information content of the joint event is equal to the sum of the individual information contents.

Finally, another useful and important property of the entropy equation is its use in the case of successive choices. To illustrate this, let us suppose we have three choices with associated probabilities of 0.5, 0.333 and 0.167. Then, if we can breakdown the choice further into two successive choices, such that we have equal probabilities for both, and then for one we have two further choices with probabilities of 0.667 and 0.333, then

$$H(0.5, 0.333, 0.167) = H(0.5, 0.5) + 0.5H(0.667, 0.333)$$

In other words, the original H is equal to the weighted sum of the Hs for the successive choices (Shannon 1948, p. 393, Guiasu 1977, pp. 57ff.).

9.2.2   Geological applications

(a) THE PROCESS OF FOSSILIZATION AS A COMMUNICATION SYSTEM

In an early, thought-provoking paper, Tasch (1965) attempted to define what happens in the process from living organism to collected fossil, in terms of a communication system. He showed that the amount of information passed (denoted by Sr) was a combination of the original information (S) less the loss due to fossilization, i.e. the loss of soft parts, loss due to distortion, breakage, chemical alteration, etc. (denoted by N), plus information gained by multiple repetition of the message, i.e. lots of individuals preserved (R) and finally additional energy input (Sc) because of the requirement to transform one information pattern to another. Thus, the equation linking these individual attributes is

$$Sr = [S - D - N] + R + Sc \qquad (1)$$

There is also an additional input of information (St) which is derived from other areas of study such as sedimentology, stratigraphy, etc., which adds to Sr to give enlarged data (Dd). Thus, we have

$$Sr + Dd = S' = k(S - D) \qquad (2)$$

where the maximum possible data retrieval after fossilization is S', which is approximately equal to the original information in the living animal (S) allowing for the irretrievable loss (D). The derivative data (Dd), Eqn 2, serve to compensate in part for the losses D and N, Eqn 1. Also, symmetry and consistency of organization allow partial compensation for the effects of N, if N is distortion or breakage. This is summarized in Figure 9.5.

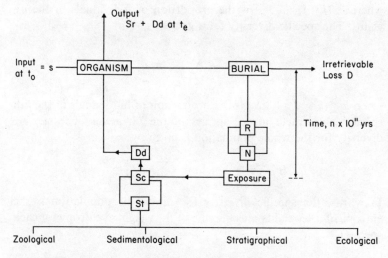

Figure 9.5 Summary of the fossil communication system (after Tasch 1965).

(b) DIVERSITY INDICES IN PALAEOECOLOGICAL STUDIES

Invertebrate community studies have frequently led to attempts to express the relationships between the number of organisms living in the community and the number of species represented, as a single number: the diversity index. We have already met one such diversity index, Fisher's α, in Chapter 7. Beerbower & Jordan (1960) proposed the use of the entropy equation for this purpose. Their equation (p. 1185) is

$$H = I_i = - \Sigma \, p_i \ln p_i$$

where H (the diversity index) $= 0$ when $p_i = 1$ and $H = \ln k$ when $p_1 = p_2 = p_3 = \ldots = p_k$. That is, the maximum diversity possible is $\ln k$ where $k =$ the number of species represented in the community. They also showed how the sample diversity related to the population diversity as well as the use of statistical tests to compare indices. For further details the reader is referred to the original paper.

In a book concerned with the use of mathematical methods in recent ecology, Pielou (1969, pp. 230–1) extended the ideas of Beerbower & Jordan and, using Shannon's concept of weighted entropy, proposed the use of generic and specific diversity. Generic diversity is defined as

$$H'_{(G)} = - \sum_{j=1}^{g} p_j \ln p_j$$

where p_j $(j = 1, \ldots, g)$ is the proportion of individuals in the jth genus. The specific diversity for a genus:

$$H'_{(S)} = - \sum_{k=1}^{S_j} q_{j,k} \ln q_{j,k}$$

where $q_{j,k}$ $(k = 1, \ldots, S_j)$ is the proportion of individuals in the kth species when there are S_j species in the jth genus. The specific diversity for the whole population is given by

$$H'_{(GS)} = - \sum p_j \ln p_j + \sum p_j H'_j (S)$$

In words, the specific diversity for the whole population is the entropy of the weights plus the sum of the weighted entropy for each species.

(c) MEASURES OF MIXING

In what is probably the earliest application of information theory in geology, Pelto (1954) used relative entropy as a measure of mixing in a sedimentological study. This idea was further developed by R. L. Miller & Khan (1962, pp. 425ff.) and applied to data relating to the distribution of recent foraminifera (R. L. Miller & Khan 1962, p. 427), and to the sorting of sediments (R. L. Miller & Khan 1962, pp. 432ff.). As a result of this study they suggested that the use might be extended into micropalaeontology, as a mixing descriptor. More recently, Ferguson (1983) suggested the use of the measure as a coefficient of elimination in the analysis of C–H–O data in the study of kerogen (kerogen is the product of the diagenesis of organic matter in rock, and its characteristics are fundamental to the study of petroleum source rocks).

In this application it was suggested that the redundancy equation could be used to relate the proportions of the three elements carbon, hydrogen and oxygen, which are the principal constituent elements of kerogen, the equation is

$$\text{coefficient of elimination} = \left[1 + \left(\frac{\Sigma_{i=1}^{3} p_i \log_2 p_i}{1.585} \right) \right] \times 100$$

The proposal was based on the idea that the generation of kerogen started with an hypothetical organic compound which is a mixture of equal proportions of the three elements, and which would have a coefficient of elimination of 0 per cent. This hypothetical compound would then undergo evolution due to geological processes which could eliminate oxygen and hydrogen, leaving graphite, i.e. 100 per cent carbon, with a coefficient of elimination of 100 per cent. In real life most organic compounds which result from biogenic reactions have values for the coefficient in the range 10–28 per cent, whereas products resulting from the action of geological processes gave considerably higher values. Indeed, it was suggested that kerogens resulting from diagenesis had values in the range 28–48 per cent, those resulting from catagenesis in the range 48–64 per cent and metagenesis > 64 per cent.

(d) INDEPENDENCE OF DATA SOURCES

The independence of data sources is an area where the least work has been done, since it does not often prove possible to study mixed data sources in geological situations. However, one area which has been considered briefly in this context is that of trend surface analysis. Proponents of the technique have suggested that trend surface analysis can, in certain circumstances, be considered to split the data into two components – the regional and local trends. In this the regional component is contained in the fitted values, and the local component is in the residuals, along with any noise in the original data. Unfortunately, this is a rather simplistic approach, and the definition of what constitutes these components can be somewhat arbitrary. In many cases trend surface analysis simply removes the noise from the data.

In some simple cases it has proved possible to split the two components from the data and then to examine the two trends separately (Ferguson 1982). If a measure of the information content of the original data and that of the two trend components can be estimated, then we can use the relationships

$$H_{(x)} = H_{(y)} + H_{(z)} \text{ (for independence)}$$

$$H_{(x)} \neq H_{(y)} + H_{(z)} \text{ (for dependence)}$$

where $H_{(x)}$ = the information content of the original data, $H_{(y)}$ = the information content of the regional trend component and $H_{(z)}$ = the information content of the local trend component.

The calculation of the information content of the three components is relatively simple. The range of the data values is subdivided to give a number of suitable class intervals (the same for each component), the width of the class interval in most applications being the contour interval at which the final maps will be displayed. The number of points which fall into each class interval is counted, and the probability of points falling into each class interval is obtained. Then the information content of the three sets can be calculated:

$$H = -\Sigma \, p \log_2 p$$

From the resulting Hs we can calculate the entropy ratio for the data sets

$$\text{entropy ratio} = \frac{H_{(y)} + H_{(z)}}{H_{(x)}}$$

where the entropy ratio = 1 for independence or > 1 for dependence (Ferguson 1982, p. 10).

In a number of practical situations the relationship between the calculated values for the surface and the residual values was examined. From this it was possible to show that as the complexity of the surface fitted increased, so the entropy ratio approached unity, indicating that the residuals were independent and probably represented random noise. In fact, the method proved particularly useful in isolating cases of overfitting of surfaces. In this situation the surface generated is largely a mathematical artefact and the entropy ratio values show a steady increase as more-complex surfaces are fitted to the data. This follows since the model itself (least squares) is generating information which is not present in the original data (Ferguson 1982, p. 42).

Appendix 1   An introduction to the methods of differentiation

A1.1   The rules of differentiation and their application

(a) The derivative of a function with a constant exponent. We have already shown that if $y = x^n$, then

$$\frac{\mathrm{d}y}{\mathrm{d}x} = nx^{n-1}$$

It follows from this that the derivative of a variable with respect to itself is unity, i.e. if $y = x$, then

$$\frac{\mathrm{d}y}{\mathrm{d}x} = 1$$

For example, differentiate $y = 4x^3 + 3x$:

$$\frac{\mathrm{d}y}{\mathrm{d}x} = (3 \times 4)x^{(3-1)} + (3 \times 1)x^{(1-1)}$$

$$= 12x^2 + 3$$

We can take, as a further example, differentiate

$$y = \mathrm{e}^x$$

Write as

$$y = 1 + x + \frac{x^2}{2!} + \frac{x^3}{3!} + \frac{x^4}{4!} + \dots$$

Then

$$\frac{\mathrm{d}\mathrm{e}^x}{\mathrm{d}x} = 0 + 1 + \frac{2x}{2!} + \frac{3x^2}{3!} + \frac{4x^3}{4!} + \dots$$

$$= 1 + x + \frac{x^2}{2!} + \frac{x^3}{3!} + \dots$$

$$= \mathrm{e}^x$$

(b) If c is any numerical constant, its derivative is zero; i.e. the rate of change of a constant is zero.

General form $y = u + c$, where $u = f(x)$.

Example: $y = 5x^2 + 6$

$$\frac{dy}{dx} = 10x$$

(c) If c is any numerical constant and the equation is of the form $y = cu$, where $u = f(x)$, then

$$\frac{d(cy)}{dx} = c\frac{dy}{dx}$$

Example: $y = 4(5x^2 + 6)$

$$\frac{dy}{dx} = 4(10x)$$

or $y = u/c$, where $u = f(x)$, then

$$\frac{dy}{dx} = \frac{1}{c}\frac{du}{dx}$$

Example: $y = (3x^3 - 7x)/8$

$$\frac{dy}{dx} = \frac{1}{8}(9x^2 - 7)$$

(d) Product rule: $y = uv$, where u and $v = f(x)$

$$\frac{d(uv)}{dx} = u\frac{dv}{dx} = v\frac{du}{dx}$$

Example: $y = (x^2 + 4)(x^3 - 1)$

$$\frac{dy}{dx} = (x^2 + 4)\frac{d(x^3 - 1)}{dx} + (x^3 - 1)\frac{d(x^2 + 4)}{dx}$$

$$= [(x^2 + 4)3x^2] + [(x^3 - 1)2x]$$

$$= (3x^4 + 12x^2) + (2x^4 - 2x)$$

$$= 5x^4 + 12x^2 - 2x$$

(e) Quotient rule: $y = u/v$, where u and $v = f(x)$

$$\frac{d(u/v)}{dx} = \frac{v\dfrac{du}{dx} - u\dfrac{dv}{dx}}{v^2}$$

Example: $y = (x^2 + 4)/(x^3 - 1)$

$$\frac{dy}{dx} = \frac{(x^3 - 1)\dfrac{d(x^2 + 4)}{dx} - (x^2 + 4)\dfrac{d(x^3 - 1)}{dx}}{(x^3 - 1)^2}$$

$$= \frac{[(x^3 - 1)2x] - [(x^2 + 4)3x^2]}{x^6 - 2x^3 + 1}$$

$$= \frac{-x^4 - 12x^2 - 2x}{x^6 - 2x^3 + 1}$$

(f) Function of a function: $y = f(v)$, e.g. $y = v/(1 - v^2)$ and $v = f(x)$, e.g. $v = 1 - x^2$. Then

$$\frac{dy}{dx} = \frac{dy}{dv}\frac{dv}{dx}$$

Example: $y = v^3 + 2$, $v = 2x$

$$\frac{dy}{dv} = 3v^2 \qquad \frac{dv}{dx} = 2$$

Now,

$$\frac{dy}{dx} = \frac{dy}{dv}\frac{dv}{dx}$$

$$= 3v^2 \times 2$$

But $v = 2x$, so

$$\frac{dy}{dx} = 3(2x)^2 \times 2 = 24x^2$$

(g) The derivative of an inverse: $y = \sqrt{x}$

$$\frac{dx}{dy} = 1\bigg/\frac{dy}{dx} \text{ or } \frac{1}{dy/dx}$$

(h) The derivative of a variable function with a constant exponent: $y = (u)^n$, where $u = f(x)$

$$\frac{dy}{dx} = n(u)^{n-1}\frac{d(u)}{dx}$$

Example: given $y = v^3 + 3$, $v = 2x$, then

$$y = (2x)^3 + 3$$

$$n(u)^{n-1} = 3(2x)^2 \quad \text{(note: constant disappears)}$$

$$\frac{d(u)}{dx} = \frac{d(2x)}{dx} = 2$$

$$\frac{dy}{dx} = \frac{3(2x^2) \times 2 = 24x^2}$$

A1.2 Standard forms and their use

A list of some of the more commonly used standard forms is given in Table A1.1. Many others can be found in mathematics textbooks dealing with calculus, to which the reader is advised to refer for a more comprehensive list.

Table A1.1 Some common standard differential forms.

Function	Derivative
x^n	nx^{n-1}
a^x	$a^x \ln a$
$\ln x$	$1/x$
$\sqrt{x}$	$\frac{1}{2}x^{-1/2}$
e^x	e^x
$\sin x$	$\cos x$
$\cos x$	$-\sin x$
$\tan x$	$(1 + \tan^2 x)$ or $\sec^2 x$

The following simple examples show how the standard forms are used in conjunction with the rules given in the previous section.

(a) Differentiate $y = (\cos x \sin x)$. Using the product rule

$$\frac{d(\cos x \sin x)}{dx} = \cos x \frac{d(\sin x)}{dx} + \sin x \frac{d(\cos x)}{dx}$$

Using the standard forms for the derivatives of $\sin x$ and $\cos x$, we get

$$= \cos x \cos x + \sin x(-\sin x)$$

$$= \cos^2 x - \sin^2 x = \cos 2x$$

(b) Differentiate $y = \tan x^3$. Using the rule for a variable function with a constant exponent and one of the standard forms for the derivative of $\tan x$, we get

$$\frac{dy}{dx} = 3x^3(\sec^2 x^3)$$

(c) The use of logarithms in differentiation can often lead to considerable simplification. Thus, using logarithms we can differentiate, for example,

$$y = x(1 + x^2)^3$$

by rewriting in the form

$$\ln y = \ln x + 3 \ln(1 + x^2)$$

Using the standard form, we get

$$\frac{dy}{dx} = \frac{1}{x} + \frac{6x}{(1 + x^2)}$$

A1.3 Implicit differentiation

In general, an implicit function is of the form $f(xy) = $ constant. For example, $3x^2 + y^2 = 12$ is an implicit function. It can be rewritten in the explicit form, i.e. $y = f(x)$:

$$y = \sqrt{(12 - 3x^2)}$$

Either form of the equation can be used for differentiation; however, the explicit form would present more difficulties than the implicit. For the solution of the implicit equation we use the function of a function rule: i.e. find dy/dx when $3x^2 + y^2 = 12$:

$$\frac{d(3x^2)}{dx} + \frac{d(y^2)}{dx} = \frac{d(12)}{dx}$$

$$6x + 2y\frac{dy}{dx} = 0$$

$$\frac{dy}{dx} = \frac{-6x}{2y} = \frac{-3x}{y}$$

Thus, as a general rule it is better to use the implicit form of the equation and differentiate using the function of a function rule.

Appendix 2 An introduction to the methods of integration

A2.1 The rules of integration

In Appendix 1, outlining the methods of differentiation, we considered the basic rules, along with some simple examples of their application. We shall follow the same procedure for integration.

(a) $\int Ky\,dx = K\int y\,dx$

For example, we are asked to integrate $4x^3$. Thus

$$\int 4x^3\,dx = 4\int x^3\,dx = \frac{4x^{3+1}}{3+1} + C = x^4 + C$$

Another example, we are asked to integrate $\sqrt[5]{x}$. Thus

$$\int \sqrt[5]{x}\,dx = \int x^{1/5}\,dx = \frac{5x^{6/5}}{6} + C$$

(b) $\int F(kx)dx = (1/k)\int f(kx)d(kx) + C$

For example, we are asked to integrate $\cos 3x$. Thus

$$\int \cos 3x\,dx = (1/3)\int \cos 3x\,d(3x) = (1/3)\sin 3x + C$$

(c) $\int (y+k)dx = \int y\,dx + kx + C$

We are asked to integrate $(1+5x)/x$. Thus

$$\int \frac{1+5x}{x}dx = \int (1/x + 5)dx = \ln x + 5x + C$$

Another example:

$$\int \frac{dx}{2x-3} = (1/2)\ln(2x-3) + C$$

(d) $\int (y_1 + y_2 + y_3 \ldots)dx = \int y_1 dx + \int y_2 dx + \int y_3 dx \ldots$

For example, integrate $(4x^3 - 6x^2 + 4)$. Thus

$$\int (4x^3 - 6x^2 + 4)dx = \int 4x^3 dx - \int 2x^2 dx + \int 4\,dx$$

$$= \frac{4x^4}{4} - \frac{6x^3}{3} + 4x + C$$

$$= x^4 - 2x^3 + 4x + C$$

(e) $\int uv\,\mathrm{d}x = u\int v\,\mathrm{d}x - \int z(\mathrm{d}u/\mathrm{d}x)\mathrm{d}x$, where $z = \int v\,\mathrm{d}x$. Thus, the integral $\sin x \cos x$ is

$$\int \sin x \cos x\,\mathrm{d}x = \sin x \int \cos x\,\mathrm{d}x - \int \sin x\,\mathrm{d}\sin x/\mathrm{d}x\,\mathrm{d}x$$

$$= \sin^2 x - \int \sin x \cos x\,\mathrm{d}x$$

$$= \tfrac{1}{2}\sin^2 x$$

A2.2　Standard forms

The most commonly used method of integrating is by using a table of standard integral forms. If the equation in question does not correspond to one of these, then it should be rewritten in a form that does. Some standard integrals are given in Table A2.1.

Table A2.1　Some standard integral forms.

Derivative	Integral
x^n	$\dfrac{x^{n+1}}{n+1} + C$
e^x	$e^x + C$
e^{kx}	$(1/k)e^{kx} + C$
a^x	$\dfrac{a^x}{\ln a} + C$
$1/x$	$\ln x + C$
$\sin x$	$-\cos x + C$
$\cos x$	$\sin x + C$
$\tan x$	$\ln(\sec x) + C$
$\sin kC$	$-(1/k)\cos kx + C$
$\cos kC$	$(1/k)\sin kx + C$
$1 + \tan^2 x$	$\tan x + C$
$\dfrac{1}{\sqrt{(1 - x^2)}}$	$\sin^{-1} x + C$
$\dfrac{1}{1 + x^2}$	$\tan^{-1} x + C$

A2.3　Substitution

We have already noted that, if necessary, equations can be rewritten to correspond with known standard forms, this is **substitution**. In other words, the function is changed and the transformed integral evaluated.

Example: evaluate $\int x \surd(5 + x^2)dx$. Substitute

$$5 + x^2 = z$$

Then

$$\frac{dz}{dx} = 2x$$

so that $dz = 2x\,dx$. By rule (b),

$$I = \tfrac{1}{2}\int x^{1/2}dz$$

$$= \tfrac{1}{3} + Cz^{3/2}$$

Returning to our original equation:

$$\int x\surd(5 + x^2)dx = \tfrac{1}{3}\surd(5 + x^2)3 + C$$

In another example, we are asked to evaluate $\int \surd(1 - x^2)dx$. Substitute

$$x = \sin\theta$$

Then

$$\frac{dx}{d\theta} = \cos\theta$$

so that $dx = \cos\theta\,d\theta$. The integral now becomes

$$\int \surd(1 - \sin^2\theta)\cos\theta\,d\theta$$

Now $\surd(1 - \sin^2\theta) = \cos\theta$ (trigonometric identity), so we can rewrite as $\int\cos\theta\cos\theta\,d\theta$

$$= \int\cos^2\theta\,d\theta$$

$$= \int\tfrac{1}{2}(1 + \cos 2\theta)d\theta$$

By rule (b)

$$y = \tfrac{1}{2}(1 + \cos\theta)d(2\theta)d\theta$$

By rule (d)

$$y = \tfrac{1}{2}\int\theta\,d\theta + \tfrac{1}{2}\int\cos 2\theta\,d\theta$$

$$y = \tfrac{1}{2}\theta + \tfrac{1}{4}\sin 2\theta + C$$

Since

$$\sin 2\theta = 2 \sin \theta \cos \theta$$

Then

$$y = \tfrac{1}{2}\theta + \tfrac{1}{2}(2 \sin \theta \cos \theta) + C$$

Then

$$\int \sqrt{(1 - x^2)} \mathrm{d}x = \tfrac{1}{2}[\sin^{-1}x + x\sqrt{(1 - x^2)}] + C$$

Appendix 3 Computer programs

The programs in this appendix have been developed to enable some of the basic mathematical techniques to be explored further. It is suggested that if a program is to be used, then the data from the appropriate example in the text should be used as test data, to ensure that the program is working correctly. All of the programs are specifically written for the BBC Micro (Model B), and have been extensively tested. Students wishing to use the programs on other systems should check some of the functions used. For example, VDU statements are specific to the version of BASIC in which the programs were written. As far as possible the programs have been kept straightforward, and hopefully, with the REM statements, should be relatively easy to follow. Also, prompts are given by the program for any input required. They are presented here in the same order as they appear in the text.

```
 10 REM PROGRAM TO PLOT A GRAPH
 20 REM Y AXIS VALUES LABEL A X AXIS VALUES LABEL B
 30 REM INPUT N - NUMBER OF PAIRS OF VALUES
 40 REM INPUT IDENT - A SUITABLE TITLE FOR THIS RUN
 50 REM INPUT A AND B  - LIST OF DATA TO BE PLOTTED
 60 REM PRODUCES GRAPH ON LINE PRINTER DATA SCALED AUTOMATICALLY
 70 REM VERTICAL AXIS 50 LINES
 80 REM HORIXONTAL AXIS 70 CHARACTERS
 90 REM RANGE FOR BOTH AXIS THE SAME - SMALLEST 0.01 TO 1.0 LARGEST
2.5 TO 250
100 REM OBSERVATIONS DO NOT HAVE TO BE ORDERED
110 REM DOES NOT PROCESS MULTIPLE DATA SETS
120 DIM A(500),B(500),BL$(3),Z$(70)
130 BL$(1)=" ":BL$(2)="*":BL$(3)="+"
140 REM SET PARAMETERS FOR PRINTING NUMBERS ON SCALE
150 @%=&01020105
160 INPUT"TYPE IN NUMBER OF PAIRS OF DATA POINTS",N
170 INPUT"TYPE IN TITLE FOR THIS RUN",ID$
180 INPUT "TYPE IN LABEL FOR Y AXIS",YAX$
190 INPUT "TYPE IN LABEL FOR X AXIS",XAX$
200 INPUT "TYPE IN UNIT OF MEASUREMENT",UN$
210 FOR I=1 TO N
220 INPUT"Y="A(I);"X="B(I)
230 NEXT I
240 PRINT "ALL DATA POINTS ENTERED"
250 REM MAKES WARNING SOUND WHEN ALL DATA ARE ENTERED
260 FOR pitch=52 TO (52+48) STEP 4
270 SOUND 1,-15,pitch,5
280 NEXT pitch
290 AR=A(1)
300 FOR I=1 TO N
310 IF A(I)>AR THEN AR=A(I)
320 NEXT I
330 SCALE=0
340 SC=40
350 PROCScale
360 SCALA=SCALE
370 FOR I= 1TO N
380 A(I)=A(I)*SCALA+0.5
390 NEXT I
400 AR=B(1)
410 FOR I=1 TO N
420 IF B(I)>AR THEN AR=B(I)
430 NEXT I
440 SCALE=0
```

```
 450 SC=70
 460 PROCScale
 470 SCALB=SCALE
 480 FOR I=1 TO N
 490 B(I)=B(I)*SCALB+0.5
 500 NEXT I
 510 PROCSort
 520 REM SWITCH ON PRINTER
 530 VDU2
 540 PROCGraph
 550 PROCIdent
 560 REM SWITCH OFF PRINTER
 570 VDU3
 580 PRINT"IF YOU REQUIRE ANOTHER GRAPH, TYPE RUN TO RESTART"
 590 END
 600 REM
 610 REM
 620 REM
 630 DEF PROCSort
 640 REM PROCEDURE TO SORT DATA
 650 REM Y VALUES IN DESCENDING ORDER
 660 REM ORDERS X VALUES TO CORRESPOND WITH Y VALUES
 670 REM BECAUSE OF ROUND OFF PROBLEMS WITH HIGH VALUES SORT USES THE
INTEGER VALUE FOR X AND Y
 680 REM SECONDARY SORT PUTS X VALUES INTO ASCENDING ORDER IF
REQUIRED
 690 MIN=N-1
 700 FOR I=1 TO MIN
 710 L=I
 720 IF INT(A(L))<INT(A(L+1)) GOTO 750
 730 IF INT(A(L))>INT(A(L+1)) GOTO 830
 740 IF INT(B(L))<=INT(B(L+1)) GOTO 830   750 DUM=A(L)
 760 A(L)=A(L+1)
 770 A(L+1)=DUM
 780 DUM=B(L)
 790 B(L)=B(L+1)
 800 B(L+1)=DUM
 810 L=L-1
 820 IF L>O GOTO 720
 830 NEXT I
 840 ENDPROC
 850 REM
 860 REM
 870 REM
 880 DEF PROCScale
 890 REM SCALE VALUES FOR BOTH AXIS
 900 REM FIRST CALL VERTICAL (Y) AXIS
 910 REM SECOND CALL HORIZONTAL (X) AXIS
 920 IF AR<0.01 GOTO 1110
 930 IF AR>1 GOTO 960
 940 SCALE=SC/1
 950 GOTO 1130
 960 IF AR>10 GOTO 990
 970 SCALE=SC/10
 980 GOTO 1130
 990 IF AR>25 GOTO 1020
1000 SCALE=SC/25
1010 GOTO 1130
1020 IF AR>50 GOTO 1050
1030 SCALE=SC/50
1040 GOTO 1130
1050 IF AR>100 GOTO 1080
1060 SCALE=SC/100
1070 GOTO 1130
1080 IF AR>250 GOTO 1110
1090 SCALE=SC/250
1100 GOTO 1130
1110 PRINT "DATA VALUES OUT OF RANGE"    1120 GOTO 590
1130 ENDPROC
1140 REM
1150 REM
1160 REM
1170 DEF PROCGraph
```

```
1180 REM START GRAPH PLOTTING LOOP
1190 L=1
1200 FOR I=1 TO 40
1210 II=41-I
1220 IF L>N GOTO 1270
1230 IF (II MOD 4)=0 GOTO 1580
1240 IF II=INT(A(L)) GOTO 1340
1250 PRINT"   I"
1260 GOTO 1880
1270 IF (II MOD 4)=0 GOTO 1300
1280 PRINT"   I"
1290 GOTO 1880
1300 SCALY=II/SCALA
1310 SC$=STR$(SCALY)
1320 PRINT RIGHT$(SC$,5)
1330 GOTO 1880
1340 M=L
1350 IF L=N GOTO 1400
1360 FOR K=L TO N
1370 IF INT(A(K))<>INT(A(K+1)) GOTO 1400
1380 M=M+1
1390 NEXT K
1400 FOR J=1 TO 70
1410 Z$(J)=BL$(1)
1420 FOR K=L TO M
1430 IF J=INT(B(K)) GOTO 1450
1440 GOTO 1490
1450 IF Z$(J)<>BL$(1) GOTO 1480
1460 Z$(J)=BL$(2)
1470 GOTO 1490
1480 Z$(J)=BL$(3)
1490 NEXT K
1500 NEXT J
1510 PR$=""
1520 FOR J=1 TO 70
1530 PR$=PR$+LEFT$(Z$(J),1)
1540 NEXT J
1550 PRINT"   I",PR$
1560 L=M+1
1570 GOTO 1880
1580 SCALY=II/SCALA
1590 IF L>N GOTO 1620
1600 IF II= INT(A(L)) GOTO 1640
1610 SC$=STR$(SCALY)
1620 PRINT RIGHT$(SC$,5)
1630 GOTO 1880
1640 M=L
1650 IF L=N GOTO 1700
1660 FOR K=L TO N
1670 IF INT(A(K))<>INT(A(K+1)) GOTO 1700
1680 M=M+1
1690 NEXT K
1700 FOR J=1 TO 70
1710 Z$(J)=BL$(1)
1720 FOR K=L TO M
1730 IF J=INT(B(K)) GOTO 1750
1740 GOTO 1790
1750 IF Z$(J)<>BL$(1) GOTO 1780
1760 Z$(J)=BL$(2)
1770 GOTO 1790
1780 Z$(J)=BL$(3)
1790 NEXT K
1800 NEXT J
1810 PR$=""
1820 FOR J=1 TO 70
1830 SC$=STR$(SCALY)
1840 PR$=PR$+LEFT$(Z$(J),1)
1850 NEXT J
1860 PRINT RIGHT$(SC$,5),PR$
1870 L=M+1
1880 NEXT I
1890 PR$="    "
1900 FOR J=1 TO 70
```

```
1910 IF(J MOD 7)=0 GOTO 1950
1920 Z$(J)="-"
1930 PR$=PR$+"-"
1940 GOTO 1960
1950 PR$=PR$+"^"
1960 NEXT J
1970 PRINT PR$
1980 PR$="        "
1990 FOR J=7 TO 70 STEP 7
2000 SCALX=J/SCALB
2010 B$=STR$(SCALX)
2020 K=LEN(B$)
2030 L=5-K
2040 IF L=0 GOTO 2080
2050 FOR M=1 TO L
2060 B$=" "+B$
2070 NEXT M
2080 PR$=PR$+B$+"    "
2090 NEXT J
2100 PRINT PR$
2110 ENDPROC
2120 DEF PROCIdent
2130 REM PRINTS TITLE AND SCALE
2140 PRINT''"Graph of - ",ID$
2150 PRINT''"Y axis represents -    ",YAX$,''"Scale factor for Y axis
is",SCALA
2160 PRINT''"X axis represents -    ",XAX$,''"Scale factor for X axis
is",SCALB
2170 PRINT''"Original data follows"
2180 PRINT''"Measurements in  ",UN$
2190 PRINT''
2200 FOR I=1 TO N
2210 A(I)=(A(I)-0.5)/SCALA
2220 B(I)=(B(I)-0.5)/SCALB
2230 PRINT A(I);"      ";B(I)
2240 NEXT I
2250 PRINT''"GRAPH COMPLETE"
2260 ENDPROC
```

Program 2.1 Program to draw a graph of *x* against *y*, using a BBC Micro and an Epson printer. The axes are scaled automatically to fit the printer paper size (22 × 28 cm). Not to be used as VDU output in its present form.

```
  10 REM DEF PROCQUAD
  20 REM REMOVE REM FROM PREVIOUS STATEMENT TO USE THIS AS A
PROCEDURE
  30 REM PROGRAM TO SOLVE A QUADRATIC
  40 REM FORM OF EQUATION Ax^2 + Bx + C = 0
  50 REM VALUES REQUIRED ARE COEFFICIENTS A & B AND THE CONSTANT C
  60 REM MULTIPLE DATA SETS PROCESSED
  70 REM SWITCH OFF PRINTER
  80 VDU3
  90 INPUT"TYPE IN COEFFICIENTS"''"REMÉMBER A = 0 TERMINATES THE
EXECUTION"'"A="A
 100 IF A = 0 GOTO 390
 110 INPUT "B="B
 120 INPUT"TYPE IN CONSTANT"'"C="C
 130 REM CALCULATE DISCRIMINANT AND TEST
 140 REM SET PARAMETERS FOR PRINTING RESULTS
 150 @%=&20206
 160 REM SWITCH ON PRINTER
 170 VDU2
 180 REM PRINT OUT DATA
 190 PRINT''''"Coefficients are:"'"A="A,'"B="B,'"Constant is:"'"C="C
 200 DISC=B^2-4*A*C
 210 REM IF DISCRIMINANT > 0 ROOTS ARE REAL AND DISTINCT
```

```
220 IF DISC>0 GOTO 280
230 REM IF DISCRIMINANT = 0 ROOTS ARE REAL AND EQUAL
240 IF DISC=0 GOTO 320
250 REM IF DISCRIMINANT < 0 ROOTS ARE COMPLEX
260 GOTO 350
270 REM CALCULATE AND PRINT ROOTS ACCORDING TO VALUE OF DISCRIMINANT
280 R1=(-B+SQR(DISC))/(2*A)
290 R2=(-B-SQR(DISC))/(2*A)
300 PRINT'''"Roots are real and distinct"'"X1 =",R1;"   X2 =",R2
310 GOTO 70
320 R=B/(2*A)
330 PRINT'''"Roots are real and equal"'"X =",R
340 GOTO 70
350 PR=-B/(2*A)
360 CN=SQR(-DISC)/(2*A)
370 PRINT'''"Roots are complex"'"X ="PR"(+ or -)"CN"i"
380 GOTO 70
390 END
```

Program 2.2   Program to solve for the roots of a quadratic equation. Requires coefficients of xs and the constant, as input.

```
 10 REM THIS PROGRAM CALLED MEAN
 20 REM CALCULATES 1. ARITHMETIC MEAN
 30 REM            2. GEOMETRIC MEAN
 40 REM            3. HARMONIC MEAN
 50 REM STORES UPTO 500 VALUES
 60 REM CAN CALCULATE ANY OR ALL OF THE ABOVE MEANS
 70 REM DOES NOT PROCESS MULTIPLE DATA SETS
 80 DIM X(500)
 90 Y$="N"
100 CLS
110 PRINT"This program calculates three means"'"They are:
Arithmetic Mean"'"         Geometric Mean"'"         Harmonic Mean"
120 PRINT''"Which will you require?"'"Type ARITHMETIC, GEOMETRIC or
HARMONIC"
130 INPUT TH$
140 IF TH$="ARITHMETIC" GOTO 190
150 IF TH$="GEOMETRIC" GOTO 190
160 IF TH$="HARMONIC" GOTO 190
170 PRINT''"BAD DATA!"
180 GOTO 120
190 IF Y$="Y" GOTO 300
200 INPUT''"How many data points?"'N
210 IF N>500 OR N<2 PRINT''"Too many or too few points!" ELSE GOTO
230
220 GOTO 200
230 PRINT''"Now input your data, one point at a time"
240 FOR I = 1 TO N
250 INPUT X(I)
260 NEXT I
270 SOUND 1,-15,53,20
280 PRINT''"All data is entered"
285 VDU2
290 PRINT''"NUMBER OF POINTS ENTERED ="N
295 VDU3
300 Y$="N"
310 IF TH$="ARITHMETIC" THEN PROCamn ELSE GOTO 360
320 VDU2
330 PRINT''"THE ARITHMETIC MEAN ="AMEAN
340 VDU3
350 GOTO 450
360 IF TH$="GEOMETRIC" THEN PROCgmn ELSE GOTO 410
370 VDU2
380 PRINT''"THE GEOMETRIC MEAN ="GMEAN
390 VDU3
400 GOTO 450
```

```
410 PROChmn
420 VDU2
430 PRINT''"THE HARMONIC MEAN ="HMEAN
440 VDU3
450 PRINT''"Calculate another mean? Y/N"
460 INPUT Y$
470 IF Y$="Y" GOTO 110
480 PRINT''"THIS EXECUTION TERMINATED"
490 STOP
500 DEF PROCamn
510 REM CALCULATE ARITHMETIC MEAN
520 XSUM=0
530 FOR I = 1 TO N
540 XSUM=XSUM + X(I)
550 NEXT I
560 AMEAN = XSUM/N
570 ENDPROC
580 DEF PROCgmn
590 REM CALCULATE GEOMETRIC MEAN
600 XPROD = LOG(X(1))
610 FOR I = 2 TO N
620 XPROD = XPROD+LOG(X(I))
630 NEXT I
640 GMEAN = 10^(XPROD/N)
650 ENDPROC
660 DEF PROChmn
670 REM CALCULATE HARMONIC MEAN
680 RXSUM = 0
690 FOR I = 1 TO N
700 RXSUM = RXSUM+(1/X(I))
710 NEXT I
720 HMEAN = N/RXSUM
730 ENDPROC
```

Program 3.1 Program to calculate the arithmetic, geometric or harmonic means of a set of data. Accepts up to 500 values.

```
  10 REM PROGRAM TO SOLVE A THIRD DEGREE POLYNOMIAL FOR MAXIMA AND
MINIMA
  20 REM INPUT NEEDED ARE THE FOUR NUMERICAL CONSTANTS
  30 REM MULTIPLE DATA SETS PROCESSED
  40 REM INPUT DATA
  50 INPUT"VALUES FOR CONSTANTS"'"SET X^3 VALUE TO ZERO TO TERMINATE
RUN"'"X^3 VALUE",A
  60 IF A=0 GOTO 490
  70 INPUT"X^2 VALUE",B'"X VALUE",C'"CONSTANT",D'"TITLE (IN INVERTED
COMMAS)",XNAM$
  80 REM SET PARAMETERS FOR PRINTING RESULTS
  90 @%=&20206
 100 REM FIND FIRST DIFFERENTIAL
 110 A1=A*3
 120 B1=B*2
 130 C1=C
 140 REM TEST FOR TWO REAL ROOTS
 150 disc=B1^2-4*A1*C1
 160 IF disc<0 GOTO 460
 170 IF disc=0 GOTO 220
 180 S=SQR(disc)
 190 X1=(-B1+S)/(2*A1)
 200 X2=(-B1-S)/(2*A1)
 210 GOTO 240
 220 X1=-B1/(2*A1)
 230 X2=X1
 240 REM FIND SECOND DIFFERENTIAL
 250 A2=A1*2
 260 B2=B1
 270 REM CALCULATE VALUES FOR FUNCTION USING ROOTS OF FIRST
DIFFERENTIAL
```

```
280 X=X1
290 J=1
300 XVAL2=A*X^3+B*X^2+C*X+D
310 J=J+1
320 IF J>2 GOTO 360
330 X=X2
340 XVAL1=XVAL2
350 GOTO 300
360 XA=A2*X1+B2
370 XB=A2*X2+B2
380 REM ENABLE PRINTER
390 VDU2
400 PRINT'""TITLE FOR THIS DATA SET        "XNAM$'""THE ORIGINAL
EQUATION WAS",A"X3",B"X2",C"X",D'""SOLUTION OF SECOND DIFFERENTIAL FOR
X="X1"  IS"XA'"                              AND FOR X="X2"  IS"XB
410 IF XA>0 GOTO 440
420   PRINT''''"        WHEN X="X1"  ,X IS MAXIMISED AT Y="XVAL1'""AND WHEN
X="X2" ,X IS MINIMISED AT Y="XVAL2
430 GOTO 470
440   PRINT''''"        WHEN X="X2"  ,X IS MAXIMISED AT Y="XVAL2'""AND WHEN
X="X1" ,X IS MINIMISED AT Y="XVAL1
450 GOTO 470

460 PRINT'""NO SOLUTION, ROOTS ARE COMPLEX"
470 VDU3
480 GOTO 50
490 END
```

Program 4.1 Program to solve problems of maxima and minima for a third-degree polynomial. Input values required are the coefficients of the equation and the constant.

```
10 REM PROGRAM CALLED SIMRULE
20 REM PROGRAM TO FIND THE AREA UNDER A CURVE
30 REM USES SIMPSONS RULE WITH N STRIPS
40 REM NUMBER OF STRIPS MUST BE EVEN
50 REM READ IN FUNCTION TO BE EVALUATED IN THE FORM OF A BASIC
STATEMENT
55 REM MULTIPLE DATA SETS PROCESSED
60 REM READ IN DATA
70 INPUT"NUMBER OF STRIPS, MUST BE AN EVEN NUMBER"'"ZERO TERMINATES
RUN",N
80 IF N=0 GOTO 380
90 IF (N MOD 2) =1 GOTO 360
100 INPUT'"TYPE IN FUNCTION AS A BASIC STATEMENT"'"REMEMBER, NO
STATEMENT NUMBER"',X$
110 INPUT"LOWER LIMIT",LL'"UPPER LIMIT",UL
120 REM SET CONSTANTS
130 H=(UL-LL)/N
140 FACT=H/3
150 N1=N+1
160 SUM=0:X=LL-H
170 REM CALCULATE AND SUM AREAS OF EACH STRIP
180 FOR I=1 TO N1
190 X=X+H
200 XX=EVAL(X$)
210 IF I=1 OR I=N1 GOTO 250
220 IF(I MOD 2)=1 GOTO 270
230 SUM=SUM+4*XX
240 GOTO 280
250 SUM=SUM+XX
260 GOTO 280
270 SUM=SUM+2*XX
280 NEXT I
290 AREA=SUM*FACT
300 REM ENABLE PRINTER
```

```
310 VDU2
320 PRINT'''"NUMBER OF STRIPS ="N"LOWER LIMIT OF INTEGRATION
="LL"UPPER LIMIT OF INTEGRATION ="UL"''"AREA ="AREA
330 REM DISABLE PRINTER
340 VDU3
350 GOTO 370
360 PRINT"ODD NUMBER OF STRIPS ENTERED, TRY AGAIN!"
370 GOTO 70
380 END
```

Program 5.1 Program to find the area under a curve between given limits, using
Simpson's Rule. The function to be evaluated is entered in the form of a BASIC
statement.

```
10 REM THE NAME OF THIS PROGRAM IS FORAN
20 REM PERFORMS FOURIER ANALYSIS ON SEQUENTIAL DATA
30 REM DATA SAMPLING MUST BE AT FIXED INTERVAL
40 REM ONE VARIABLE OR PROPERTY MEASURED AT EACH POINT
50 REM MAXIMUM NUMBER OF SAMPLE POINT IS 401
60 REM BASED ON EQUATIONS GIVEN BY HARBAUGH AND MERIAM (1968)
p.114ff.
70 REM USES NUMERICAL INTEGRATION METHOD
80 REM BASIC VERSION OF AN UNPUBLISHED FORTRAN PROG. BY FERGUSON
90 DIM ADEG(201),cnt(401),U(401),ACOSC(201),ASINC(201),PSPECT(201)
100 REM
110 REM                    CLEAR SCREEN AND SET NEW PAGE
120 REM              MAIN PROGRAM READS DATA AND CALLS PROCEDURES
130 REM           NUMBER OF DATA POINTS IS KMAX AND MUST BE ODD
140 REM                   VALUE FOR SAMPLE INTERVAL IS TH
150 REM                MEASURED VARIABLE IS U(I), I= 1 TO KMAX
160 REM      CUMULATIVE SAMPLE INTERVAL FOR KMAX POINTS IS cnt(I)
170 VDU2
180 CLS
190 VDU3
200 INPUT "TYPE IN NUMBER OF SAMPLE POINTS"'"MAXIMUM NUNBER OF
POINTS IS 401"'"MUST BE AN ODD NUMBER"'"TYPE O(ZERO) TO END RUN",KMAX
210 IF KMAX=0 GOTO 600
220 INPUT"TYPE IN TITLE",T$
230 VDU2
240 PRINT"TITLE OF THIS DATA SET:"',T$,'''
250 VDU3
260 INPUT "TYPE IN VALUE FOR SAMPLE INTERVAL",TH
270 PRINT"TYPE IN MEASURED VARIABLE"'"FOR EACH SAMPLE POINT"
280 FOR I = 1 TO KMAX
290 INPUT U(I)
300 NEXT I
310 REM CALCULATE THE CUM. INTERVAL VALUE FOR EACH SAMPLE POINT
320 cnt(1)=0
330 FOR K = 2 TO KMAX
340 cnt(K) = cnt(K-1)+TH
350 NEXT K
360 REM SET UP PARAMETERS TO PRINT NUMBERS
370 @%=&0002040A
380 REM CALL PROCEDURE TO CALCULATE BASIC STATISTICS
390 REM THE PROCEDURE IS CALLED stat
400     PROCstat
410 VDU 2
420 PRINT"RESULTS OF STATISTICS OF ORIGINAL
DATA"'"MEAN",AVG'"VARIANCE",VAR'"STANDARD DEVIATION",STDEV'"TOTAL SUMS
OF SQUARES",STOTSS
430 PRINT'''"THE ORIGINAL DATA SET IS AS FOLLOWS:"'"   INTERVAL
VARIABLE"
440 FOR I = 1 TO KMAX
450 PRINT cnt(I),U(I)
460 NEXT I
470 VDU 3
480 REM CALL PROCEDURE TO CALCULATE SIN AND COS TERMS AND POWER
SPECTRUM
```

```
 490 REM THE PROCEDURE IS CALLED forft
 500    PROCforft
 510 VDU 2
 520 PRINT'''
 530 PRINT "RESULTS OF FOURIER ANALYSIS"
 540 PRINT"    HARMONIC   COSINE    SINE      POWER SPEC"
 550 FOR I = 1 TO LK
 560 PRINT ADEG(I),ACOSC(I),ASINC(I),PSPECT(I)
 570 NEXT I
 580 VDU 3
 590 GOTO 160
 600 END
 610 REM
 620 REM PROCEDURE TO CALCULATE FOURIER COEFFICIENTS FROM TIME TREND
DATA
 630 REM
 640   DEF       PROCforft
 650 REM                    CALCULATES COSINE TERM (ACOSC)
 660 REM                    CALCULATES SINE TERM (ASINC)
 670 REM    CALCULATES POWER SPECTRUM FOR EACH PAIR OF TERMS
(PSPECT)
 680 REM       CALCULATES EACH OF THE ABOVE FOR EACH HARMONIC (ADEG)
 690 REM                THERE ARE (ABS(KMAX/2))+1 HARMONICS
 700 L%=KMAX/2+1
 710 LK=L%
 720 ADEG(1)=0
 730 FOR L= 2 TO LK
 740 II=L-1
 750 ADEG(L)=ADEG(II)+1
 760 NEXT L
 770 AMAX1=cnt(KMAX)
 780 SMCON=0
 790 FOR L= 1 TO LK
 800 SMCON=(U(1)+U(KMAX))/2
 810 KMAXJ=KMAX-1
 820 FOR K=2 TO KMAXJ
 830 SMCON=SMCON+(U(K)*COS((ADEG(L)
*PI*cnt(K))/(AMAX1/2.0)))
 840 NEXT K
 850 ACOSC(L)=(2.0/(KMAX-1))*SMCON
 860 NEXT L
 870 ACOSC(1) = ACOSC(1)/2.0
 880 FOR L = 2 TO LK
 890 SMCON =0.
 900 FOR K=2 TO KMAXJ
 910 SMCON=SMCON+(U(K)*SIN((ADEG(L)
*PI*cnt(K))/(AMAX1/2.0)))
 920 NEXT K
 930 ASINC(L)=(2.0/(KMAX-1))*SMCON
 940 NEXT L
 950 ASINC(1)=0.0
 960 PSPECT(1)=0.0
 970 FOR L = 2 TO LK
 980 PSPECT(L)=SQR(ACOSC(L)^2
+ASINC(L)^2)
 990 NEXT L
1000 ENDPROC
1010 REM
1020 REM PROCEDURE TO CALCULATE STATISTICS FOR DATA
1030 REM
1040 DEF        PROCstat
1050 REM                CALCULATES MEAN (AVG)
1060 REM                CALCULATES VARIANCE (VAR)
1070 REM            CALCULATES STANDARD DEVIATION (STDEV)
1080 REM      CALCULATES THE TOTAL SUM OF SQUARES (STOTSS)
1090 SUM=0
1100 SUMSQ=0
1110 SUMSQD=0
1120 FOR K = 1 TO KMAX
1130 SUM = SUM + U(K)
1140 SUMSQ=SUMSQ+U(K)^2
1150 NEXT K
1160 AVG=SUM/KMAX
```

```
1170 A=SUM^2
1180 B=A/KMAX
1190 STOTSS=SUMSQ-B
1200 VAR=STOTSS/(KMAX-1)
1210 STDEV=SQR(VAR)
1220 ENDPROC
```

Program 5.2 Program to perform Fourier analysis on sequential data. Maximum number points 401 (must be odd) and sampled at set interval.

```
   10 REM PROGRAM TO MULTIPLY A MATRIX BY
   20 REM            (1) A SCALAR
   30 REM            (2) A VECTOR
   40 REM VECTOR MUST HAVE SAME NUM. ROWS (NR2%) AS THE MATRIX HAS
COLUMNS (NC1%)
   50 REM NR2%=NC1%=NRC%
   60 REM            (3) A MATRIX
   70 REM FIRST MATRIX HAS SAME NUMBER OF COLUMNS (NC1%)
   80 REM AS SECOND HAS ROWS (NR2%)
   90 REM NC1%=NR2%=NRC%
  100 REM OTHER PARAMETERS - NO. OF ROWS OF FIRST MATRIX NR1%
  110 REM                    NO. OF COLUMNS OF SECOND MATRIX NC2%
  115 REM MULTIPLE DATA SETS PROCESSED
  120 DIM AMAT(10,10),BMAT(10,10),
CMAT(10,10),AVECT(10),CVECT(10)
  130 REM READ IN OPTION AS ABOVE
  140 INPUT"TYPE IN NUMBER TO INDICATE CHOSEN OPTION"'"1 = MULT. BY A
SCALAR"'"2 = MULT. BY A VECTOR"'"3 = MULT. BY A MATRIX"'"A VALUE
GREATER THAN 3 TERMINATES THE EXECUTION",IOPT
  150 IF IOPT>3 GOTO 630
  160 IF IOPT=3 GOTO 440
  170 IF IOPT=2 GOTO 270
  180 REM READ IN DATA
  190 INPUT"VALUE OF SCALAR",SCALAR
  200 INPUT"NO. OF ROWS OF MATRIX",NR1%'"NO. OF COLUMNS OF
MATRIX",NC1%
  210 PRINT"TYPE IN THE MATRIX ROW-WISE ONE ELEMENT AT A TIME"
  220 FOR I%=1 TO NR1%: FOR J%=1 TO NC1%
  230 INPUT AMAT(I%,J%)
  240 NEXT J%: NEXT I%
  250 PROCMscalar
  260 GOTO 610
  270 INPUT" NO. OF ROWS OF VECTOR",NR2%'"NO. OF ROWS OF
MATRIX",NR1%'"NO. OF COLUMNS OF MATRIX"NC1%
  280 IF NC1%<>NR2% GOTO 400
  290 NRC%=NC1%
  300 PRINT"TYPE IN THE MATRIX ROW-WISE ONE ELEMENT AT A TIME"
  310 FOR I%=1 TO NR1%: FOR J%=1 TO NRC%
  320 INPUT AMAT(I%,J%)
  330 NEXT J%: NEXT I%
  340 PRINT"TYPE IN THE VECTOR ONE ELEMENT AT A TIME"
  350 FOR I%=1 TO NRC%
  360 INPUT AVECT(I%)
  370 NEXT I%
  380 PROCMvector
  390 GOTO 610
  400 PRINT"BAD DATA"'"NO. OF COLUMNS OF MATRIX NOT EQUAL TO NO. OF
ROWS OF VECTOR"
  410 SOUND 1,-10,97,10: SOUND 1,-10,105,10
  420 SOUND 1,-10,89,10: SOUND 1,-10,41,10: SOUND 1,-10,69,20
  430 GOTO 140
  440 INPUT"NO. OF ROWS OF 1ST. MATRIX",NR1%,'"NO. OF COLUMNS OF 1ST.
MATRIX",NC1%'"NO. OF ROWS OF 2ND. MATRIX",NR2%'"NO. OF COLUMNS OF 2ND
MATRIX",NC2%
  450 IF NC1%<>NR2% GOTO 570
  460 NRC%=NC1%
  470 PRINT"TYPE IN THE 1ST. MATRIX ROW-WISE ONE ELEMENT AT A TIME"
```

```
 480 FOR I%=1 TO NR1%: FOR J%=1 TO NRC%
 490 INPUT AMAT(I%,J%)
 500 NEXT J%: NEXT I%
 510 PRINT"TYPE IN THE 2ND. MATRIX ROW-WISE ONE ELEMENT AT A TIME"
 520 FOR I%=1 TO NRC%: FOR J%=1 TO NC2%
 530 INPUT BMAT(I%,J%)
 540 NEXT J%: NEXT I%
 550 PROCMmatrix
 560 GOTO 610
 570 PRINT"BAD DATA"'"NO. OF COLUMNS IN 1ST. MATRIX NOT EQUAL TO NO.
OF ROWS IN 2ND."
 580 SOUND 1,-10,97,10: SOUND 1,-10,105,10
 590 SOUND 1,-10,89,10: SOUND 1,-10,41,10: SOUND 1,-10,69,20
 600 GOTO 140
 610 PROCPrdata
 620 GOTO 140
 630 END
 640 REM
 650 REM
 660 REM
 670 DEF PROCMscalar
 680 REM MULTIPLY A MATRIX BY A SCALAR
 690 FOR I%=1 TO NR1%
 700 FOR J%=1 TO NC1%
 710 CMAT(I%,J%)=AMAT(I%,J%)*SCALAR
 720 NEXT J%: NEXT I%
 730 ENDPROC
 740 REM
 750 REM
 760 REM
 770 DEF PROCMvector
 780 REM MULTIPLY A MATRIX BY A VECTOR
 790 FOR I%=1 TO NR1%
 800 CVECT(I%)=0.0
 810 FOR J%=1 TO NRC%
 820 CVECT(I%)=CVECT(I%)+AMAT(I%,J%)
*AVECT(J%)
 830 NEXT J%: NEXT I%
 840 ENDPROC
 850 REM
 860 REM
 870 REM
 880 DEF PROCMmatrix
 890 REM MULTIPLY A MATRIX BY A MATRIX
 900 FOR I%=1 TO NR1%
 910 FOR J%=1 TO NC2%
 920 CMAT(I%,J%)=0.0
 930 FOR K%=1 TO NRC%
 940 CMAT(I%,J%)=CMAT(I%,J%)+
AMAT(I%,K%)*BMAT(K%,J%)
 950 NEXT K%: NEXT J%: NEXT I%
 960 ENDPROC
 970 REM
 980 REM
 990 REM
1000 DEF PROCPrdata
1010 REM TO PRINT RESULTS OUT
1020 REM SET PRINT PARAMETERS AND SWITCH ON PRINTER
1030 @%=&20206
1040 VDU2
1050 IF IOPT=3 GOTO 1290
1060 IF IOPT=2 GOTO 1160
1070 PRINT''"Multiplication by a scalar"'"Scalar =",SCALAR
''"Original data"
1080 FOR I%=1 TO NR1%: PRINT': FOR J%=1 TO NC1%
1090 PRINT AMAT(I%,J%);
1100 NEXT J%: NEXT I%
1110 PRINT''"Resulting matrix"
1120 FOR I%=1 TO NR1%: PRINT': FOR J%=1 TO NC1%
1130 PRINT CMAT(I%,J%);
1140 NEXT J%: NEXT I%
1150 GOTO 1440
1160 PRINT ''"Multiplication by a vector"'"Original vector"''
```

```
1170 FOR I%=1 TO NRC%
1180 PRINT AVECT(I%)
1190 NEXT I%
1200 PRINT''"Original matrix"
1210 FOR I%=1 TO NR1%: PRINT': FOR J%=1 TO NC1%
1220 PRINT AMAT(I%,J%);
1230 NEXT J%: NEXT I%
1240 PRINT''"Resulting vector"''
1250 FOR I%=1 TO NR1%
1260 PRINT CVECT(I%)
1270 NEXT I%
1280 GOTO 1440
1290 PRINT''"Multiply by a matrix"''Original matrices"''
1300 PRINT "Matrix 1"
1310 FOR I%=1 TO NR1%: PRINT': FOR J%=1 TO NC1%
1320 PRINT AMAT(I%,J%);
1330 NEXT J%: NEXT I%
1340 PRINT'' "Matrix 2"''
1350 FOR I%=1 TO NR2%: PRINT': FOR J%=1 TO NC2%
1360 PRINT BMAT(I%,J%);
1370 NEXT J%: NEXT I%
1380 PRINT''"Resulting matrix"
1390 FOR I%=1 TO NR1%: PRINT': FOR J%=1 TO NC2%
1400 PRINT CMAT(I%,J%);
1410 NEXT J%: NEXT I%
1420 PRINT''
1430 REM SWITCH OFF PRINTER
1440 VDU3
1450 ENDPROC
```

Program 6.1 Program to perform multiplication operations on any matrix up to size 10 × 10. Will multiply by a scalar, a vector or another matrix.

```
   10 REM PROGRAM EIGVAL
   20 REM   THIS VERSION IN BASIC, AFTER DAVIS (1973) PROG 4.10,
P166-67
   30 REM USES JACOBI METHOD
   40 REM TO CALCULATE THE EIGENVALUES AND EIGENVECTORS OF A
SYMETRICAL MATRIX
   50 REM RESULTING EIGENVECTORS IN MATRIX A (IN DIAG)
   60 REM EIGENVALUES IN MATRIX B (COLUMN-WISE)
   65 REM MULTIPLE DATA SETS PROCESSED
   70 DIM A(10,10),B(10,10)
   80 REM SET PARAMETERS FOR PRINTING RESULTS
   90 @%=&20206
  100 REM INPUT DATA
  110 REM INPUT ORDER OF MATRIX - O%
  120 INPUT"TYPE IN ORDER OF MATRIX"''"TYPE IN 0 TO TERMINATE
EXECUTION",O%
  130 IF O%=0 GOTO 1120
  140 REM INPUT MATRIX
  150 PRINT "INPUT MATRIX, ONE ELEMENT AT A TIME - ROW WISE"
  160 FOR I%=1 TO O%
  170 FOR J%=1 TO O%
  180 INPUT A(I%,J%)
  190 NEXT J%: NEXT I%
  200 REM B IS SET AS IDENTITY MATRIX
  210 REM SET UP CONSTANTS AND COMPUTE THRESHOLD
  220 N=O%
  230 INORM=0
  240 FOR I%=1 TO O%
  250 FOR J%=1 TO O%
  260 IF (I%-J%)<>0 GOTO 290
  270 B(I%,J%)=1.0
  280 GOTO 310
  290 B(I%,J%)=0.0
```

```
300 INORM=INORM+A(I%,J%)*A(I%,J%)
310 NEXT J%: NEXT I%
320 INORM=SQR(INORM)
330  FLORM=INORM*1.0E-08/N
340 THR=INORM
350 THR=THR/N
360 IND%=0
370 REM FIND OFF-DIAGONAL ELEMENTS WITH VALUES GREATER THAN
THRESHOLD
380 FOR I%=2 TO O%
390 II%=I%-1
400 FOR J%=1 TO II%
410 IF ((ABS(A(J%,I%)))-THR) < 0 GOTO 760
420 REM COMPUTE SIN AND COS
430 IND%=1
440 AL=-A(J%,I%)
450 AM=(A(J%,J%)-A(I%,I%))/2.0
460 AO=AL/SQR(AL*AL+AM*AM)
470 IF AM<0 GOTO 490
480 GOTO 500
490 AO=-AO
500 SX=AO/SQR(2.0*(1.0
+SQR(1.0-AO*AO)))
510 SX2=SX*SX
520 CX=SQR(1.0-SX2)
530 CX2=CX*CX
540 REM ROTATE COLUMNS
550 FOR K%=1 TO O%
560 IF (K%-J%)=0 GOTO 610
570 IF (K%-I%)=0 GOTO 610
580 AT=A(K%,J%)
590 A(K%,J%)=AT*CX-A(K%,I%)*SX
600 A(K%,I%)=AT*SX+A(K%,I%)*CX
610 BT=B(K%,J%)
620 B(K%,J%)=BT*CX-B(K%,I%)*SX
630 B(K%,I%)=BT*SX+B(K%,I%)*CX
640 NEXT K%
650 XT=2.0*A(J%,I%)*SX*CX
660 AT=A(J%,J%)
670 BT=A(I%,I%)
680 A(J%,J%)=AT*CX2+BT*SX2-XT
690 A(I%,I%)=AT*SX2+BT*CX2+XT
700 A(J%,I%)=(AT-BT)*SX*CX+A(J%,I%)
*(CX2-SX2)
710 A(I%,J%)=A(J%,I%)
720 FOR K%=1 TO O%
730 A(J%,K%)=A(K%,J%)
740 A(I%,K%)=A(K%,I%)
750 NEXT K%
760 NEXT J%
770 NEXT I%
780 IF IND%>0 GOTO 360
790 IF (THR-FLORM)>0 GOTO 350
800 REM SORT EIGENVALUES AND EIGENVECTORS
810 FOR I%=2 TO O%
820 J%=I%
830 IF(A(J%-1,J%-1)-A(J%,J%))<0 GOTO 850
840 GOTO 950
850 AT=A(J%-1,J%-1)
860 A(J%-1,J%-1)=A(J%,J%)
870 A(J%,J%)=AT
880 FOR K%=1 TO O%
890 AT=B(K%,J%-1)
900 B(K%,J%-1)=B(K%,J%)
910 B(K%,J%)=AT
920 NEXT K%
930 J%=J%-1
940 IF (J%-1)>0 GOTO 830
950 NEXT I%
960 REM PRINT OUT EIGENVALUES AND EIGENVECTORS
970 REM SWITCH ON PRINTER
980 VDU2
990 FOR I%=1 TO O%
```

```
1000 FOR J%=1 TO O%
1010 IF J%<>I% GOTO 1030
1020 PRINT"Eigenvalue "I%"         ="A(I%,J%)
1030 NEXT J%
1040 FOR K%=1 TO O%
1050 PRINT"Eigenvector"I%","K%"
="B(K%,I%)
1060 NEXT K%
1070 PRINT'
1080 NEXT I%
1090 REM SWITCH OFF PRINTER AND RETURN TO START
1100 VDU3
1110 GOTO 120
1120 END
```

Program 6.2   Program to find the eigenvalues and eigenvectors of a real symmetrical matrix up to size 10×10. Based on the Jacobi method.

```
10 REM DEF PROCMpow
20 REM TAKE REM OUT OF PREVIOUS STATEMENT TO USE AS A PROCEDURE
30 REM PROGRAM TO POWER A MATRIX
40 REM PRINCIPLE USE WITH TRANSITION PROBABILITY MATRICES
50 REM BASED ON HARBAUGH AND BONAHM CARTER (1970) P.119
55 REM MULTIPLE DATA SETS PROCESSED
60 DIM TM(25,25),PM(25,25), pmat(25,25)
70 REM SET PARAMETERS TO PRINT RESULTS
80 @%=&01020205
90 REM INPUT DATA
100 INPUT "TYPE NUMBER OF LITHOLOGIES, TYPE 1 TO TERMINATE
EXECUTION",M
110 IF M=1 GOTO 440
120 INPUT"TYPE NUMBER OF STEPS",N%
130 FOR I=1 TO M:FOR J=1 TO M
140 INPUT"TYPE RAW DATA, ROW WISE",TM(I,J)
150 NEXT J: NEXT I
160 REM SWITCH ON PRINTER
170 VDU2
180 FOR I=1 TO M:FOR J=1 TO M
190 PM(I,J)=TM(I,J)
200 NEXT J:NEXT I
220 PRINT''"INPUT MATRIX"
230 FOR I=1 TO M:PRINT':FOR J=1 TO M
240 PRINT TM(I,J);
250 NEXT J:NEXT I
260 FOR L=1 TO N%
270 L1%=L+1
280 PRINT''''"INPUT MATRIX TO THE POWER",L1%
290 FOR I=1 TO M: FOR J=1TO M
300 pmat(I,J)=0
310 FOR K=1 TO M
320 pmat(I,J)=pmat(I,J)+TM(I,K)
*PM(K,J)
330 NEXT K: NEXT J: NEXT I
340 FOR I=1 TO M: FOR J=1 TO M
350 PM(I,J)=pmat(I,J)
360 NEXT J
370 PRINT'
380 FOR J=1 TO M
390 PRINT PM(I,J);
400 NEXT J: NEXT I: NEXT L
410 REM SWITCH OFF PRINTER AND CLEAR SCREEN
420 VDU3:CLS
430 GOTO 100
440 END
```

Program 6.3   Program to raise a matrix to any given power. Handles matrices up to 25×25 in its present form.

```
  10 REM PROGRAM TO MULTIPLY A MATRIX BY ITS TRANSPOSE
  20 REM THIS PROGRAM CALLED MULTR
  30 REM ALSO CALCULATES THE DISPERSION OR CORRELATION MATRICES
  35 REM MULTIPLE DATA SETS PROCESSED
  40 DIM X(50,10),XMT(10,10),XMEAN(10),XDEV(10)
  50 REM SET PARAMETERS FOR PRINTING OUT RESULTS
  60 @%=&0102020A
  70 REM INPUT MATRIX SIZE, TITLE AND DATA
  80 INPUT"TYPE NUMBER OF ROWS = NUMBER OF VARIABLES"'"VALUE GREATER
THAN 50 TERMINATES EXECUTION",N%
  90 IF N%>50 GOTO 610
 100 INPUT"TYPE NUMBER OF COLUMNS = NUMBER OF SAMPLES",C%
 110 INPUT"TYPE TITLE"T$
 120 PRINT"INPUT MATRIX ROW WISE"
 130 NS=C%
 140 FOR I%=1 TO N%
 150 FOR J%=1 TO C%
 160 INPUT"ELEMENT VALUE",X(I%,J%)
 170 NEXT J%
 180 NEXT I%
 190 REM CHOOSE TYPE OF CALCULATION
 200 REM 1 = USE RAW DATA ONLY
 210 REM 2 = CALC. EITHER DISPERSION OR CORRELATION MATRICES
 220 INPUT"DO YOU WISH TO USE RAW DATA ONLY?"'"IF YES TYPE 1, IF NO
TYPE 2",M
 230 IF M=1 GOTO 270
 240 PROCTRSF
 250 GOTO 360
 260 REM SWITCH ON PRINTER AND PRINT OUT INPUT DATA
 270 VDU2
 280 PRINT''"TITLE:",T$
 290 PRINT''"INPUT MATRIX"''
 300 FOR I%=1 TO N%
 310 PRINT'
 320 FOR J%=1 TO C%
 330 PRINTX(I%,J%);
 340 NEXT J%
 350 NEXT I%
 360 REM MULTIPLY MATRIX BY ITS TRANSPOSE
 370 FOR I%=1 TO N%
 380 FOR J%=1 TO N%
 390 XMT(I%,J%)=0
 400 NEXT J%
 410 NEXT I%
 420 FOR I%=1 TO N%
 430 FOR J%=1 TO N%
 440 FOR K%=1 TO C%
 450 XMT(I%,J%)=XMT(I%,J%)
+X(I%,K%)*X(J%,K%)
 460 NEXT K%
 470 NEXT J%
 480 NEXT I%
 490 PRINT''"RESULTANT MATRIX"''
 500 FOR I%=1 TO N%
 510 PRINT'
 520 FOR J%=1 TO N%
 530 PRINT XMT(I%,J%);
 540 NEXT J%
 550 NEXT I%
 560 PRINT''"This data set finnished"
 570 REM SWITCH OFF PRINTER AND CLEAR SCREEN
 580 VDU3:CLS
 590 PRINT"RETURNING TO BEGINING OF PROGRAM"'"FOLLOW INSTRUCTIONS TO
TERMINATE THE EXECUTION"
 600 GOTO 80
 610 END
 620 REM
 630 REM
 640 REM
 650 DEF PROCTRSF
 660 REM PROCEDURE TO NORMALIZE RAW DATA MATRIX USING MEAN OR MEAN
AND STANDARD DEVIATION
 670 REM SWITCH ON PRINTER AND PRINT OUT ORIGINAL DATA
```

```
680 VDU2
690 PRINT''"TITLE:",T$
700 PRINT''"INPUT MATRIX"''
710 FOR I%=1 TO N%
720 PRINT'
730 FOR J%=1 TO C%
740 PRINTX(I%,J%);
750 NEXT J%:NEXT I%
760 VDU3
770 REM CALC MEAN FOR EACH VARIABLE
780 FOR I%=1 TO N%
790 XSUM=0.0
800 FOR J%=1 TO C%
810 XSUM=XSUM+X(I%,J%)
820 NEXT J%
830 XMEAN(I%)=XSUM/NS
840 NEXT I%
850 REM SUBTRACT MEAN FROM EACH DATA VALUE
860 REM DESTROYS ORIGINAL DATA MATRIX
870 FOR I%=1 TO N%
880 FOR J%=1 TO C%
890 X(I%,J%)=X(I%,J%)-XMEAN(I%)
900 NEXT J%:NEXT I%
910 REM CLEAR SCREEN AND SWITCH OFF PRINTER
920 CLS:VDU3
925 PRINT"PROGRAM WILL NOW CALCULATE EITHER"'"THE DISPERSION MATRIX
OR"''"THE CORRELATION MATRIX, YOUR CHOICE"
930 INPUT"DO YOU WISH TO CALCULATE THE DISPERSION MATRIX?"''"IF YES
TYPE 2, IF NO (IMPLIES CORR. MATRIX), TYPE 1",R
940 IF R=1 GOTO 1050
950 REM SWITCH ON PRINTER
960 VDU2
970 PRINT''"DISPERSION MATRIX HAS BEEN CHOSEN"'" MATRIX WHICH
FOLLOWS HAS BEEN NORMALIZED, WITH A MEAN OF ZERO FOR EACH VARIABLE"
980 FOR I%=1 TO N%
990 PRINT '
1000 FOR J%=1 TO C%
1010 PRINT X(I%,J%);
1020 NEXT J%
1030 NEXT I%
1040 GOTO 1260
1050 REM CALCULATE STANDARD DEVIATION
1060 FOR I%=1 TO N%
1070 XSUM=0.0
1080 FOR J%=1 TO C%
1090 XSUM=XSUM+X(I%,J%)*X(I%,J%)
1100 NEXT J%
1110 XDEV(I%)=SQR(XSUM/NS)
1120 NEXT I%
1130 REM DIVIDE EACH VALUE BY THE CORRESPONDING STD. DEV.
1140 FOR I%=1 TO N%
1150 FOR J%=1 TO C%
1160 X(I%,J%)=X(I%,J%)/XDEV(I%)
1170 NEXT J%: NEXTI%
1180 REM SWITCH ON PRINTER
1190 VDU2
1200 PRINT''"CORRELATION MATRIX HAS BEEN CHOSEN"'" MATRIX WHICH
FOLLOWS HAS BEEN NORMALIZED, WITH A MEAN OF ZERO"''"AND STANDARD
DEVIATION OF UNITY FOR EACH VARIABLE"''
1210 FOR I%=1 TO N%
1220 PRINT'
1230 FOR J%=1 TO C%
1240 PRINTX(I%,J%);
1250 NEXT J%: NEXT I%
1260 ENDPROC
```

Program 6.4 Program to calculate either the dispersion matrix or a correlation matrix. Based on the transposition method outlined in the text. Maximum number of samples = 50, maximum number of variables = 10.

```
   5 REM PROGRAM TO SOLVE SIMULTANEOUS LINEAR EQUATIONS USING
GAUSSIAN ELIMINATION, MULTIPLE DATA SETS PROCESSED
  10 DIM A(10,11),C(11),X(11)
  15 REM READ IN DATA MAXIMUM NO. OF EQUATIONS IS 10, TO TERMINATE
RUN ENTER VALUE  > 10
  20 INPUT"NUMBER OF EQUATIONS"''"MAXIMUM ALLOWED IS 10"''"A NUMBER
GREATER THAN 10 TERMINATES THE EXECUTION",N%
  30 IF N%>10 THEN END
  40 M%=N%+1
  50 PRINT"INPUT COEFFICIENTS"''"ONE AT A TIME, ROWISE"
  60 FOR I%=1 TO N%:FOR J%=1 TO M%
  70 INPUT A(I%,J%)
  80 NEXT J%: NEXT I%
  90 VDU2
 100 PRINT''''"DATA ENTERED IS"'''
 110 FOR I%=1 TO N%:FOR J%=1 TO M%
 120 PRINT A(I%,J%);
 130 NEXT J%:NEXT I%
 140 VDU3
 145 REM FIND LARGEST PIVOT AND RE-ORDER EQUATIONS
 150 FOR R%=1 TO N%-1
 160 Q%=R%
 170 P%=Q%
 180 IF Q% = N% GOTO 220
 190 Q%=Q%+1
 200 IF A(P%,R%)<A(Q%,R%) GOTO 170
 210 GOTO 180
 220 FOR J%=R% TO M%
 230 C(J%)=A(R%,J%):A(R%,J%)=A(P%,J%)
:A(P%,J%)=C(J%)
 240 NEXT J%
 245 REM CALCULATE UNKNOWNS USING GAUSSIAN ELIMINATION
 250 FOR I%=R%+1 TO N%
 260 FOR J%=R%+1 TO M%
 270 A(I%,J%)=A(I%,J%)-(A(I%,R%)
*A(R%,J%))/A(R%,R%)
 280 NEXT J%: NEXT I%
 290 NEXT R%
 300 X(N%)=A(N%,M%)/A(N%,N%)
 310 FOR R%=N%-1 TO 1 STEP -1
 320 D=0
 330 FOR J%=R%+1 TO N%
 340 D=D+A(R%,J%)*X(J%)
 350 NEXT J%
 360 X(R%)=(A(R%,M%)-D)/A(R%,R%)
 370 NEXT R%
 375 REM FIND DETERMINANT AS THE PRODUCT OF THE PIVOTS
 380 D=A(1,1)
 390 FOR I% = 2 TO N%
 400 D=D*A(I%,I%)
 410 NEXT I%
 415 REM OUTPUT RESULTS
 420 VDU2
 430 PRINT''''"SOLUTION IS"''"UNKNOWNS"
 440 FOR J%=1 TO N%
 450 PRINT X(J%): NEXT J%
 460 PRINT''''"THE PIVOTS ARE"
 470 FOR I%=1 TO N%
 480 PRINT A(I%,I%):NEXT I%
 490 PRINT''''"DETERMINANT IS"
 500 PRINT D
 510 VDU3
 515 REM RETURNS TO START TO PICK UP NEXT DATA SET
 520 GOTO 20
 530 END
```

Program 7.1 Program to solve simultaneous linear equations using Gaussian elimination. The largest pivots are chosen at each stage. The maximum number of equations is 10.

```
   10 REM PROGARAM TO SOLVE SIMULTANEOUS LINEAR EQUATIONS USING THE
GAUSS-SEIDEL METHOD
   15 REM USES METHOD OF SUCCESSIVE CORRECTIONS
   20 REM MULTIPLE DATA SETS PROCESSED
   25 REM TOLERANCE (TLR) SET AT 0.0001, MAXIMUM ITERATIONS (KK%)
1000
   30 REM BASED ON ORIGINAL FORTRAN PROGRAM BY FERGUSON
   35 REM INITIAL ESTIMATES OF X SET TO ZERO
   40 DIM X(10),COEF(10,10),D(10)
   50 REM READ IN DATA
   60 VDU3
   70 INPUT "TYPE NUMBER OF UNKNOWNS"'"MAXIMUM 10"'"A LARGER VALUE
TERMINATES THE RUN",N%
   80 IF N% > 10 THEN END
   90 CLS
  100 INPUT"TYPE TITLE FOR THIS RUN",TITLE$
  110 PRINT "INPUT COEFFICIENTS"'"1 AT A TIME, ROWISE"
  120 FOR I% = 1 TO N%: FOR J% = 1 TO N%
  130 INPUT COEF(I%,J%)
  140 NEXT J%
  150 INPUT"REM. THIS IS VALUE FOR"'"R.H.S.OF EQUATION",D(I%)
  160 NEXT I%
  170 CLS
  171 VDU2
  172 PRINT'''"DATA ENTERED IS"'''
  173 FOR I% = 1 TO N%: FOR J% = 1 TO N%
  174 PRINT COEF(I%,J%);
  175 NEXT J%
  176 PRINT D(I%)'
  177 NEXT I%
  178 VDU3
  180 REM SET CONSTANTS AND DUMMY LISTS TO ZERO
  190 TLR = 0.0001
  200 KK% = 0
  210 FOR I% = 1 TO N%
  220 X(I%)=0
  230 NEXT I%
  240 REM CALCULATE VALUES OF X(I%)
  250 FOR I%  = 1 TO N%
  260 DUM = 0.0
  270 DUM=DUM+D(I%)
  280 FOR J% = 1 TO N%
  290 IF I% = J% GOTO 310
  300 DUM = DUM-(COEF(I%,J%)*X(J%))
  310 NEXT J%
  320 X(I%)=(1.0/COEF(I%,I%))*DUM
  330 NEXT I%
  340 REM TEST IF ENOUGH ITERATIONS USING TOLERANCE
  350 DD=0.0
  360 FOR J% = 1 TO N%
  370 DD = DD+(X(J%)*COEF(1,J%))
  380 NEXT J%
  390 IF ABS (D(1)-DD) < TLR GOTO 430
  400 KK%=KK%+1
  410 IF KK% = 1000 GOTO 490
  420 GOTO 250
  430 VDU2
  440 PRINT"TITLE IS  ",TITLE$,'"SOLUTION OF EQUATIONS"'"NUMBER OF
ITERATIONS",KK%
  450 FOR I%=1 TO N%
  460 PRINT X(I%)
  470 NEXT I%
  480 GOTO 60
  490 VDU2
  500 PRINT"NO SOLUTION AFTER 1000 ITERATIONS"
  510 PRINT'''"TITLE IS   ",TITLE$,'"ESTIMATE OF X(1) - X(N)"'"AFTER
1000 ITERATIONS"'''
  520 FOR I%=1 TO N%
  530 PRINT X(I%)
  540 NEXT I%
  550 VDU3
  560 GOTO 60
  570 END
```

Program 7.2 Program to solve simultaneous linear equations by the Gauss–Seidel method, using successive corrections. The maximum number of equations is 10.

```
    10 REM PROGRAM TO SOLVE SIMULTANEOUS LINEAR EQUATIONS BY MATRIX
INVERSION
    20 REM MATRIX INVERSION BASED ON DAVIS (1973) P.142
    30 REM COEF IS THE MATRIX OF COEFFICIENTS, ICOEF IS THE INVERSE
    40 REM Z IS THE VECTOR OF VALUES FOR THE RHS OF THE EQUATION, DET
IS THE DETERMINANT
    50 REM THE COEFFECENT MATRIX IS REDUCED TO AN IDENTITY MATRIX
    60 REM THE MAXIMUM MATRIX SIZE IS 10*10
    70 REM X IS THE VECTOR OF UNKNOWNS
    75 REM MULTIPLE DATA SETS PROCESSED
    80 DIM COEF(10,10),ICOEF(10,10),
Z(10),X(10)
    90 REM READ IN AND PRINT OUT DATA
   100 CLS
   110 VDU3
   120 INPUT"TYPE IN NUMBER OF UNKNOWNS"'"A VALUE > 10 TERMINATES THE
RUN",N%
   130 IF N%>10 GOTO 670
   140 PRINT"TYPE IN COEFFICIENTS"'"ONE AT A TIME, ROWISE"
   150 FOR I%=1 TO N%: FOR J%=1 TO N%
   160 INPUT COEF(I%,J%)
   170 NEXT J%
   180 INPUT"VALUE FOR RHS OF EQUATION",Z(I%)
   190 NEXT I%
   200 VDU2
   210 PRINT''"DATA IS"''
   220 FOR I%=1 TO N%: FOR J%=1 TO N%
   230 PRINT COEF(I%,J%);
   240 NEXT J%
   250 PRINT Z(I%)
   260 NEXT I%
   270 REM SET ICOEF TO IDENTITY MATRIX
   280 FOR I%=1 TO N%: FOR J%=1 TO N%
   290 ICOEF(I%,J%)=0
   300 NEXT J%
   310 X(I%)=0
   320 ICOEF(I%,I%)=1.0
   330 NEXT I%
   340 DET=1.0
   350 REM FIND INVERSE OF COEFF. MATRIX
   360 FOR I%=1 TO N%
   370 IDIV=COEF(I%,I%)
   375 IF IDIV=0 GOTO 515 :REM THIS IMPLIES DET = 0
   380 DET = DET*IDIV
   390 FOR J%=1 TO N%
   400 COEF(I%,J%)=COEF(I%,J%)/IDIV
   410 ICOEF(I%,J%)=ICOEF(I%,J%)/IDIV
   420 NEXT J%
   430 FOR J%=1 TO N%
   440 IF(I%-J%)<0 OR (I%-J%)>0 GOTO 450 ELSE GOTO 500
   450   IRATIO=COEF(J%,I%)
   460 FOR K%=1 TO N%
   470 COEF(J%,K%)=COEF(J%,K%)-IRATIO
*COEF(I%,K%)
   480 ICOEF(J%,K%)=ICOEF(J%,K%)-IRATIO *ICOEF(I%,K%)
   490 NEXT K%
   500 NEXT J%
   510 NEXT I%
   512 GOTO 520
   515 PRINT''''"DETERMINANT OF COEFFICIENT MATRIX ZERO!"''"THEREFORE NO
SOLUTION": GOTO 110
   520 REM PRINT OUT INVERSE OF COEFFICIENT MATRIX
   530 PRINT''''"INVERSE OF COEFFICIENT MATRIX IS"'''
   540 FOR I%=1 TO N%: FOR J%=1 TO N%
   550 PRINT ICOEF(I%,J%);
   560 NEXT J%:PRINT': NEXT I%
   570 PRINT '''"DETERMINANT =",DET,'''
   580 REM CALCULATE UNKNOWNS AND PRINT RESULTS
   590 FOR I%=1 TO N%:FOR J%=1 TO N%
   600 X(I%)=X(I%)+ICOEF(I%,J%)*Z(J%)
   610 NEXT J%: NEXT I%
   620 PRINT"UNKNOWNS ARE"'''
   630 FOR I%=1 TO N%
```

```
640 PRINT X(I%)
650 NEXT I%
660 GOTO 110
670 VDU3
680 END
```

Program 7.3 Program to solve simultaneous linear equations by the method of matrix inversion. The maximum number of equations is 10.

```
 10 REM PROGRAM TO SOLVE THE EQUATION d2y/dx2 = 5X
 20 REM FOR THE RANGE OF VALUES X = 0 TO 0.5
 30 REM THE INTERVAL DELTA X = 0.05
 40 REM USES THE METHOD OF FINITE DIFFERENCES
 50 REM SIMULTANEOUS LINEAR EQUATIONS SOLVED BY GAUSS-SIEDEL
 60 DIM Y(11)
 70 REM BOUNDARY VALUES
 80 Y(1)=0.0
 90 Y(11)=100.0
100 REM REMAINING Y VALUES TO ZERO
110 FOR I=2 TO 10
120 Y(I)=0.0
130 NEXT I
140 REM ENABLE PRINTER
150 VDU2
160 REM SET UP TITLE FOR PRINTING RESULTS
170 TBTITLE$="ITER.     Y1       Y2       Y3       Y4       Y5       Y6
    Y7       Y8       Y9"
180 PRINT '',TBTITLE$,'
190 REM ITERATIVE  PROCEDURE STARTS NEXT
200 FOR J = 1 TO 99
210 FOR I = 2 TO 10
220 K=I-1
230 Y(I)=(Y(I-1)+Y(I+1)-0.000625*K)
/2.0
240 NEXT I
250 IF J<70 GOTO 370
260 REM CONVERT CURRENT SOLUTION INTO STRINGS FOR PRINTING
270 A$=""
280 IF J>9 GOTO 310
290 B$=STR$(J)+"        "
300 GOTO 320
310 B$=STR$(J)+"       "
320 FOR I = 2 TO 10
330 A$=STR$(Y(I))
340 B$=B$+LEFT$(A$,6)+"   "
350 NEXT I
360 PRINT B$,'
370 NEXT J
380 REM DISABLE PRINTER
390 VDU3
400 END
```

Program 8.1 Program to solve the second-order differential equation $d^2y/dx^2 = 5x$. See text for details.

References

Atkinson, K. 1985. *Elementary numerical analysis*. New York: Wiley.

Barnes, J. W. 1981. *Basic geological mapping*. Milton Keynes: The Open University Press.

Beerbower, J. R. & D. Jordan 1960. Application of information theory to palaeontological problems: taxonomic diversity. *Journal of Palaeontology* **43**, 1184–98.

Bischoff, J. L. 1968. Kinetics of calcite nucleation: magnesium ion inhibition and ionic strength catalysis. *Journal of Geophysical Research* **73**, 3315–22.

Bischoff, J. L. & W. S. Fyfe 1968. Catalysis, inhibition and the calcite–aragonite problem. (1) The aragonite–calcite transformation. *American Journal of Science* **266**, 65–79.

Blackman, R. B. & J. W. Tukey 1959. *The measurement of power spectra*. New York: Dover.

Buntebarth, G. 1984. *Geothermics – an introduction*. Berlin: Springer-Verlag.

Camina, A. R. & G. J. Janacek 1984. *Mathematics for seismic data processing and interpretation*. London: Graham and Trotman.

Cheeney, R. F. 1983. *Statistical methods in geology*. London: Allen and Unwin.

Cobbold, P. R., J. W. Cosgrove & J. M. Summers 1971. Development of internal structures in deformed anisotropic rocks. *Tectonophysics* **12**, 23–53.

Coll, J. 1982. *BBC microcomputer user guide*. London: British Broadcasting Corporation.

Cosgrove, J. W. 1976. The formation of crenulation cleavage. *Quarterly Journal of the Geological Society of London* **132**, 155–78.

Cubitt, J. M. & B. Shaw 1976. The geological implications of steady-state mechanisms in catastrophe theory. *Mathematical Geology* **8**, 657–62.

Davis, J. C. 1973. *Statistics and data analysis in geology*. New York: Wiley.

Doornkamp, J. C. & C. A. M. King 1971. *Numerical analysis in geomorphology – an introduction*. London: Edward Arnold.

Elliott, R. E. 1970. Simulation of a productive coal measures sequence. *The Mercian Geologist* **3**, 319–35.

Elliott, R. E. 1985. Quantification of peat to coal compaction stages, based especially on phenomena in the east Pennine coalfield, England. *Proceedings of the Yorkshire Geological Society* **45**, 163–72.

Falini, F. 1965. On the formation of coal deposits of lacustrine origin. *Bulletin of the Geological Society of America* **76**, 1317–46.

Ferguson, J. 1978. Some aspects of the ecology and growth of the Carboniferous gigantoprodutids. *Proceedings of the Yorkshire Geological Society* **42**, 41–54.

Ferguson, J. 1980. Application of information theory in geological data processing. *Quarterly Journal of the Geological Society of London* **137**, 107–8.

Ferguson, J. 1982. *The application of information theory to trend surface analysis. Computer applications in geology iii*. Geological Society of London Miscellaneous Paper No. 15, 3–44.

Ferguson, J. 1983. The analysis of C–H–O data in kerogen studies using a coefficient of elimination. *Journal of Petroleum Geology* 5, 400–8.

Ferguson, J., P. R. Bush & B. A. Clarke 1984. The role of organic matter in the early diagenesis of carbonate ooids – an experimental study. *Journal of Petroleum Geology* 7, 245–66.

Fox, W. T. & R. A. Davis, Jr 1971. *Computer simulation model of coastal processes in eastern Lake Michigan*. Technical Report No. 5, O.N.R. Task No. 388–092/10–18–68(414), Contract NOO 14–69–c–0151. Williamstown, Mass.: Williams College.

Friedman, G. M. & J. E. Sanders 1978. *Principles of sedimentology*. New York: Wiley.

Garrels, R. N. & F. T. Mackenzie, Jr 1971. *Evolution of sedimentary rocks*. New York: Norton.

Glass, J. C. 1980. *An introduction to mathematical methods in economics*. New York: McGraw-Hill.

Gould, P. 1967. On the geographic interpretation of eigenvalues: an initial exploration. *Transactions of the Institute of British Geographers* 42, 53–86.

Gow, M. M. 1960. *A course in pure mathematics*. London: Unibooks, English University Press.

Graham, D., C. Graham & A. Whitcombe 1984. *A-level mathematics course companion*. London: Charles Letts.

Gray, J. R. 1967. *Probability*. Edinburgh: Oliver and Boyd.

Guiasu, S. 1977. *Information theory with applications*. New York: McGraw-Hill.

Harbaugh, J. W. & G. Bonham-Carter 1970. *Computer simulation in geology*. New York: Wiley.

Harbaugh, J. W. & D. F. Merriam 1968. *Computer applications in stratigraphic analysis*. New York: Wiley.

Henley, S. 1976. Catastrophe theory models in geology. *Mathematical Geology* 8, 649–55.

Higginbotham, P. G. 1985. *Microtab – an all purpose statistical package (BBC version)*. London: Edward Arnold.

Hogben, L. 1967. *Mathematics for the million*, revised edn. London: Pan.

Hollingdale, S. H. & G. C. Toothill 1975. *Electronic computers*, revised edn. Harmondsworth: Penguin.

Horai, K. & G. Simmons 1969. Thermal conductivity of rock-forming minerals. *Earth and Planetary Science Letters* 6, 359–68.

Horvitz, L. 1939. On geochemical prospecting. *Geophysics* 4, 210–25.

James, A. N. & A. R. R. Lupton 1978. Gypsum and anhydrite in foundations of hydraulic structures. *Géotechnique* 28, 249–72.

King, L. J. 1969. *Statistical analysis in geography*. Englewood Cliffs, Prentice-Hall.

Koch, G. S., Jr & R. F. Link 1971. *Statistical analysis of geological data*, vol. 2. New York: Wiley.

Krumbein, W. C. & F. A. Graybill 1965. *An introduction to statistical models in geology*. New York: McGraw-Hill.

Lasaga, A. C. 1981. Rate laws of chemical reactions. *Reviews in Mineralogy, Mineralogical Society of America* 8, 69–110.

Lisle, R. J. 1977. Estimation of the tectonic strain ratio from the mean shape of deformed elliptical markers. *Geologie en Mijnbow* 56, 140–4.

Means, W. D. 1976. *Stress and strain. Basic concepts of continuum mechanics for geologists.* New York: Springer-Verlag.

Miller, A. R. 1981. *Pascal programs for scientists and engineers.* Berkeley, California: SYBEX.

Miller, R. L. & J. S. Khan 1962. *Statistical analysis in the geological sciences.* New York: Wiley.

Moroney, M. J. 1951. *Facts from figures.* Harmondsworth: Penguin.

Nettleton, L. L. 1976. *Gravity and magnetics in oil prospecting.* New York: McGraw-Hill.

Noble, B. 1964. *Numerical methods: 1. Iteration programming.* Edinburgh: Oliver and Boyd.

Pelto, C. R. 1954. Mapping of multicomponent systems. *Journal of Geology* **62**, 501–11.

Pielou, E. C. 1969. *An introduction to mathematical ecology.* New York: Wiley-Interscience.

Prentice, J. E. 1956. *Gigantoproductus edelburgensis* (Phillips) and related species. *Proceedings of the Yorkshire Geological Society* **30**, 299–358.

Ragan, D. M. 1968. *Structural geology: an introduction to geometrical techniques,* 2nd edn. New York: Wiley.

Ramsay, J. G. & M. I. Huber 1983. *Techniques of modern structural geology.* Vol.1: *Strain analysis.* London: Academic Press.

Reeve, C. R. & J. S. Huxley 1945. Some problems in the study of allometric growth. In *Essays on growth and form presented to D'Arcy Wentworth Thompson,* W. E. LeGros Clark and P. R. Medawar (eds). Oxford: Oxford University Press.

Rendu, J.-M. 1981. *An introduction to geostatistical methods of mineral evaluation.* South African Institute of Mines and Metals.

Saunders, P. T. 1980. *An introduction to catastrophe theory.* Cambridge: Cambridge University Press.

Sawyer, W. W. 1966. *A path to modern mathematics.* Harmondsworth: Penguin.

Selley, R. C. 1970. Studies of sequence in sediments using a simple mathematical device. *Quarterly Journal of the Geological Society of London* **125** (for 1969), 557–81.

Shannon, C. E. 1948. A mathematical theory of communication. *Technical Journal of the Bell System* **27**, 379–423.

Shelley, J. 1984. *Essentials of Fortran 77.* New York: Wiley.

Sherlock, A. J., E. M. Roebuck & M. G. Godfrey 1982. *Calculus: pure and applied.* London: Edward Arnold.

Shioya, M. & R. Ishiwatari 1983. Laboratory thermal conversion of sedimentary lipids to kerogen-like matter. *Organic Geochemistry* **5**, 7–12.

Sloss, L. L. 1962. Stratigraphic models in exploration. *Journal of Sedimentary Petrology* **32**, 415–22.

Stegna, L. 1961. On the principles of geochemical oil prospecting. *Geophysics* **26**, 447–51.

Stephenson, G. 1973. *Mathematical methods for science students,* 2nd edn. London: Longman.

Tasch, P. 1965. Communications theory and the fossil record of invertebrates. *Transactions of the Kansas Academy of Science* **68**, 322–9.

Tasch, P. 1980. *Palaeobiology of the invertebrates*, 2nd edn. New York: Wiley.
Thom, R. 1972. *Stabilite structurelle et morphogenèse*. New York: Benjamin.

Unwin, D. J. & J. A. Dawson 1985. *Computer programming for geographers*. London: Longman.

Verruijt, A. 1970. *Theory of groundwater flow*. London: Macmillan.

Waddington, C. H. 1974. A catastrophe theory of evolution. *Annals of the New York Academy of Science* **231**, 32–41.
Wang, H. F. & M. P. Anderson 1982. *Introduction to groundwater modeling*. New York: W. H. Freeman.
Williams, C. B. 1964. *Patterns in the balance of nature*. London: Academic Press.
Wilson, C. D. V. 1980. A seismic survey of the former channel of the River Doe, Ingleton. *Proceedings of the Yorkshire Geological Society* **42**, 617–20.
Woodcock, A. E. R. & T. Poston 1974. A geometric study of elementary catastrophes. *Lecture notes in mathematics* **373**. Berlin: Springer-Verlag.

Zeeman, E. C. 1971. The geometry of catastrophe. *Times Literary Supplement*, 1556–7 (10 December).
Zeeman, E. C. 1976. Catastrophe theory. *Scientific American* **234**, 65–83.

Index

Index